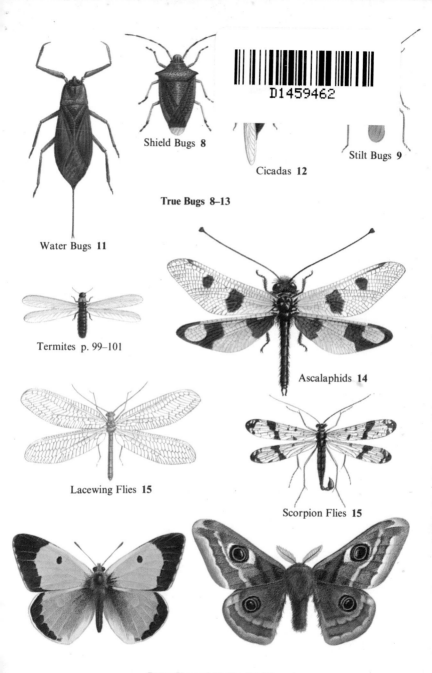

Shield Bugs **8**

Cicadas **12**

Stilt Bugs **9**

True Bugs **8–13**

Water Bugs **11**

Termites p. 99–101

Ascalaphids **14**

Lacewing Flies **15**

Scorpion Flies **15**

Butterflies and Moths **16–27**

A FIELD GUIDE TO THE
Insects of Britain and
Northern Europe

There are also Collins Pocket and Field Guides to:

THE BUTTERFLIES OF BRITAIN AND EUROPE
L. G. Higgins and N. D. Riley

THE BIRDS OF BRITAIN, EUROPE AND THE MIDDLE EAST
Hermann Heinzel, Richard Fitter and John Parslow

THE TREES OF BRITAIN AND NORTHERN EUROPE   *Alan Mitchell*

THE WILD FLOWERS OF BRITAIN AND NORTH-WESTERN EUROPE
Marjorie Blamey, Richard Fitter and Alastair Fitter

THE BUTTERFLIES OF AFRICA   *John G. Williams*

THE BIRDS OF EAST AND CENTRAL AFRICA   *John G. Williams*

THE BIRDS OF BRITAIN AND EUROPE
Roger Peterson, Guy Mountfort and P. A. D. Hollom

THE MAMMALS OF BRITAIN AND EUROPE   *F. H. van den Brink*

THE BIRDS OF NEW ZEALAND   *R. A. Falla, R. B. Sibson and E. G. Turbott*

BRITISH BIRDS   *Richard Fitter and R. A. Richardson*

WILD FLOWERS   *David McClintock and R. S. R. Fitter*

MUSHROOMS AND TOADSTOOLS   *Morten Lange and F. Bayard Hora*

THE SEA SHORE   *John Barrett and C. M. Yonge*

THE BIRDS OF TRINIDAD AND TOBAGO   *G. A. C. Herklots*

THE BIRDS OF THE WEST INDIES   *James Bond*

THE LARGER MAMMALS OF AFRICA   *Jean Dorst and P. Dandelot*

THE STARS AND PLANETS   *Donald Menzel*

A FIELD GUIDE TO THE

Insects of Britain and Northern Europe

Michael Chinery

with 60 color plates by
Gordon Riley, Denys Ovenden
and Brian Hargreaves

COLLINS
St James's Place, London

William Collins Sons & Co Ltd
London · Glasgow · Sydney · Auckland
Toronto · Johannesburg

First edition 1972
Second edition 1976
Reprinted 1977

Contents

CONTENTS

Colour Plates

Plates 1-15 and 28-29 are by Denys Ovenden; 16-27 are by Brian Hargreaves; 30-60 are by Gordon Riley

Acknowledgements

This book could never have been written without the assistance of many people and I have much pleasure in acknowledging the help given to me by numerous friends and colleagues. In particular, I would like to thank Dr Paul Freeman, Keeper of Entomology at the British Museum (Natural History), and the following members of his staff who have always been ready to help by discussing problems and criticising manuscripts, and by allowing the artists and myself to examine material in the Museum collections: Dr J. D. Bradley, Mr P. S. Broomfield, Dr T. Clay, Mr B. H. Cogan, Mr. A. L. Goodson, Mr D. E. Kimmins, Dr. W. J. Knight, Mrs J. A. Marshall, Mr H. Oldroyd, the late Mr J. V. Pearman, Mr R. D. Pope, Dr D. R. Ragge, Mr W. A. Sands, Mr F. G. A. M. Smit, Mr P. H. Ward, and Dr I. H. H. Yarrow. I am also indebted to Mr G. E. Woodroffe, who gave me a great deal of help with the sections on Hemiptera and Coleoptera, but I must stress that these people are in no way responsible for any errors that may be present in the book.

I have drawn information from a great number of books in the preparation of this Field Guide and I am indebted to the Royal Entomological Society of London for permission to use and adapt the keys to the families of Plecoptera, Diptera, and Coleoptera that appear in their Handbooks for the Identification of British Insects. I also wish to thank Frederick Warne & Co. Ltd. for permission to use and modify the key to the families of Heteroptera which appears in *Land and Water Bugs of the British Isles* by Southwood and Leston.

I am deeply grateful to my three colleagues – Brian Hargreaves, Denys Ovenden, and Gordon Riley – for the meticulous way in which they have drawn and painted the insects right down to the last vein and bristle. I would like to say a special thank you to Denys Ovenden, who accompanied me on several 'bug hunts' when collecting material for it. My thanks are also due to Mr I. M. Evans of Leicester Museum, who provided a large number of the specimens illustrated in the book.

Many other people, too numerous to mention, have assisted me in the preparation of this book, but special thanks are due to Sheila Kinsey and Sylvia Bambridge who undertook the arduous task of typing the manuscript. Lastly, I want to thank my wife Jill, who has put up with a house full of living and dead insects for many years and who recently brought me a beetle saying: 'This must be an interesting one: it just bit me.'

Michael Chinery
Hundon, Suffolk, 1973

How to use this book

The **endpapers,** inside the front and back covers, illustrate insects characteristic of each order in Northern Europe. All are shown approximately life size except for those in blue circles on the back endpaper. Note the insect most like the specimen you want to identify and turn to the plates indicated.

On the **plates** are illustrated all the major families, the species being chosen to show the typical features of each family.

On the **caption pages,** facing the plates, will be found the names of the species illustrated and brief notes on the orders and families concerned, indicating how they may be distinguished. Where necessary, diagnostic features are shown in enlargements on the caption pages. The small ▲ for a species and △ for a family indicate that it does not normally occur in the British Isles. Most of the insects shown on the plates are enlarged. The degree of magnification is given by each name, unless the insect is shown at its natural size.

Text. After a general introduction to insect biology there is a key to the insect orders of Europe on pages 43 to 50. Following the instructions on page 43 it should be possible to place almost any adult insect in its correct order.

Keys are also given to the families of nearly all the orders, but the butterflies and moths, the bees and wasps, and the beetles, contain so many families that these orders have been given keys to super families.

Most of the family keys are applicable to the whole of Western Europe, but some of them are restricted to British insects. This has been done in those few instances where the additional European families are so small or insignificant that it was thought that their inclusion would not justify destroying the simplicity of the keys for British use. In these instances the additional families are briefly mentioned in the text.

Introduction

Throughout recorded history insects have been both the delight and despair of mankind, though it is certain that the massed assault of locusts on a bush will eclipse any feeling of pleasure from watching the butterfly that was feeding on the flowers of the same bush.

No other group of living creatures has such variety of form, colour, function, and habitat and, although they are often dismissed simply as 'bugs' or 'creepy-crawlies', many people 'love' them. Not least among these is the bug-hunter and it is hoped that this book will be of some service to him, be he amateur or professional.

It is impossible to give a simple definition of insects – beyond the fact that most of them have six legs at some time in their lives. There are so many kinds of insects and they vary so much that no simple definition could take in all the variations. The best that can be done is to list those features of insects that distinguish them from other animals.

Insects belong to the large animal phylum called the Arthropoda – a name that refers to the jointed limbs and body. The arthropod body is covered by a hard shell or skeleton, and soft joints between the skeletal plates allow the animal to move.

As well as the insects, the Arthropoda contains the crustaceans (crabs, shrimps, woodlice, etc), the myriapods (centipedes and millipedes), and the arachnids (spiders, mites, scorpions, etc). It is with these groups that the insects – especially the wingless ones – are most likely to be confused and the figures below show the main features by which each group can be distinguished.

An insect's body is divided up into three regions – head, thorax, and abdomen. The head bears one pair of antennae and the thorax usually carries three pairs of

Insect: 3 pairs of legs: 3 body divisions: usually winged

Arachnid: 4 pairs of legs: no antennae, though palps may resemble antennae: no wings

Crustacean: several pairs of legs: 2 pairs of antennae: no wings

Myriapod (centipede): many pairs of legs: no wings

legs – hence the alternative name Hexapoda (six feet) for the Insecta. Wings are usually present on the thorax. All winged arthropods – in fact all winged invertebrates – are insects, but this does not mean that all insects have wings. In the pages of this book you will see many wingless creatures but they are insects just as much as the familiar butterflies and moths. The three body-regions and the three pairs of legs prove that these wingless creatures are insects.

Using the information given so far, the beginner should have no difficulty in deciding whether an adult specimen is an insect or some other arthropod. But what about the young stages? Many young insects resemble their parents in all but size and the lack of wings – a young grasshopper or cockroach is easily recognisable as such – but there are many more in which the young are completely different from the adults. To take but two examples, there is very little similarity between a caterpillar and the adult butterfly or between a maggot and a bluebottle fly, yet one develops into the other. According to the chart, the adults are clearly insects but the caterpillar might be classified as a myriapod, while the legless maggot would not appear to be an arthropod at all.

It is these great differences between adults and young that make it impossible to give a definition that will cover all insects at all stages of their lives.

The bug-hunter is often regarded as a crank but there is a great deal to be gained from studying insects. By studying we do not simply mean chasing butterflies and popping them into a killing bottle. This teaches nothing except that butterflies can be very elusive. By studying we mean searching for insects, watching them, and getting to know their habits and life-histories. To get to know insects properly certainly necessitates killing a few here and there but the aim should be to know how they *live* and not to have cabinet drawers full of dead ones – there are thousands of specimens in museums to be looked at if one is merely interested in shapes and colours. There is probably little left to learn about insect anatomy but a great deal remains to be discovered about the habits of insects – especially the lesser-known groups – and there is plenty to absorb the interest of anyone wishing to investigate them.

Insects are more than interesting, however. There are about a million known kinds of insects – about 80 per cent of all known animals – and many species exist in enormous numbers: just think of the numbers of ants you see in a disturbed nest or of the numbers of gnats swarming over a single small pond. Even greater are the number of tiny soil-living insects – E. B. Ford estimated there to be nearly 230 million in the top 9 inches of an acre of meadow-land soil. Insects clearly play a tremendous part in the economy of nature as predators, parasites, and scavengers and as prey for larger animals. Few fields of natural history can be pursued far without coming into contact with insects, and human activities are not without insect interference. Who would have thought that insects could interfere with the building of the Panama Canal? The yellow-fever mosquito, however, did just that. About 16,000 labourers died of yellow fever and work had to stop for several years until the disease could be controlled. A great many other diseases of man, his animals, and his crops are transmitted by insects. Ten or even 15 per cent of the world's food production is destroyed annually by insects, either in the fields or in store after harvesting. Further huge sums of money are spent in combating the ravages of beetles that bore into timber. Nevertheless, relatively few insect species are harmful. On the credit side, bees and many other insects do us great service by pollinating our crops and ensuring fruit and seed production. Many insects are useful because they destroy pests, examples being the ladybirds that feed upon the damaging greenfly. More tangible benefits include honey, beeswax, and silk. The study of insects therefore has a great part to play in man's economy.

Whether you meet insects in the course of your job as farmer, botanist, zoologist, and so on, or whether you are simply someone interested in insects, you will want to know the names of the insects you meet or at least to know the groups to which they belong. There are more than 20,000 species on the British list and no single book could deal with all of them – it would need quite a thick book merely to list them all and arrange them in their groups, let alone describe them. Many specialist works exist, dealing with individual orders of insects, or even families, and these works go into the detail necessary to identify individual species. A certain amount of specialised knowledge is needed to be able to understand these works, and in any case the non-specialist often does not know the family to which his specimen belongs: he does not know whether he has a chalcid wasp or a cynipid wasp, he may not know whether he has a wasp at all. This book has been designed to help the non-specialist with just this sort of problem, to enable him to place an insect in its correct group and to provide the basic knowledge necessary for tackling the more detailed works. It is hoped that the specialist may also find this book of use in dealing with those orders with which he is less familiar.

The Biology of Insects

If the success of an animal group were based solely on the number of species the insects, with about a million different kinds already known and many more undoubtedly still to be discovered, would be the most successful of all animals. Many factors have contributed to their outstanding success but the five features that take most of the credit for the insects' numerical superiority are: (1) the horny skeleton, (2) small size, (3) adaptability, (4) ability to fly, and (5) metamorphosis during life.

1. The Skeleton In common with other arthropods, the insects have a hard outer skeleton composed largely of horny chitin. This protects the body very efficiently but above all, by restricting water loss, it has allowed the insects – and some other arthropods – to leave the damp surroundings to which their unprotected, wormlike ancestors must have been confined. Freed from this necessity to remain in damp places, the insects were able to spread into new habitats and in this they have been aided by the next three features.

2. Size All insects are relatively small creatures, ranging from under $\frac{1}{4}$mm to about 30cm long and from $\frac{1}{2}$mm to about 30cm across the wings. The British Isles can claim some of the smallest insects but we cannot get anywhere near the largest – the Death's Head Hawk Moth being our largest species with a caterpillar about 12cm long and an adult wing span about the same. Although stick insects may reach 30cm in length and moths 30cm in wing span, their bodies are always rather slender: very few insects have bodies more than about 1cm in diameter and rarely is any point in the body more than about 5mm from the surface. The main reason for this small size lies in the insects' breathing mechanism. Vertebrates and most groups of invertebrate animals have special breathing organs – lungs or gills – in one part of the body and a transport system – the blood – which carries the oxygen from the breathing organs to all other parts of the body. The insects, however, use a different system. The body is permeated by a system of fine canals called tracheae which open on to the surface of the body at the spiracles. The air enters through the spiracles and the tissues absorb oxygen from the air in the fine branches of the tracheae. Fresh oxygen supplies are obtained by the diffusion of oxygen along the tracheae from the outside. But diffusion is a very slow process and is effective only in small animals where the distances are small. The insects, having once evolved along the path of tracheal respiration, were restricted in size thereafter.

The small size, however, conveys a definite advantage to the insects in their spread for it allows them to live in very tiny places, filling ecological niches that would be unsuitable for larger animals. Individuals need only small amounts of food and large numbers can therefore exist in restricted places. To take an extreme example, it is quite common for a single oak leaf to support 100 tiny spangle galls on its surface (Pl. 37). Each gall may contain two or three 'guests' as well as its rightful gall-wasp occupant and so it is possible for a single oak leaf to support 300 tiny insects, although not all of them may reach maturity.

3. Adaptability The adaptability of insects appears almost unlimited. There are very few places on earth without insects – mountain tops, hot deserts, lakes and rivers, and even hot springs have their insect inhabitants. Only the sea remains unconquered by the insects for, although there are many shore-living species, there is only a handful of insects that actually live in the sea.

The limbs of insects have been adapted to suit various modes of life and some of the most important adaptations have been in connection with feeding habits. The jaws, which are actually modified limbs, have been adapted to cope with a variety of foods both liquid and solid. Few things are immune from insect attacks. One could almost say 'You name it and an insect feeds on it'. Every plant, except perhaps the marine seaweeds, plays host to one or more insects. Even such (to us) poisonous plants as the Deathcap fungus (*Amanita phalloides*) are readily consumed by certain insects. Other insects feed on animal material, consuming smaller creatures or sucking the blood of larger ones. Many more feed on decaying material and bacteria in the soil. Furniture beetles, carpet beetles, flour beetles, clothes moths, booklice, hide beetles, dung-flies, cigarette beetles – these names suggest just a few of the strange materials that support insect life and indicate that insects are not short of ideas when it comes to finding food.

4. Flight Among invertebrate animals, the insects are the only ones that can really fly. Spiders and many other small creatures can drift in the wind but they have no wings and they cannot direct their travels. The ability to fly has been a very big factor in the spread of insects. It enables them to escape from their enemies more effectively, to find mates more easily, and to reach new areas and feeding grounds in which to leave their offspring.

5. Metamorphosis During Life Although less obviously perhaps than the preceding features, the metamorphosis undergone by many insects plays a large part in their abundance. When the two stages feed on different food, as for example the leaf-eating caterpillar and the nectar-sipping butterfly, a given area can clearly support more insects than it could if the insects fed on one type of food throughout their lives.

Add to these five main features the rapid and prolific breeding habits of many insects and you have the answer to their success, and it is easy to understand why 80 per cent of all animal species are insects – because so many places are open to them that would not be suitable for larger or less adaptable animals – and why their individual numbers far outweigh (literally) all other animals.

The Structure of Insects

This book is no place for a detailed account of insect anatomy but the classification of insects depends upon structural features and a general description of external anatomy is necessary here so that the terms used in the keys will be readily understood. Internal anatomy is of little concern in the present work for, with the exception of the genitalia, it is of no value in the identification of living or complete specimens and only the briefest account of internal anatomy is attempted here.

The insects are characterised by having three distinct parts to the body – head, thorax, and abdomen. The head carries one pair of antennae and the thorax usually carries three pairs of legs. One or two pairs of wings are also usually present on the thorax. The abdomen has no legs in the adult stage although it may carry a number of filaments or cerci at the hind end.

Like all arthropods, the insect body is a segmented structure, composed of a number of fundamentally similar 'rings' or segments. There are basically 20 segments in the insect body – six in the head, three in the thorax, and 11 in the abdomen – but some are fused together and it is not possible to count them all. The walls of the segments are strengthened and protected by numerous hard, chitinous plates called sclerites. Between these plates are soft-walled areas (joints) which allow the body to move.

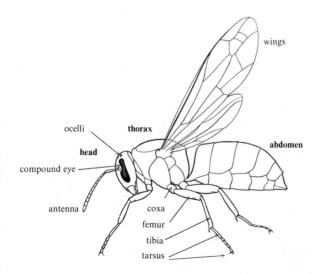

A typical insect showing the major features of the insect body

The Head The six segments of the head are intimately welded together to form a rather tough capsule. There are many grooves or sutures on the head capsule but they do not necessarily correspond with the original segments and sclerites of which the head is formed. The figure shows the basic structure of the head of a cockroach which is regarded as a rather primitive and generalised insect. The regions shown can be distinguished in most other insects but the pattern is often complicated by the fusion and/or subdivision of various sclerites.

Insects have no internal jaws like our own and the limbs of the head segments have been modified to assist in the capture and eating of food. All cutting and chewing is performed by these external mouth-parts before the food is passed into the mouth. Again, the cockroach serves as an example of the basic structure. Its simple biting mouth-parts, unspecialised and suited to a wide variety of food materials, are believed to be similar to those of the early insects.

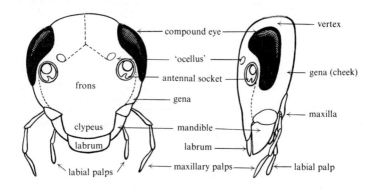

Front and side views of the cockroach head – a typical hypognathous head. The ocelli of the cockroach are, in fact, very poorly developed and represented by little more than pale patches near the antennae

The paired mandibles are the cutting parts of the feeding apparatus and are usually called simply the jaws. They are hard and heavily sclerotised and are often provided with powerful muscles. Many of our larger insects can give the unwary handler a painful nip with their mandibles: the Wart-biter, a bush cricket rare in the British Isles, gets its name from the old Swedish custom of allowing this insect to bite off warts. Arising on the underside of the head, the mandibles are not normally conspicuous but in a number of insects they have taken on new functions and have developed accordingly. The male Stag Beetle (Pl. 50) has enormous antler-like mandibles, sometimes as long as the rest of the body but they are of sexual significance only and are not nearly as powerful as one might imagine. The soldier castes of some termite species, however, have muscles worthy of their large mandibles and they are formidable creatures. Certain African tribes use similarly endowed soldier ants to 'stitch' wounds: the ants are made to bite into the skin across the cut and are then beheaded. The mandibles stay closed and are left in position until the wound has healed.

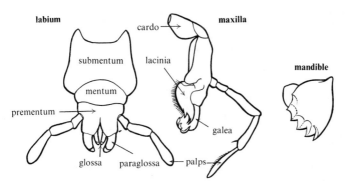

The mouth-parts of the cockroach dissected out to show their structure

Behind the mandibles there is a pair of maxillae or secondary jaws. In the cockroach these help to hold the food while the mandibles cut it. The palps of the maxillae are well-supplied with sense organs and are concerned with finding food and determining its acceptability. The labium, or lower lip as it is often called, is formed by the fusion of two maxilla-like appendages and it performs similar functions to the maxillae themselves.

Lying in the middle of the underside of the head, just behind the mouth, is the hypopharynx. It is not one of the paired head appendages but is associated with the ducts of the salivary glands. In the cockroach and most other insects it is a small tongue-like structure but is well-developed in two-winged flies, especially the blood-sucking forms.

The mouth-parts are completed by the labrum. This is a single structure, derived from a single plate at the very front of the head. It forms a 'roof' over that region in which the mandibles cut up the food and so is aptly called the upper lip. Its under-surface sometimes bears a small lobe called the epipharynx.

Biting mouth-parts similar to those described are found in most of the lower orders of insects – cockroaches, grasshoppers, dragonflies, and so on – as well as in some of the higher ones such as the beetles and wasps. Sucking mouth-

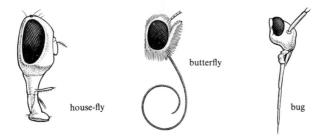

Three entirely different modifications of the mouth-parts for taking liquid food

parts, adapted for liquid food, are found among the butterflies and moths, true bugs, two-winged flies, fleas, and a few other insects. There is a great variety among these sucking mouths – witness the differences between the slender proboscis of a butterfly, the sharp piercing stylets of a true bug, and the 'suction pad' of a house-fly. Nevertheless, they all seem to have evolved from the primitive biting type of mouth-parts by differential development – especially of the maxillae and labium.

The single pair of antennae are found in almost all adult insects and in the majority of young insects, although they are not always clearly visible in the latter. They are concerned largely with the senses of smell and touch and their use in this respect can be seen by watching ants running over the ground. The antennae wave continuously and touch the ground here and there as the ant picks its way over the soil and seeks food. The antennae of certain male moths are extremely well developed in connection with their use in finding a mate. The female moths emit a specific scent which attracts the males, sometimes as much as a mile away. The concentration of scent particles at such a distance is very low but the feathery development of the male antennae make up for this by presenting the largest possible area of receptive cells to detect the scent.

The antennae are made up of a number of segments ranging from one in a few beetles to more than 100 in cockroaches, bush crickets, and others. In the lower orders of insects, the antennal segments are all similar and the antennae are simple and thread-like, but there is a great deal of variation in the higher orders. Three regions can be recognised in the antennae of the higher insects. The first segment, which is often longer than any other, is called the scape. This is followed by the pedicel, which is usually a short segment, and the rest of the antenna forms the flagellum. This may consist of a number of separate segments or the component segments may be fused together. When the scape is particularly long and the rest of the antenna hinges on it, the antenna is said to be geniculate or elbowed.

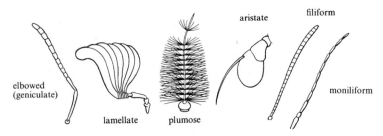

Some types of insect antennae

There are two main types of visual receptor among insects – the compound eye and the simple ocellus. A great many insects have both types but one or the other, or both, may be missing. The compound eye is the larger of the two types and is quite conspicuous in many insects.

Compound eyes are composed of a number of separate visual units called ommatidia. These are cone-shaped and each has its own lens or facet at the surface of the eye (see Fig.). This arrangement is responsible for the reticulated appearance of the insect eye when seen under a lens. Each ommatidium makes its

THE BIOLOGY OF INSECTS 19

own image and sends its own signal to the insect's brain, so that the insect sees a mosaic image made up of many small pieces. The picture is not sharp but this arrangement of the eye is well suited to detect movement, for any movement results in the stimulation of different ommatidia. The greater the number of ommatidia, the better the insect can see – the picture will be sharper and smaller movements can be detected. Dragonflies, which capture their food on the wing, have up to 30,000 ommatidia and extremely good sight. The eyes are so large that they appear to take up almost the whole of the head. Associated with their almost complete dependence on sight, the dragonflies have very small antennae. At the other end of the scale, workers of several ant species, which depend mainly on the senses of smell and touch, have at most a few hundred ommatidia and their antennae are well developed. Large, well-developed antennae, however, do not necessarily imply poor sight. Butterflies and moths, for example, have relatively large antennae and several thousand facets in each compound eye.

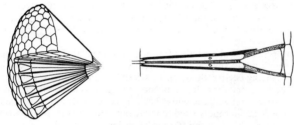

An insect's compound eye, showing how the surface is composed of numerous lenses or facets. Each lens is at the end of a conical body called an ommatidium, shown much enlarged on the right. Each ommatidium is insulated from its neighbours by pigmented collars, and light passes straight down to the nerve fibres at the base. Only rays coming perpendicularly through the lens can reach the nerves, so each ommatidium has a very limited field of view.

Compound eyes are never found in larvae.

The simple ocelli, when present, are usually three in number and they are arranged in a triangle on the top of the head. They are quite small and inconspicuous, although quite easily seen in some of the larger hymenopterans (Pls. 37–46). The ocelli have no focusing mechanism and are probably used solely for measuring light intensity in adult insects. It is also suggested that they are stimulated by light and that they somehow increase the sensitivity of the compound eyes. The ocelli of larvae are placed on the sides of the head and probably give a rather vague indication of the nature of the surroundings, sufficient at least for the insect to distinguish between exposed and shaded regions.

The Thorax The three thoracic segments are named, from front to back, the prothorax, mesothorax, and metathorax. Each segment carries a pair of legs and the wings, if present, are carried on the meso- and metathoracic segments. Wings are never found on the prothorax which is often small and insignificant. The meso- and metathoracic segments are usually fused together, forming the pterothorax and the two component segments are not always easy to distinguish. The front wings, carried on the mesothorax, are normally larger than the hind wings and in consequence the mesothoracic segment is normally larger than the metathoracic segment. In the two-winged flies (Diptera), whose hind wings are reduced to pin-like halteres, the mesothorax makes up almost the whole thoracic region, the pro- and metathoracic segments being reduced to small rings fore and aft. Among beetles, whose front wings are modified as the protective elytra, the mesothorax is small.

The sclerites of the thoracic segments are usually divided up into numerous smaller plates and there is an elaborate system for naming them. At this point, however, we shall confine ourselves to the main divisions only. The primary sclerites of the dorsal surface – the nota – are each divided transversely into three regions, the prescutum, scutum, and scutellum, but the divisions of the pronotum and metanotum are usually obscured. Unless otherwise stated, the terms scutum and scutellum refer to the mesothorax.

The pleural sclerites, on the sides of the thorax, consist basically of an episternum and an epimeron in each segment. The episternum is the anterior of the two and divided from the epimeron by the pleural suture. There are many subdivisions of these pleural sclerites but we shall not concern ourselves with the details in this book. The ventral sclerites, or sterna, are divided into three main regions corresponding to the division of the nota and called the presternum, basisternum and sternellum.

Six legs are present in almost all adult insects. Clearly their primary use is for walking or running and their typical structure is best seen in the cockroach or certain ground-living beetles. Some of the sclerites of the pleura are derived from the original leg bases, but for practical purposes the coxa is the basal segment of the leg. The coxa articulates with the body. The trochanter is always a small segment, movable on the coxa but rigidly fixed to the femur. The latter is usually the largest segment of the leg, although the tibia is often longer. The tibia often carries a number of spines and these are particularly well developed near the distal end where they form the tibial spurs, important aids in classification. The tarsus consists of between one and five segments plus a pretarsus. The latter usually bears two claws and a small pad called the arolium.

This basic structure is common to all insects but there are a great many variations associated with the habits of the insects. Notable variations include the enlargement of the hind femur in grasshoppers and certain other jumping insects, fringes of hairs on the swimming legs of aquatic insects, and the enlargement of the front legs in certain burrowing insects such as the Mole Cricket.

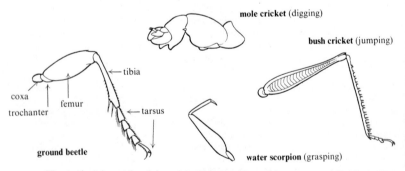

The typical insect leg (ground beetle), together with some specialised modifications

The Wings The classification of winged insects depends to a great extent upon the nature of the wings. Most of the insect orders have names ending in -ptera which is derived from the greek word *pteron* meaning a wing. Thus we get Lepidoptera (scale wings), Diptera (two wings), and so on.

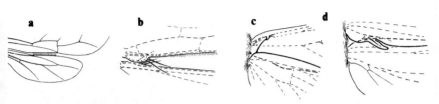

Some wing-coupling mechanisms: **a**, a row of small hooks on the hind wing (Hymenoptera); **b**, overlapping bristles (Mecoptera); **c**, frenulum (some Lepidoptera, p. 162); **d**, jugum (Swift moths and some other Lepidoptera, p. 162)

There are usually two pairs of wings, carried on the meso- and metathoracic segments. Wings are never found on the prothorax, although in certain insects, extinct and living, there are flap-like extensions of the prothorax. The typical insect wing is a membranous outgrowth of the integument, supported and strengthened by a framework of veins. The two pairs of wings may have similar textures as in the dragonflies, butterflies, and others, or they may be different as, for example, in the beetles and cockroaches where the front wings are hard or leathery and protective in function.

Among the wingless insects, there are two distinct groups – the Apterygota, primitive springtails and bristle-tails whose thoracic structure indicates that they have never had wings during their existence, and the secondarily wingless insects, such as the lice and fleas. The thoracic structure of this latter group indicates that these insects have passed through a winged stage during their evolution. The loss of the wings is associated with their parasitic habits. To an insect that spends all its adult life crawling through fur or feathers, any tendency towards reduction or loss of wings would be an advantage. These tendencies have therefore been favoured by natural selection and the once-winged parasites evolved into wingless forms.

Dragonflies and a few other insects move their two pairs of wings independently during flight and the early winged insects are believed to have done the same. It cannot be said that such an arrangement is inefficient – the dragonflies are the most aerobatic of all insects, being swift, manoeuvrable, and even able to fly backwards – but during insect evolution there has been a tendency for the two pairs of wings to develop a coupling apparatus and to act as a single pair. The coupling apparatus varies from a simple overlap, as in many butterflies and moths, to elaborate systems of hooks. Associated with the wing-coupling, there has been a general reduction in the size of the hind wing, especially among the fast fliers such as bees and wasps and many moths. In the two winged flies of the order Diptera, the hind wings have been reduced to tiny halteres. These are concerned with balance – hence their alternative name of balancers – and they give no lift or thrust to the insects.

Within the individual winged orders, especially those with membranous front

Wings of damsel fly (left) and chalcid wasp, showing the wide variation in venation

wings, the arrangement of the veins is of great importance in classification and identification. We must therefore discuss wing venation in some detail.

You have only to look at the wings of a dragonfly and a chalcid wasp to realise the tremendous range of variation in wing venation. Between these two extremes comes every possible stage of complexity, yet the veins are not arranged haphazardly and it is possible to relate the venation to a basic pattern. Much of the credit for uncovering this pattern must go to Comstock and Needham who, after a great deal of work, put forward a hypothetical wing venation from which all other wing venations can be, and presumably have been evolved. Their original ideas were put forward around the end of the nineteenth century and have been modified in the light of later work but the essence of their scheme is still accepted by entomologists.

The costal vein or costa (C) does not branch and it normally forms the anterior border of the wing. Behind it is the sub-costa (Sc), normally a relatively thin vein that forks rarely and meets the edge of the wing somewhere along the costal margin. The radius (R) is generally quite prominent in the anterior section of the wing. It gives off a branch called the radial sector (Rs) which divides into four, making five branches of the radius in all. These are numbered R_1 to R_5 in the order in which they reach the wing margin. Running more or less through the centre of the wing is the median vein or media (M) which divides into an anterior and a posterior branch (MA and MP). MA is absent in most living insects and MP (usually abbreviated to M) sends four branches to the wing margin. These are numbered M_1 to M_4. Prominent in the posterior section of the wing is the cubitus (Cu) which divides into two main branches of which Cu_1 may divide again into Cu_{1a} and Cu_{1b}. The three anal veins are usually unbranched.

The figure below also shows the principal cross veins denoted by small letters.

Hypothetical venation pattern of an ancestral winged insect, showing the major veins and cross veins. No living insect possesses all the veins, but the main ones can be recognised in most winged species.
C=costa Sc=sub-costa R=radius Rs=radial sector M=media
MA=anterior branch of media MP=posterior branch of media
Cu=cubitus A=anal veins m-cu=cross vein from media to cubitus
r-m=cross vein from radius to media

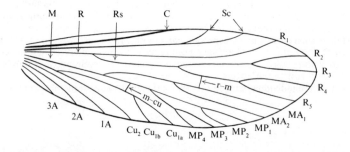

The membranous areas between the veins and cross veins are called cells. If completely surrounded by veins they are said to be closed cells and if they reach the wing margin they are said to be open cells. The cells are named according to the vein forming the anterior margin and so we get costal cell, radial cell, and so on.

The variations of this pattern include additional cross veins, extra branches of the main veins, addition of secondary longitudinal veins between the main veins, or disappearance of some veins. In no known insect is there any increase in the number of primary veins arising from the base of the wing.

When the venation is reduced, by degeneration of a vein or veins, or by fusion of neighbouring veins, it is often very difficult to decide what veins are still present. Comstock and Needham understandably came to the wrong conclusions in some of the groups they studied. For example, the vein which Comstock called Cu_1 in Diptera has now been shown to be M_4. Studies of the development of wing tracheae, particularly by Tillyard, have been largely responsible for the correct interpretation of the venation.

Tracheation studies are definitely for the expert but many insect wings do carry simpler clues to the venation. The wings of the lower insects are not flat but thrown into a number of shallow ridges and furrows. Some veins follow the ridges and others the furrows and a given vein always keeps to its station. The radius is always on a ridge (convex) and therefore more prominent on the upper surface of the extended wing. Veins Cu_{1a} and 1A are also convex. The radial sector and median veins are concave (in furrows) and less prominent on the upper surface. By looking for the convex veins it is therefore possible to work out which veins are which in many of the lower insects. Unfortunately, in the higher insects this pattern is usually obscured.

Before leaving this section on wing venation, it must be said that the Comstock–Needham system of naming veins and cells is not the only system in use, and that the radius of one system may not necessarily correspond to the radius of another system. Lepidopterists and dipterists, many of whose subjects exhibit a reduced venation, frequently employ a system of numbering veins as they reach the margin.

The Abdomen The insect abdomen is basically 11-segmented but the eleventh segment is always small and it disappears in the higher insects, leaving only 10 abdominal segments. The first segment is also small. Fusion of segments, particularly at each end of the abdomen, may give the appearance of fewer segments than are really present.

The Protura and Collembola are unusual among insects in that they have less than the normal number of abdominal segments. Young proturans have only eight abdominal segments plus a tail or telson but segments 9, 10, and 11 are added in front of the telson during development. This form of growth is not found in other insects, although it is common in many other arthropods, and this fact is evidence of the primitive nature of these wingless insects. The Collembola (springtails) never have more than six abdominal segments at any stage of their lives and some zoologists consider this sufficient to separate the springtails from the insects and put them into a class of their own.

Each abdominal segment has a dorsal tergum and a ventral sternum but there are no pleural (side) sclerites. Appendages are present on some or all of the abdominal segments of the apterygote insects – again indicating their primitive nature. Abdominal appendages are found in the embryos of other insects and in many larvae but they are confined to the hind end of the abdomen in the adults of pterygote insects. The appendages of segments 8 and 9 are modified to form the genitalia, concerned with mating and egg-laying. The structure of these organs is often quite important in separating closely related species but this topic is beyond the scope of the present book. The genitalia are generally quite small and are often withdrawn into the body but in the females of some insects they are expanded into a conspicuous egg-layer or ovipositor. Examples of these insects include bush crickets, sawflies, and ichneumons. The long ovipositor enables them to lay their eggs in otherwise inaccessible places – under the surface of the soil, inside plant stems, and even inside other insects. In the bees and wasps, the ovipositor has lost its egg-laying function and has become modified into a sting used for defence and for paralysing prey.

Apart from the conspicuous ovipositors of the insects mentioned, the most conspicuous abdominal appendages are the *cerci* which spring from the last abdominal segment. They may be long and slender as in mayflies, short and stubby as in grasshoppers, or even modified into pincers as in earwigs. Cerci are absent from most of the higher insects. In some insects, the dorsal sclerite of the eleventh segment extends backwards as the *epiproct*. In thysanurans and some mayflies it is long and slender and forms the third 'tail' in between the two cerci. (Fig. p. 52).

Internal Anatomy

This book is intended primarily for use in the field and little need be said on internal structure but the following brief summary, although not taking all the organ systems into account, will provide the basic classroom information needed by the elementary student.

The digestive canal is a relatively simple tube running from the mouth to the anus and bearing a greater or lesser number of pouches. It is commonly not much more than the length of the body, although in some insects there is much coiling and therefore a much greater length. In general, and perhaps somewhat surprisingly, the liquid feeders have longer canals than the solid feeders. The first part of the canal is a fairly slender tube called, as in most animals, the oesophagus, although there is often, especially in sucking insects, a muscular pharynx at the mouth end of the tube. The oesophagus leads into a very variable, thin-walled region called the crop, which is a food storing region. Following this is the gizzard, a muscular region where the food is broken up. The gizzard is well developed in those insects that eat solid food – cockroaches, grasshoppers, beetles, and many more – but is hardly differentiated in the two-winged flies.

Up to this point, the whole canal is lined with cuticle and it is known as the fore gut. Beyond the gizzard is the mid gut and this has no cuticular lining, although there is a special membrane lining it and keeping the food out of direct contact with the cells of the gut wall. Digestive enzymes are produced in the mid gut and some absorption takes place there. The effective surface area of the region is often increased by the development of a number of pouches or caeca. In a number of liquid feeding larvae, whose food contains little indigestible residue, there is no exit from the mid gut and what residue there is accumulates there until it is connected with the hind gut in the adult. The larvae of lacewings and of bees and wasps usually exhibit this condition.

The Malpighian tubules mark the division between the mid gut and the hind gut. The latter, like the fore gut, is lined with cuticle, and its surface is often thrown into folds. Food absorption is completed here and water is reabsorbed in the rather globular chamber at the end.

Excretion is performed mainly by the Malpighian tubules, which are narrow, blind tubes attached to the gut near the mid gut/hind gut junction. They are well supplied with tracheae and lie freely in the blood from which they extract waste matter. Uric acid is the principal substance excreted and the lower parts of the tubules reabsorb useful salts. In some young insects, such as certain lacewing larvae, some of the Malpighian tubules have become silk-producing organs.

The blood system in insects, in common with that of other arthropods has relatively few vessels, the blood existing mainly in large cavities and freely bathing the organs of the body. These cavities collectively form the haemocoel which effectively replaces the true body cavity or coelom in arthropods. The main blood vessel consists of the heart and aorta and it runs along the greater length of the insect, just under the dorsal body wall. The heart is closed at the hind end and lies in a blood-filled space. Waves of contraction run rhythmically forward along the heart and blood is drawn in through tiny valves known as ostia. Some of the blood may then pass out through outlet valves or lateral vessels and the remainder flows through the aorta and into the head. Simple vessels are found in the wing veins and in the legs but circulation is otherwise at low pressure through the blood spaces. General body movements aid circulation but larger insects often have accessory 'pumps' at various parts of the body, especially in the thorax in connection with circulation in wings and legs.

The blood itself, which may account for as much as 75 per cent of an insect's weight, consists of plasma and cells. The cells may number 100,000/cu. mm and their main function is scavenging – clearing the blood of bacteria and particles from cell breakdown. The blood plays almost no part in carrying oxygen round the body and haemoglobin is found in only a relatively small number of insects. A good deal of waste carbon dioxide, however, is carried in the blood.

Respiration is by a system of air tubes called tracheae which penetrate all parts of the body and open to the exterior at the spiracles (Fig. p. 163). There are basically 10 pairs of these openings – one pair per segment starting with the mesothorax – but this number is often reduced. In all higher insects, the spiracles can be closed and opened as required. The tracheae are really ingrowths of the body wall and they are therefore lined with cuticle. This is not evenly developed but forms spiral ridges along the tube and thus provides support. Some bristle-tails and other primitive insects have a separate tracheal system for each spiracle but the higher insects have a single system, with all the spiracles leading into one maze of tubes.

When the spiracles are open oxygen diffuses along the tracheae and it has been shown that diffusion, although slow, is quite sufficient for the needs of small or inactive insects. Larger insects increase their supplies of oxygen through the development of air sacs and breathing movements. The air sacs are thin-walled expansions of the tracheae which become filled with air. Pumping movements of the body squeeze the air out of these sacs and then, when they relax, they fill with fresh air. Such pumping movements can easily be seen in a resting wasp or hover-fly.

Each trachea ends in a tiny star-shaped cell, the branches of which are minute tubes ($< 1\mu$ in diameter) called tracheoles. These are often partly filled with liquid. From the ends of these tracheoles the oxygen diffuses in to the tissues. The amount of liquid in the tracheoles depends upon the activity of the insects and Wigglesworth has shown that the accumulating waste products in active muscle exert an osmotic pressure that draws fluid from the tracheoles. This neat arrangement increases the oxygen supply as required. Carbon dioxide escapes mainly through the tissues of the body and out through the body wall.

All adult insects are air breathers, even the aquatic ones, although many aquatic larvae get their oxygen by simple diffusion from the water. Most aquatic adults are either beetles or bugs and they carry a bubble of air under their elytra or trapped by hairs on other parts of the body. The air is in contact with the spiracles and so, as far as breathing goes, the insects might just as well be in the air. Such an air bubble actually provides more than its own oxygen content. As oxygen is used up by the insect the concentration in the bubble is maintained by diffusion of oxygen in from the water and so the insect gets extra oxygen. Gases are lost to the water, though, and the bubble gradually gets smaller, needing replacement at the surface every now and then.

There are quite a few aquatic adults that have taken this 'physical gill' a stage further and, although still air breathers, they can remain permanently under the surface. The body surface is covered with very fine water-repelling hairs and traps a very thin layer of air which is in contact with the spiracles. The hairs prevent loss of the gases and so the air film acts as a permanent physical gill. Oxygen continuously diffuses in to make up for that taken up by the insect. This is known as plastron respiration. Examples of such insects include the bug *Aphelocheirus* (Pl. 11) and various beetles of the family Elmidae. They can live only in well-aerated streams, with a high oxygen content.

Insects are very active creatures and the nervous system is better developed in them than in any other invertebrates, with the exception of the squids and octopuses. The brain is at the head end and often completely surrounds the oesophagus. Running back from the brain and lying under the gut is a double nerve cord with ganglia and cross connections in each segment. The whole arrangement looks rather like a ladder. The ganglia of certain segments, such as the thoracic segments, are often large and the thoracic ganglia may even merge to form a structure larger than the brain. These ganglia act as 'local brains', directing activities in their immediate vicinity, although they can be over-ruled by the brain which is the centre of co-ordination.

Associated with the efficient nervous system, the insects are well equipped with sense organs (receptors). The organs of sight and of smell (antennae) have already been dealt with. The stimulus of touch is detected over a large part of the insect body, but especially on the antennae and the legs where sensitive hairs are connected to nerve fibres. Taste is also well developed in many insects, although the taste receptors are not confined to the mouth region. House-flies and several others have taste receptors on their feet and they determine the suitability of food simply by landing on it. Other sense organs detect heat – female mosquitoes may detect their bird or mammal hosts in the first instance by the heat radiating from them – and humidity changes.

The Insect's Life History

Although a few insects, notably the summer generations of aphids, give birth to active young, the vast majority of them lay eggs. Protected by a tough shell and one or more internal membranes that render them waterproof, the eggs can survive a wide range of conditions and many insect eggs pass the winter freely exposed on twigs. When the young insect is ready to leave the egg it either chews its way out or bursts its way out by muscular action, sometimes assisted by tooth-like projections (hatching spines) on the cuticle.

The insect that hatches from the egg rarely resembles the adult of the species, one of the principal differences being the absence of wings in the young insect. There may also be differences in mouth-parts as well as the obvious difference in size. It follows that most young insects must undergo considerable changes before they reach the adult state. These changes are collectively called metamorphosis.

The primitive apterygote insects and some of the secondarily wingless parasites hatch from the egg in a form very like that of the adult except for size and the lack of reproductive organs. There is therefore little visible change in the insect as it grows up and metamorphosis is said to be slight or absent. In most of the pterygote insects, however, metamorphosis is a much more profound process, involving the development of wings and frequently the rebuilding of the whole body.

Because of the hard external skeleton, an insect cannot grow steadily: it has to grow in stages, shedding the skeleton each time it gets too tight. Every so often the inner layers are digested away and a new, looser covering is secreted under the old skin. By muscular action, or by swallowing air or water, the insect then swells up and splits the old coat and crawls out of it. The insect remains swollen until the new coat has hardened and then, by getting rid of the air or water, it makes room for the next growth stage. Until the new coat hardens the insect is rather pale and delicate, and it may hide away at this time to avoid its enemies.

This moulting or ecdysis occurs anything between once and 50 times during the insect's life but these extremes are unusual and the majority of species moult between four and 10 times. The stages between moults are called instars and it is common practice to refer to 2nd-instar larvae and so on.

Insects can be split into two groups according to the way in which the wings develop in the young. Among the so-called 'lower insects' – the cockroaches, grasshoppers, dragonflies, and so on – the wings develop gradually on the outside of the body and get larger at each moult until they are fully developed. The young stages of these insects are called nymphs and they frequently resemble the adults in general appearance, inhabiting similar places, and eating similar food. This group of insects is called the Exopterygota in reference to the fact that the wings develop outside the body.

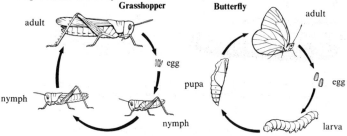

The life history of the grasshopper – an exopterygote insect – and of the butterfly – an endopterygote insect

The other group of winged insects includes the butterflies and moths, beetles, true flies, and so on in which the young stages are very unlike the adults. These young stages are called larvae and they often exist on a diet different from that of the adults and occupy completely different ecological niches. Instead of undergoing a series of small changes until the adult form is attained, the larvae undergo one very dramatic change – so great as to require a resting stage during which the transformation can take place. This resting stage is the pupa or chrysalis and, although the insect may be capable of a limited amount of movement at this stage, it does not feed. The wing buds develop internally in this group and are not visible externally until the pupal stage. These insects are therefore referred to as the Endopterygota.

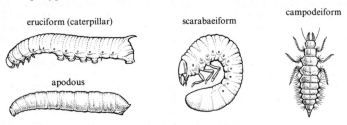

eruciform (caterpillar)   scarabaeiform   campodeiform

apodous

The four basic types of insect larvae

Whether the new adult emerges from a nymphal skin or a pupa, its first reaction is usually to find a suitable support where its crumpled wings can unfurl freely. This unfurling is brought about by pumping blood into the wings to distend them. Some insects can fly immediately or within a short time of emerging (see p. 59) but others need a few hours in which the wings can harden before taking to the air. Many species time their emergence very efficiently so that their wings are ready for flight at the appropriate time of day. Dragonflies, for example, tend to emerge early in the morning and are ready for flight as soon as the sun warms them. Many moths emerge in late afternoon or early evening and are ready to fly at dusk. The fully developed adult is known as the imago.

a

b

The two main kinds of pupa: **a,** *obtect,* in which all the appendages are fixed down; **b,** *exarate,* in which some or all of the appendages are free

When the wings have reached their full development, or when sexual maturity has been reached, most insects stop growing and moult no more: small flies will not grow into larger flies, to give an oft-quoted example. The only exceptions to this are the bristle-tails – silver-fish and their allies, which moult throughout their lives and may have 50 or more moults – the springtails, and the mayflies which are unique in moulting once more after the wings have developed.

With this very brief account of insect life-histories we must leave the biology of insects. A great deal has been omitted but there are several excellent text-books to which the reader can refer for further information. We hope this chapter has fulfilled our intention that it should provide a foundation and a framework on which the reader can build. The following chapters will assume that this framework is fixed in the reader's mind and will concentrate on the variations on which classification and identification are based.

Collecting and Preserving Insects

The aim of this book is to enable its readers to get to know insects in the field and not to help them fill cabinets and store boxes. Nevertheless, a certain amount of collecting will be necessary and this book would not be complete without some guidance in this direction. Many insects have disappeared for ever and others are on the brink of extinction as a result of over-collecting coupled with destruction of their habitats. The accumulation of rows of attractive specimens was an end in itself to many early collectors. If they had paid more attention to the biology of the insects, particularly their habitat requirements, several species would probably have been with us now. It should not really be necessary to stress the dangers of over-collecting today, but it is. The destruction of habitats has reduced the numbers of many of our insects to levels where further interference with breeding populations could be serious: a species could take years to build up again – or it may die out altogether. It should not be necessary to take more than a couple of each species and this is unlikely to harm the populations of most insects.

The collection, therefore, should not be an end in itself but an aid to understanding the biology of insects. When we have gained this understanding we will be able to do more towards the conservation of our insect fauna and the rest of our wildlife.

A notebook is as important as a net to the entomologist and should be used to record details of behaviour as well as date and place of capture. If I may quote from Harold Oldroyd's book *Collecting, Preserving, and Studying Insects*: '. . . do not be in a hurry to catch and kill the insects, but spend as much time as you can watching them going about their daily life.' When you have captured your specimens and identified them (maybe only determined their family) you will be able to recognise them again in the field without catching them. You will then be able to add further to the information obtained earlier and gradually build up your knowledge of an insect species or group. You will be surprised how much has still to be found out even about our relatively small British insect fauna.

After a period of general collecting, during which you will familiarise yourself with the various orders of insects and many of the more prominent and important families, you may wish to specialise in one particular order, or even one large family. This is the only way to become a real expert – no one can ever know everything about all insects – but always try to avoid becoming so 'wrapped up' in your own little group that you never see any other insects.

The following notes on collecting and preserving are rather general and very brief but they cover the basic methods necessary for the formation of a representative insect collection. Not all orders can be treated in the same way and each of the following sections contains an indication of the most suitable methods for the insects concerned. More detailed information and more elaborate methods may be found in the books listed on page 334.

Insects can be found at any time of the year (although the summer months are more profitable for the collector) and in almost every place. It is never necessary to go far to find them, and a representative collection may even be obtained without leaving the house: the writer has obtained specimens of 15 orders simply by leaving a window open for a few days and nights, and three more can be added by searching the household cats and the captures they bring in from time to time. At least two, and probably four, of the remaining orders are to be found in the garden.

The study of household insects is an absorbing one but relatively few species are found in houses, and many of those are accidental visitors. The collector will want to get out and about and collect insects from their natural homes. These cover such a wide variety of habitats that several collecting methods are needed. For a discussion of these methods, it is convenient to divide insects into four groups: flying insects, crawling insects, soil and litter dwellers, and aquatic insects The collecting methods themselves can be divided into active hunting on the one hand and baiting or trapping on the other.

Hunting

1. **Flying Insects** The majority of insects fly at some time or other but, in the context of collecting methods, flying insects may be regarded as those that spend most of their time on the wing and are caught in flight or during brief periods of rest on the vegetation. The main groups included here are the dragonflies, butterflies and certain moths, true flies, and Hymenoptera. The principal equipment here, of course, is the net. Many patterns are available from dealers (see page 340) but it is not too difficult to make a suitable net at home if the materials are available. The frame should be light, but strong, and the most favoured material now is nylon, either in one piece or several pieces fitted together. A heavy-gauge wire, about 2mm in diameter, is probably the best material for a home-made frame as it can be bent to shape and yet is not so light that it 'whips' as the net is swept through the air. A triangular shape is better than a circle, especially if the net is to be used for sweeping as well (see page 32), and it should be at least 30cm across – big enough to get your hands and a killing bottle in. The nets so often sold as

The butterfly net in use: turning the net traps the insect so that it can be examined

butterfly nets in toy shops are almost useless for catching flying insects, although they can be used as water nets. The net frame should be attached firmly to a short handle – much easier to use than a long one for general collecting, although provision for attaching a longer handle when necessary would be an advantage.

The net bag must be soft and light, not too closely woven but close enough to prevent the escape of the small insects. It must also be reasonably tough and able to withstand attack by bramble and briar. Re-inforcement is needed at the rim to prevent the frame from wearing through the material. The length of the net bag should be at least twice the diameter as this allows the net to be folded at the end of each stroke, thus trapping any insects caught in it. The colour of the net is not vital but dark colours – green, brown, or black – are best for lepidoptera and for dragonflies.

The use of the net is a matter of common sense and practice: one cannot learn how to use a net from a book. The capture of insects resting on flowers or on the ground sometimes poses problems, however: 'Do I net it where it is or do I put it up first?' The answer depends on many factors, such as the nature of the vegetation and the surface of the ground, or the state of the insect. On a flat surface, the net can be dropped over the insect which will fly up and be trapped in the end. Many drowsy insects can also have the net lowered over them – they may even be boxed without the use of the net at all. In other situations, it is usually better to disturb the insect, with the net ready for action as soon as the insect is clear of hazards.

2. **Crawling Insects** Under this heading, we can consider those insects that spend most of their time sitting or crawling on the ground or vegetation. This includes beetles, bugs, grasshoppers and crickets, psocids, and insects like stoneflies, caddis flies, and moths that fly in the evening and hide away during the day. The simplest method of finding these insects, although not the most rewarding, is to search for them in likely places – on tree trunks and walls, under leaves, etc. The larger insects can often be collected directly into a pill box but the smaller ones are best

The aspirator or pooter in use to pick up small insects

The sweep net in use: the strut across the mouth gives it extra rigidity

collected with the aid of a pooter or aspirator. More productive than searching are the techniques of sweeping and beating. Sweeping involves the use of a net and is usually confined to the relatively low herbage of fields and verges. The net is swept to and fro in front of the collector as he walks slowly along. The net contents must be examined at frequent intervals to prevent seeds and leaves from damaging specimens and also so that the collector can be sure of the plants from which the insects came. An ordinary general purpose net, such as was described above, may be used for sweeping but a better pattern is shown here. The handle is continued across the mouth of the net and allows a more controlled sweep. A stout hem is absolutely essential in a sweep net.

Beating is used to obtain insects from taller vegetation – trees, shrubs, and hedgerows. All that are needed are a stick to do the beating and something to catch insects in. A white sheet laid on the ground will do but it is better to have one stretched on a frame about 1 metre square. This can be held in one hand and thrust under the branches much more easily than an ordinary sheet. Beating is a particularly good method for obtaining caterpillars but will also yield bugs, beetles, and other leaf-feeding insects.

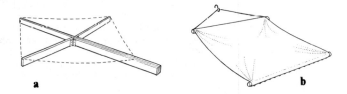

Two forms of beating tray: in **a** the material is permanently attached to the handle and to the two arms, and when it is looped over the far end the arms are automatically opened out. **b,** which is easier to carry, is attached to a convenient branch and unrolled with the other hand

3. **Soil and Litter Dwellers** Ants, beetles, and apterygotes are the main types of insect found in this situation, which is dominated by various arachnids. The habitat is moist and dark and the two main collecting methods involve driving the insects out with light and heat. The Berlese funnel is widely used for this purpose. In its simplest form, it is a glass funnel with a gauze platform fixed about half-way down it. The upper part of the funnel is filled with litter and it is then suspended over a killing bottle or tube of alcohol. An electric light bulb (not too powerful) is placed over the funnel and left on for a few hours, or even days. This gradually dries out the material and the insects, seeking darker and damper surroundings, gradually move down the funnel and then fall out at the bottom. An even simpler method of getting some of these litter dwellers is to spread some litter on a white sheet and suspend a strong light over it while turning the pieces over. Disturbed insects scuttle for cover and are easily picked up with a moist brush or pooter. This method is suitable only if the amount of litter is small, because it is very time-consuming.

4. **Aquatic Insects** Mayflies, dragonflies, stoneflies, and caddis flies all spend their early lives in water. Several moths and flies do as well, but the only insects to have mastered the water in the adult state are certain bugs and beetles, whose stiff front wings enclose an air-chamber for breathing. A net is needed to catch these water-dwelling insects but it should not be the one used for catching flying insects. A much stronger net is needed for use in water, together with a stout handle about 5ft or so long – water exerts a surprisingly large resistance and a

slender handle simply bends when the net is swept through the water. A broom handle is ideal for this purpose. The net frame should have a square end so that it can be used to scrape the bottom, rather like a shrimping net. It is not necessary for the bag of the water net to be more than about 6in deep. Another useful piece of equipment is the grab. This is like a tiny anchor, made of three or four pieces of stout wire bound together and turned up at the ends. Attached to a length of rope, it is excellent for dragging pond weeds to the edge for examination.

Baits and Traps

Almost any insect can be caught by putting down an appropriate bait or other attraction, but baits and traps are used mainly for Lepidoptera, particularly for night-flying moths. The commonest lures are 'sugar' and light (see page 191). Flowers are simple and attractive bait for many kinds of insects, while carrion and dung are also worth watching for flies and beetles. Jam-jars sunk in the soil and baited with carrion make good pitfall traps for beetles, as long as the tops are covered sufficiently to prevent the entry of mice and other mammals.

One of the most interesting methods of collecting Lepidoptera, especially certain moths, is that known as assembling. The bait here is an unmated female which is placed in a wire or muslin cage and left in an exposed position or at an open window. Several dozen males may arrive and there is always the chance of a colour variation among them, leading to the possibility of an interesting breeding programme. Unmated females are not easy to find in the wild because many females tend to stay put where they emerge until after they have been mated. The best way to obtain the virgin moths is to collect larvae and rear them: about 50 per cent will be females. The emperor moths are the best known assemblers but they are by no means the only ones and it is worth trying any virgin female as a lure. The method can also be tried with some of our larger beetles.

Preservation

When once they have been caught, the insects must be boxed or bottled for the journey home. Whenever possible, insects should be transferred into 'pill boxes' or specimen tubes so that they can be examined before killing. This avoids the all-too-common fault of killing first and then finding that the specimen is not really worth keeping. Also, many female insects, especially moths, will lay eggs after capture and present one with the opportunity to rear the species and study the young stages. Most insects will travel in the living state better than they will if killed and, if a large enough supply of containers is available, this is the best way of getting them home. Exceptions to this are most of the Diptera and some other fragile insects which should be killed at once and pinned or properly packed in the field. Cellulose wadding or soft tissue should be used to pack the insects, not cotton wool. Dead insects should never be carried home loosely in jars and boxes as they will soon be damaged.

The standard type of killing bottle is a wide-mouthed bottle with a securely fitting bung. It should be large enough for the largest insects likely to be collected. If you are interested only in certain small insects, then specimen tubes 20mm in diameter will do quite well. Pieces of tissue should be inserted to prevent the dead insects from rolling about in the jar.

There are many different types of killing agent but cyanide is the choice of most professional entomologists. This is a lethal substance and, if one wishes to use it, the cyanide bottle is best made up by a chemist. Lumps of potassium cyanide are mixed with *dry* plaster of Paris and put in the bottom of a strong bottle to form a layer about 1cm deep. This should be covered with a layer of wet plaster some 15mm deep and the bottle then placed *open* in a well ventilated place to dry for a day or two. It will then be ready for use. The cyanide gradually decomposes and gives off hydrogen cyanide gas which diffuses out through the plaster. The life of the cyanide bottle is quite long* and this killing agent is certainly useful if one does a lot of collecting. If collecting is infrequent, however, then one of the liquid killing agents is a safer proposition. These substances include ethyl acetate, chloroform, carbon tetrachloride, and ammonia.

The various liquid killing agents all have their supporters and opponents, and several of them have one or more drawbacks. Ammonia, for example, has an adverse effect on certain greens. Ethyl acetate and carbon tetrachloride are probably the most widely used and are certainly quite satisfactory for general collecting. For use with liquid agents, the killing bottle should have a layer of plaster poured into it. When the plaster is set, sufficient liquid is added to moisten the plaster thoroughly, but not enough to leave surplus liquid in the killing bottle. The liquid will gradually evaporate but the bottle can be recharged again and again and its life is indefinite. Most of these liquid killing agents destroy plastic, so do not put them into plastic tubes.

In the absence of a specific killing agent, one can always resort to crushed young laurel leaves. Surprisingly enough, these give out the same poison as cyanide but they are relatively harmless to handle. One big advantage of laurel leaves over most killing agents, is that they keep the insects in a soft or relaxed condition for quite a long time, without allowing them to go mouldy. Laurel leaves may also be used for relaxing specimens that have already dried.

Boiling water is another useful standby as a killing agent and is the quickest of the lot. It is especially useful for the tougher insects, such as beetles, but must not be used for those with hairy or scaly wings.

Because of their relatively small bodies, most insects can be preserved simply by drying them in the air. Thus dried, they will keep indefinitely if protected from mould and other pests. Some large-bodied insects are best cleaned out before drying but there are few of these in Britain, although dragonflies sometimes need special treatment if they are to retain their colours (page 72). Drying is not suitable, however, for many of the smaller insects with thin cuticles. These shrivel on drying and the insects become unrecognisable. Such insects should be preserved in spirit or else in cavity slides for use with microscopes. Methyl alcohol and industrial meths are the most convenient forms of spirit but a permit is necessary from the Excise Office to buy industrial meths. After-shave lotion is also a good preservative, although more expensive! Insects can be put straight into the preservative from the net or pill-box. The smaller insects are fragile and spirit bottles should be completely full to avoid damage by shaking.

Insects that can be preserved dry can be treated in one of four ways: direct pinning, staging, carding, or pointing. In direct pinning, the pin passes directly through the insect, usually through the thorax, although some insects are best pinned elsewhere. Ordinary pins should not be used because they are too thick

* Old cyanide bottles must be *destroyed*, not merely thrown away. Put them in a really hot bonfire or a furnace, or else bury them *deeply* with the bung out.

and they also tend to rust. Specially manufactured entomological pins should be used. These are obtainable from entomological dealers (see page 340) and come in various lengths and thicknesses. Several sizes will be needed for a general collection. Insects should always be pinned when relaxed, preferably when they are fresh, because the cuticle is then elastic and grips the pin properly.

Those insects with large or showy wings are generally set after pinning. This involves spreading out the wings and flattening them to show them to their best advantage. Setting boards are normally used for this. They are cork or polystyrene boards of various widths and bearing a groove down the centre. The insects are placed on suitable boards, with their bodies in the grooves. The wings can then be arranged on the board and pinned into position with retaining strips of paper. It is general practice to arrange the wings so that the hind edge of the front wing is at right angles to the body, but this is not possible with all insects. When both pairs of wings are of a similar nature and are coupled in flight, it is usual to overlap them slightly when setting. The length of time needed for the specimens to dry obviously depends upon the temperature and the bulk of the insects' bodies but 3–4 weeks will generally be sufficient. The insects can then be removed to the cabinet or store box. Insects that are usually set include Lepidoptera, dragonflies, mayflies, and lacewings. Some grasshoppers are also set, especially just on one side. Bees, wasps, and true flies, although they have 'settable' wings, are not usually set because many useful features of the thorax are obscured by setting.

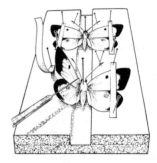

Arranging insects on a setting board

Staging is used only for small insects. The specimens are first of all pinned directly with very fine, headless pins. The smallest specimens may simply be impaled on the point of one of these pins. The pin is then stuck into a strip of polyporus or polystyrene – two of the few materials soft enough to take these fine pins without bending them – and the stage, as this strip of material is called, is then pinned through with a stouter pin which attaches it to the store box.

Carding is widely used for displaying beetles but it is not really suitable for a scientific collection because the underside of the specimen is obscured. The method involves sticking the insects to small pieces of card and then spreading the legs and antennae out with a lightly gummed brush so that they stick to the card at their tips. A wide variety of adhesives can be used but they must not dry too quickly, otherwise you will not have time to arrange the specimens properly. Carding may also be used for earwigs, cockroaches, and most heteropteran bugs

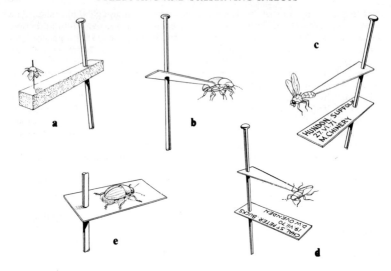

Methods of dealing with small insects: **a,** staging; **b, c, d,** pointing; **e,** carding

if these are being preserved merely for display purposes. Otherwise, these insects should be pinned.

Pointing is another very satisfactory method for the smaller insects that cannot be directly pinned. The points are small triangles of thin card or celluloid (Polyglaze is a useful material) and the insects are attached to them by small spots of adhesive. The points are then pinned into the store box. The pins must obviously be put through the points before the insects are attached and the safest way to attach the insects is to put the gum on the tip of the point and then pick the insect up with it. No attempt is made to set these small insects, other than to arrange them so that the important features are visible.

One very important aspect of collecting insects, whatever methods are used for catching and preserving them, is labelling. All specimens should bear labels giving details of place and time of capture, together with any other relevant information on the habitat. It is usual also to add the collector's name to the label. Although all this information may seem unnecessary for a small, personal collection, it all adds to the scientific value of the specimens: there is always the chance that someone will want to make a detailed study of the insect fauna in your area and fully labelled specimens will provide a background for any future study. The labels should always be on the same pin as the specimen so that the two cannot be separated.

Finally, a warning about the storing of insect collections. Remember that almost everything is eaten by something or other, and dead insects are no exception. Booklice and other small insects seem to make their way into the tightest fitting boxes and can wreak havoc with the collection if not checked. Most store boxes and cabinet drawers have special 'camphor cells' into which you can put naphthalene to ward off these pests. If there is no such cell, you can pin a small muslin bag into one corner of the box, or you can spray the collection periodically with one of the aerosol moth-proofing products (not if you have living caterpillars in the same room!). Mould is another possible problem but it can generally be avoided by complete drying of the specimens before storing them and by storing them in a dry place. Do not stack your boxes against an outside wall – there is always a chance of damp, however well built the house may be.

Breeding Insects

This is a very worth-while occupation because it not only produces good adult specimens for study, but allows one to study the young stages as well. Life history details are poorly known for many of our insects but they must be discovered if we are to understand the insects' habitat requirements. Breeding insects is not usually difficult, although certain species, notably some of the larger butterflies, will not pair in a confined space. It is always worth keeping adult females alive for a time to see if they produce eggs. Rearing the young stages is quite easy for most species. One simply needs to provide them with the correct food and conditions as near as possible to those found in their natural habitats. Detailed information on insect breeding is outside the scope of this book but plenty can be found in the books listed in the Bibliography.

The Classification of Insects and a Key for the Identification of the Orders

The young entomologist will often find himself faced with a bewildering assortment of foreign-sounding names and he might well feel like the gnat in Alice Through the Looking Glass: 'What's the use of their having names if they won't answer to them?' Alice's wise reply was 'No use to them but it's useful to the people that name them I suppose,' and this is precisely why we name things – so that we can refer to any particular object without going into a lengthy description of it.

Most of our larger and more conspicuous animals – mammals, birds, and so on – have acquired common English names but among insects, only the butter-flies and larger moths, together with a few large or economically important members of other groups, have English names. The layman cannot distinguish between the smaller and less conspicuous insects and therefore cannot give them common names. He may recognise some as grasshoppers or dragonflies but the rest are dismissed as 'flies' or 'bugs', and it is left to the entomologist to name them.

Biologists always use Latin or latinised Greek words when naming plants or animals and, although this may seem rather unfair to the beginner, there are good reasons for it. In the seventeenth and eighteenth centuries, when the classification of living things was in its infancy, Latin was the principal written language for educated people and Latin was automatically used for naming plants and animals. Although it was later replaced by modern languages for most purposes, biologists saw no reason for abandoning Latin names, for biology is a world-wide science and there would be disadvantages in using any single modern language. Several European languages are derived from Latin and this reduces the problem involved. If it is to be of the best possible use, a scientific name must give some indication of the nature of the organism and Latin or latinised Greek is usually better at doing this than modern languages because the word 'stems' can be compounded to convey the description in a shorter space. For example, *Hydrometra stagnorum* is a much better way of saying 'water-measurer of stagnant water'.

Each different kind, or species, is given a double-barrelled name. This is known as the binominal system and more will be said about this a little later.

Names of the species are not the only ones that confront the entomologist. There are many others referring to orders, families, genera, and so on in the hierarchy of classification, and these are just as important as the names of the species themselves. Classification is a way of arranging living things in logical groups for convenient use. Each group contains species with certain features in common and each group must have a name. The group name should give some indication of the nature of the component species, just as the specific name describes the species.

Just imagine what would happen if the insects had not been classified into groups and you wanted to find out if an insect you had found was new to science.

You would have to look at every picture and description of every specimen ever collected to be sure that there was no other one like yours. This would clearly be an impossible task, but with classification and the arrangement of the insects in groups, the search can be narrowed down straight away. If your specimen has features that place it in the earwig group, then no time need be spent searching the other groups.

The arrangement of insects into named groups according to major structural features also makes it much easier to describe an insect. Merely by reading that a new fly belongs, for example, to the genus *Pollenia* in the family Calliphoridae, an entomologist has a fairly good idea what the new insect looks like. All that is necessary to complete the description is a list of features that separate the new species from other species of *Pollenia*. Without such classification, it would be necessary to describe the insect in full – number of wings, form of antennae, venation of wings, and so on. Classification is clearly necessary.

The characteristic features of insects and their position in the Arthropoda have already been discussed. We must now move on to the classification of the insects themselves. Here, the major division is into two sub-classes – the primitive, wingless **Apterygota** and the more advanced **Pterygota** whose members are winged or secondarily wingless. Within these sub-classes there are sufficient structural variations to justify their division into a number of orders. Among the Pterygota, wing structure is one of the most important features in classification and many of the order names refer to the nature of the wings. There are, however, many variations within the orders and several orders are wingless, so that wing characteristics are not the only ones that have to be taken into account.

Classification, or taxonomy as it is properly called, is not an exact science because much depends upon the opinions of the workers involved. Two main lines can be distinguished among taxonomists – the 'splitters' and the 'lumpers'. The splitters may erect two or more orders for a group of insects which the 'lumpers' regard as a single order. Whether one is a splitter or a lumper depends upon the importance one attaches to certain features. As an example, we can take the alder flies, the snake flies, and the lacewing flies. The major differences between them are in the larvae and the splitter regards these differences as sufficient to split these insects into three separate orders. The lumper, however, feels that the larval differences are less significant than the adult similarities and includes the three groups in a single order, the Neuroptera. Different workers may therefore list different numbers of orders.

In this book we shall follow the classification given by Imms (1957) and recognise 29 orders. Not all of them are represented in the British Isles and we are lucky that the termites (Isoptera) are absent from our country. Other absentees are the orders Grylloblattodea (wingless soil-living insects), Embioptera (web-spinners), and Zoraptera (strange little insects living in decaying wood and humus). The order Phasmida (stick and leaf insects) has no British species, although there are a few colonies of introduced stick insects in the warmer parts of these islands.

THE CLASSIFICATION OF INSECTS

40 THE CLASSIFICATION OF INSECTS

The 29 orders recognised by Imms are as follows:

Class Insecta

Sub-class Apterygota These are primitive insects without wings and their thoracic structure suggests that they have never had wings during their history.

Order Thysanura	Silver-fish and other bristle-tails
Order Diplura	Tiny soil-living insects
Order Protura	Minute soil-living insects
Order Collembola	Springtails

Sub-class Pterygota These are basically winged insects, although a number of them have lost their wings during the course of evolution.

Division Exopterygota The wings develop externally and there is no marked change during the life history. The young stages, called nymphs, usually resemble the adults in all but size and the absence of fully developed wings. This division is also called the Hemimetabola.

Order Ephemeroptera	Mayflies
Order Odonata	Dragonflies
Order Plecoptera	Stoneflies
*Order Grylloblattodea	Soil-living insects of American mountains
Order Orthoptera	Crickets and Grasshoppers
Order Phasmida	Stick and leaf insects
Order Dermaptera	Earwigs
Order Embioptera	Web-spinners
Order Dictyoptera	Cockroaches
Order Isoptera	Termites
*Order Zoraptera	Minute insects of uncertain affinity
Order Psocoptera	Booklice or psocids
Order Mallophaga	Biting lice
Order Anoplura	Sucking lice
Order Hemiptera	True bugs
Order Thysanoptera	Thrips

Division Endopterygota The wings develop inside the body of the young stages and there is a marked change (metamorphosis) during the life history. The young stages are very different from the adults and are called larvae. The change from larva to adult takes place during a resting stage – the pupa. This division is also called the Holometabola.

Order Neuroptera	Alder flies, snake flies, and lacewing flies
Order Mecoptera	Scorpion flies
Order Lepidoptera	Butterflies and moths
Order Trichoptera	Caddis flies
Order Diptera	True flies (two-winged flies)
Order Siphonaptera	Fleas
Order Hymenoptera	Bees, wasps, and ants
Order Coleoptera	Beetles
Order Strepsiptera	Stylopids – parasites of bees.

Orders marked with an asterisk do not occur in Europe.

The orders themselves can be grouped into several super-orders according to their evolutionary relationships but this aspect of classification is of technical interest only and of no concern in the present practical book.

Classification does not stop at orders, however. Most of them are too large and embrace too much variation to be handled as a whole and the orders are therefore split up into a greater or lesser number of smaller groups. It may happen that there are within an order two or more distinct lines, although not sufficiently distinct to merit separate orders. These lines may be designated sub-orders. Another worker may decide that these lines *do* merit ordinal rank and erect orders for them. This has been done for the alder flies, snake flies, and lace-wing flies already referred to but it is of minor importance in the general scheme of classification as long as there still remain well-labelled 'pigeon holes' for these insects.

One of the most important categories is the family, often called the natural family to emphasise the fact that it is a natural grouping as opposed to the some-what artificial higher groups. The family contains a number of different species which are clearly related to each other because of detailed similarities. By con-vention, family names always end in -idae. When there are several families in an order or sub-order they may be grouped into superfamilies, the members of each superfamily resembling each other more than they resemble members of other superfamilies. Superfamily names always end in -oidea.

Just as orders are sometimes split into sub-orders, so families are often split into sub-families with names ending in -inae. All the sub-families share the main features of the family but there are minor differences between them. A genus is an even smaller group consisting of closely related species. The species themselves are the kinds of animals: the units of the living world. It is not easy to say just what is a species but it is usually described as an assemblage of individuals with clear similarities in appearance and structure, inhabiting the same area and inter-breeding freely among themselves.

As mentioned above, the scientific name of a species consists of two words. The first, always spelled with a capital letter, is the name of its genus – its generic name. The second is always spelled with a small letter and is the specific name. These names are usually printed in italics. This binominal system was introduced by the Swedish naturalist Linnaeus in 1758 and it has two great advantages over a single name system, for one thing, it indicates the relationship of the animal by giving the genus to which it belongs: if we see the names *Pieris brassicae* and *Pieris rapae* we know at once that the two insects are closely related. If the insects had only one name each, *brassicae* and *rapae*, there would be no indication of their relationship. The other big advantage in having two names is that the specific names can be used over and over again with different generic names. Every genus must, of course, have a different name but the specific name, describing a particular member of the genus, can be used many times, although never more than once in a given genus. For example, members of several genera may inhabit similar places and, because the specific name can be used again and again, all can have a specific name indicating the type of place in which they live. Thus, when we see *Musca domestica* and *Thermobia domestica* we know that the two species inhabit domestic premises. If there were only one name, only one insect could be called *domestica* and the domestic nature of the other would not be apparent.

Although the species is regarded as the biological unit, it can be sub-divided. Genetic variation can produce abnormal forms very different from the normal form, although still able to interbreed freely. Perhaps more important is geographical variation. When geographical barriers, such as mountains, seas, or simply unsuitable habitats, divide a population into isolated units differences can gradually evolve between the two separated populations. If brought together, the animals can still interbreed but the differences may be sufficiently constant and clear for the species to be split into two or more sub-species or geographical races. This has happened quite often with British insects cut off from the main populations of Europe and we have quite a number of sub-species of our own. One of the best known is the British race of the Swallowtail butterfly, *Papilio machaon brittanicus* (Pl. 16), which is quite different from the European races. When a sub-species is recognised, a third word is added to the scientific name – *brittanicus* being clearly appropriate for the British Swallowtail.

The name of the person who first described the insect should strictly be given after the insect's name. A name in brackets indicates that the person concerned first described the insect but gave it a different generic name. This brings us to a common cause of complaint – name changing. The scientific naming of animals is strictly governed by the rules of the International Commission for Zoological Nomenclature and one of the most important rules is that the first correct name given to an animal is the only valid name.

When people began to name insects and other animals there was not the degree of communication that we enjoy today. Quite often a name was published but became buried in the literature and failed to reach another entomologist who gave a different name to the same species. When the earlier publication comes to light and it is proved that the two names refer to the same species, the law of priority dictates that the earlier name shall be adopted even though the later name may have become established. To take an example, the Clouded Yellow butterfly (Pl. 18) was for a long time known as *Colias edusa* Fabricius but it was then found that Geoffroy had described the insect and named it *Colias crocea* in 1785, two years before Fabricius published his description. The correct name for the species is therefore *Colias crocea* Geoffroy. Generic names may also have to be changed if earlier names are found.

The early entomologists frequently made mistakes in classification and tended to be large scale 'lumpers'. This resulted in many quite different insects being grouped in a single genus. Linnaeus, for example, proposed the generic name *Libellula* for all the dragonflies he knew and when Amos Harris first described our beautiful demoiselle *Agrion splendens* (Pl. 2) he followed Linnaeus' lead and called it *Libellula splendens*. It was later shown that this insect belongs to the genus *Agrion* and its correct name is therefore *Agrion splendens* (Harris), although this is a later name than the original *Libellula splendens*. Harris is still credited with the original description but, because he described the insect under a different generic name, his own name is in brackets. Most changes in generic names have arisen in this way through the splitting up of the original genera. Only two of the 11 species Linnaeus described in *Libellula* retain that name, although they still retain the specific names given to them by Linnaeus.

The Key

The first thing to do when trying to identify an unknown insect is to assign it to its correct order, and with the help of a lens and of the following key you should be able to place almost any adult British insect in its correct order. We say 'almost' because there is enormous variation within the orders as well as between them and most orders contain a few species that are atypical. These 'odd-men-out' cannot be run down with a general key but you will soon learn to recognise them. In fact, the characteristics of most of the orders are so clear that before long you will be able to place an insect in its order without reference to this key at all. You will be able to say that a particular specimen is a stonefly (or what ever it is) *because it looks like it.* A combination of features such as resting attitude or method of flying, or simply general appearance will indicate the order without your having to examine the wing structure. These features are less precise and less easy to describe than those in the key, but when once they are known they are equally important in identification.

In order to use the key, the beginner must always start at the beginning and work through systematically. Each clue has two (occasionally three) alternatives. Read these carefully and select the one that applies to the specimen you are investigating. To take the simplest example, clue 1 has as its alternatives 'winged' or 'wingless'. Having selected the appropriate one, look at the figure on the right. If your insect has wings, the figure 2 is shown and this is the number of your next clue. Follow this procedure with every clue you meet. If you follow the clues accurately and in sequence each insect studied will fall in with one or other of the alternatives. If you come to a clue neither of whose alternatives appear to fit the insect then you have gone wrong earlier in the key, or more probably you are looking at a young insect.

As you go through the key you will find that the clues become more and more detailed as the search is narrowed down to the group to which the insect belongs. Eventually a clue will be followed not by a number but by a name – the name of the order to which the insect belongs. To identify your insect further it is necessary to turn to the section concerned. There you will find descriptions of the order and usually further keys that will enable you to discover the family to which your specimen belongs.

As with the orders, it is possible to recognise many families by general appearance and this is where the illustrations play their part. The species illustrated are, in general, those that 'look like' the family, and there are many small diagrams which point out the distinguishing features between related families.

From the descriptions and illustrations you may even be able to find out the name of your insect but, with more than 20,000 species in the British Isles, only a very small proportion can be included in this book. If you wish to pursue the identification further you will have to refer to a specialist work dealing with the order concerned. The most appropriate of these works are listed at the end of the book but it is as well to remind the reader that the structural differences between individual species, or even genera, are very much smaller than the differences between families and a microscope is indispensable for work with the smaller insects. More specialised knowledge is necessary for further work of this kind but it is hoped that the glossary will provide help in this direction.

Key to the Orders of European Insects

1. Insects winged   2
   Insects wingless or with vestigial wings   28

2. One pair of wings   3
   Two pairs of wings   7

3. Body grasshopper-like, with enlarged   Orthoptera, p. 78
   hind legs and pronotum extending
   back over abdomen

   Insect not like this   4

4. Abdomen with 'tails'   5
   Abdomen without 'tails'   6

5. Insects <5mm long, with relatively   Hemiptera, p. 111
   long antennae: wing with only one
   forked vein

   Larger insects with short   Ephemeroptera, p. 58
   antennae and many wing
   veins: tails relatively long

6. Front wings forming club-shaped   Strepsiptera, p. 320
   halteres

   Hind wings forming halteres   Diptera, p. 207
   (may be hidden)

7. Front wings hard or leathery   8
   All wings membranous   13

8. Front wings horny except for   Hemiptera, p. 111
   membranous tip

   Front wings of uniform texture throughout   9

9. Front wings hard and veinless, meeting in centre
line 10

Front wings with many veins, overlapping at least a
little and often held roofwise over the body 11

10. Abdomen ending in a pair Dermaptera, p. 89
of 'forceps'

Abdomen without forceps Coleoptera, p. 290

11. Insects with piercing and sucking beaks Hemiptera, p. 111

beak

Insects with chewing mouths: cerci usually present 12

12. Hind legs modified for jumping Orthoptera, p. 78

Hind legs not modified for jumping Dictyoptera, p. 93

13. Small slender insects with  Thysanoptera, p. 140
narrow, hair-fringed wings:
often found in flowers

Insects not like this 14

14. Head extending downwards Mecoptera, p. 152
into a beak

beak

No such beak 15

15. Wings more or less covered with minute Lepidoptera, p. 154
flattened scales: coiled proboscis
(tongue) usually present

Wings usually transparent, although often hairy 16

16. Wings with a network of veins, including many
    cross veins   17
    Wings with relatively few cross veins   21

17. Abdomen ending with long threads   18
    Terminal appendages short or absent   19

18. Front wings much larger than hind   Ephemeroptera, p. 58
    wings: wings
    held vertically
    over body at rest:
    2 or 3 terminal
    appendages

    Wings more or less equal in size,   Plecoptera, p. 72
    or hind wings larger: wings folded
    close to body at rest: 2 terminal
    appendages

19. Antennae very short: body at   Odonata, p. 63
    least 25mm long

    Antennae longer, greater than width of head   20

20. Tarsi with 3 segments   Plecoptera, p. 72

    Tarsi with 5 segments   Neuroptera, p. 142

21. Wings noticeably hairy   22
    Wings not noticeably hairy   23

22. All wings more or less alike: front
    tarsi swollen

Embioptera, p. 92*

Hind wings usually broader
than front wings: front tarsi
not swollen

Trichoptera, p. 195

23. Tiny insects covered with white powder

Neuroptera, p. 142

    Wings transparent   24

24. Tarsi with 4 or 5 segments   25
    Tarsi with 1–3 segments   26

25. All wings alike

Isoptera, p. 99*

    Hind wings much smaller than
    front wings

Hymenoptera, p. 247

26. Hind wings similar to or larger than
    front wings: abdomen with cerci

Plecoptera, p. 72

    Hind wings smaller than front wings: no cerci   27

27. Tiny insects with at least 12
    antennal segments

Psocoptera, p. 102

Never more than 10 antennal segments: piercing and sucking beak present

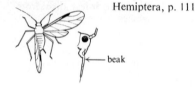

Hemiptera, p. 111

28. Insects with long, slender, twig-like body

Phasmida, p. 88

Insects not like this   29

29. Insects with grasshopper-like body, with long hind legs

Orthoptera, p. 78

Insects not like this   30

30. Small soft-bodied insects living on plants under a protective shield or scale

Hemiptera, p. 111

Insects not like this   31

31. Minute soil-living insects (<2mm long), without antennae

Protura, p. 54

Insects not like this   32

32. Insects with cerci or other abdominal appendages   33
     Insects without such appendages   40

33. Appendages long and conspicuous   34
     Appendages short or hidden under body   37

34. Appendages forming pincers   35
     Appendages not forming pincers   36

35. Tarsi with 3 segments

Dermaptera, p. 89

     Tarsi with only 1 segment   Diplura, p. 53

36. Abdomen with 3 long appendages

Thysanura, p. 52

     Abdomen with only two appendages

Diplura, p. 53

37. Small jumping insects with head
produced into a   beak: vestigial wings
present   Mecoptera, p. 152

No sign of a beak   38

38. Small or minute insects with a
forked springing organ under the   Collembola, p. 55
hind end of the body: found in
soil or decaying vegetation
Insects not like this   39

39. Tarsi usually with 4 segments   Isoptera, p. 99*

Tarsi with 3 segments: front tarsus   Embioptera, p. 92*
swollen

40. Parasites in fur or feathers: insects generally flattened side-to-side or dorso-ventrally   41
Insects not parasitic and not usually flattened   45

41. Jumping insects flattened from side   Siphonaptera, p. 243
to side

Insects flattened dorso-ventrally   42

42. Insects of moderate size: head partly withdrawn into
thorax   43
Small or minute insects: head not withdrawn into
thorax   44

43. Antennae short: very 'leggy' insects with   Diptera, p. 207
strong claws well suited to clinging to the
host mammal

Antennae longer: body somewhat circular: Hemiptera, p. 111
claws less prominent

prothorax

44. Biting mouths: prothorax distinct   Mallophaga, p. 108

Sucking mouths: thoracic segments fused   Anoplura, p. 109
into one unit

45. Abdomen constricted to a 'waist';   Hymenoptera, p. 248
    antennae often 'elbowed'

    No such features   46

46. Body clothed with flattened hairs and scales: wing
    vestiges present   Lepidoptera, p. 154
    Body naked   47

47. Head as wide, or nearly as wide   Psocoptera, p. 102
    as body: antennae long and
    slender: insects frequently found
    among dried materials

    Head narrower than body: Hemiptera, p. 111
    antennae shorter: abdomen often
    with a pair of tubular outgrowths
    near hind end: insects found on
    growing plants

THE APTERYGOTE INSECTS

The sub-class Apterygota (=without wings) contains a rather heterogeneous assortment of wingless insects. Some 2,500 species are known but, because of the small size and secretive habits of these insects, many more are undoubtedly awaiting discovery, even in the British Isles. Most of them live in the soil and among decaying vegetation.

It is believed that the apterygotes are the most primitive insects and that they have never had wings in their evolutionary history. Detailed study of the thorax of these insects has revealed no vestige of the wing-bearing apparatus such as is found in the wingless lice and fleas. The fossil records provide further evidence of the primitive nature of the apterygotes: Devonian rocks more than 300 million years old have yielded a fossil (*Rhyniella*) which appears to be a springtail and which is a good deal older than the earliest known winged insects. Yet more evidence is provided by the presence of abdominal appendages other than the normal cerci and genitalia. These probably indicate a closer affinity with some multi-legged ancestral arthropod than is shown by the more advanced insects.

Four orders are recognised among the Apterygota but their relationship to each other is not clear. They may well be a polyphyletic group, evolved independently from more than one ancestral type. The springtails and proturans are so distinct that some workers even question the wisdom of including them among the insects. Present practice, however, is to regard them as rather aberrant off-shoots from the insectan line. Only the bristle-tails can be regarded as close to the main line of insect evolution leading to the winged forms.

Among the apterygotes, metamorphosis is slight or absent. The young insects resemble their parents in all but size and reproductive organs.

The soil-living apterygotes may be collected in the usual ways and preserved in alcohol. Slide mounts can be made with whole specimens of the smaller species.

Order Thysanura – Bristle-Tails

Recognition features Small wingless insects up to 20mm long. Tapering, carrot-shaped body with shiny scales. Long, thread-like antennae and three long, segmented 'tails' at the hind end.

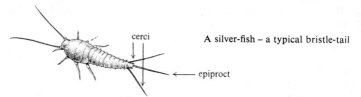

A silver-fish – a typical bristle-tail

Of the apterygotes, the bristle-tails are the most likely to come to the notice of the casual observer because they include our largest species and because some of them inhabit domestic premises. Most housewives will have seen a silver-fish dart away from some spilled flour in that neglected corner of the kitchen cupboard.

The bristle-tails are extremely primitive insects with simple biting mouths. The body is carrot-shaped and usually covered with tiny, shiny scales, hence the name Silver-fish for our common household representative. If you try to pick up one of these insects you are likely to retain nothing but a coating of scales on your fingers, the insect itself slipping quietly away. The antennae are long and thread-like. The tarsi have two, three, or four segments and most of the abdominal segments carry small appendages. The last abdominal segment carries two long, jointed cerci and a central, segmented 'tail'. These processes are fringed with bristles and are responsible for the name of the order, derived from the Greek words *thysanos* (fringe) and *oura* (tail).

The only insects with which the bristle-tails are likely to be confused are the two-pronged bristle-tails of the order Diplura. Complete specimens are readily identified by the number of 'tails' but if the central one is lost other features must be examined. The 1-segmented tarsi of the diplurans are useful distinguishing features, as is the general body shape. Size is important in the British species: our bristle-tails are all more than 9mm long *when adult*, whereas the diplurans are never more than 5mm long.

Metamorphosis in the thysanurans is very slight, the main external change being the appearance of scales after the first few moults. There are at least six instars and often many more. Many members of the order continue to moult throughout their lives, which may be four or five years. This is unusual because insects normally stop growing and moulting when once they reach maturity.

The order is divided into two families, both of which are represented in the British Isles. They may be distinguished as follows:

Compound eyes large: ocelli small: living under stones and
among low-growing vegetation   Machilidae
Compound eyes small and inconspicuous: no ocelli: living in
domestic premises

Lepismatidae

Of our seven representatives of the family Machilidae, the largest and most frequently seen is *Petrobius maritimus*, a metallic-coloured creature about 18mm long. It lives on the sea shore among organic detritus brought in by the waves.

The firebrat

Our two members of the Lepismatidae are better-known. The Silver-fish, *Lepisma saccharina*, is a common insect in food cupboards and similar places where it feeds on scraps of paper, the glue of cartons, spilled flour, and so on. The Firebrat, *Thermobia domestica*, as one would expect from its name, frequents warmer places such as bakeries and kitchens where, like the Silver-fish, it feeds on carbohydrate material. It can be distinguished from the Silver-fish by its much longer antennae and cerci.

Order Diplura – Two-Pronged Bristle-Tails

Recognition features Small wingless, soil or detritus-living insects with two cerci. British species never more than 5mm long.

A typical dipluran

These insects were formerly grouped with the three-pronged bristle-tails in the order Thysanura but are now placed in an order of their own because of a number of differences. The most constant and important of these is the arrangement of the mouth-parts; in the diplurans, the mouth-parts are partially sunk into the head capsule whereas those of the thysanurans are free. This difference, however, is not readily detected and for recognition purposes, certainly as far as the British species are concerned, the general body shape, number of 'tails', and number of tarsal segments can be relied on.

The diplurans live in soil, under bark, and in other dark, humid places where there is decaying material on which they can feed. They are all pale in colour and have neither compound eyes nor ocelli. Their antennae are relatively stouter than those of the thysanurans and the segments more clearly visible. The thoracic segments are clearly separated and the tarsi have only one segment. Like the thysanurans, these insects have paired appendages on most of the abdominal segments, although these are not visible without a microscope. There is no extension of the 11th abdominal segment into a central 'tail' so that the body ends merely with the two cerci (Diplura = two tails).

It is probable that the diplurans are the closest to the origin of insects from some arthropod ancestor for they have a number of features in common with centipedes.

Two European genera of Diplura: **a**, *Japyx*; **b**, *Anajapyx*

Three families are recognised in the Diplura. All are present in Europe but only one, the family **Campodeidae**, is found in the British Isles. Twelve species have been discovered in these islands so far, all belonging to the genus *Campodea*. They all have long, slender cerci. The other two families occur mainly in the tropics, although they extend into Southern Europe. The cerci in the family **Japygidae** are in the form of pincers, while those of the **Projapygidae** are short and stout.

Order Protura

Recognition features Minute white soil-living insects less than 2mm long. Antennae and eyes absent. Front legs held forwards in the manner of antennae.

A typical proturan

These tiny creatures, not at all resembling the normal idea of insects, were not discovered until 1907 but since then they have been uncovered in all parts of the world. About 50 species have been recognised so far, 12 of them in Britain. The proturans feed on decaying material and can be found in leaf litter and in moist soil with plenty of organic matter, but a microscope is almost indispensable for the search, the largest known species being under 2mm long. There is no common name for the group, the name Protura meaning 'simple tail' and referring to the simple pointed telson.

Although it is possible to see the proturans with the naked eye, a microscope is essential if one wishes to make out any of their anatomy. The head is rather conical in shape, pointed at the front and ending in piercing mouth-parts. There are no eyes or antennae but the front legs are held forwards at the sides of the head and probably concern themselves with the sense of touch. The tarsi have only one segment and end in a single claw. The cylindrical abdomen has the full complement of 11 segments in the adult but the young proturan has only eight abdominal segments plus the pointed telson. Segments 9, 10, and 11 are added during development so that there is slight metamorphosis. Such increase in segments during post-embryonic development is not found in other insects but it is a feature of arthropods in general. This is one of the main reasons given by those who think the proturans should not be classified as insects.

The first three segments of the abdomen each bear a pair of tiny appendages and the classification of the order into families depends on the structure of these appendages. Three families are recognised at present and all are represented in the British fauna.

The only satisfactory way to preserve these insects is by making slide mounts.

Order Collembola – Springtails

Recognition features Small wingless insects, rarely more than 5mm long. Body cylindrical or globular and usually provided with a forked springing organ at the hind end that enables the insects to leap into the air when disturbed. Living in soil, leaf litter and vegetation in general.

A typical springtail, with the 'spring' released

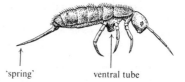

'spring'   ventral tube

This is by far the largest order of apterygotes as far as present knowledge goes, containing about 1,500 species. Its distribution is world-wide and certain species even occur beyond the permanent snow lines of the Arctic and Antarctic regions, apparently feeding on sparse algae or pollen grains deposited by the wind. The majority of species, however, live in soil, leaf litter and refuse where the humidity is high, for these insects are very susceptible to drying. A few even live in and around water, the common *Podura aquatica* being found in large numbers on the surface of ponds. Greys and browns are the predominant colours for springtails, although some are white and many litter-living species are mottled with brown and pale yellow. The body is often clothed with hairs or scales and many species have a prominent collar of bristles just behind the head.

The mouth-parts of springtails are of the biting type and are partially sunk into the head capsule. The antennae are variable in length although they never contain more than six segments: four is the usual number. There are no compound eyes but a number of ocelli are usually present and are often surrounded by a pigmented area that gives the impression of an eye. The thoracic segments are not readily distinguishable from those of the abdomen apart from the fact that they carry the legs, but the legs themselves are unusual in that they have no tarsal segments: the tibiae end in single or double claws.

It is in the abdomen that the springtails differ so much from other insects, to the extent that their insectan status is sometimes questioned. The abdomen contains only six segments compared with eleven in all other adult insects. In all springtails, the first abdominal segment bears a characteristic organ called the ventral tube, formed by the fusion of the appendages of that segment. The tube contains eversible sacs or vesicles that are expanded by forcing blood into them. Respiration, water absorption, and adhesion are among the functions suggested for this organ. Springtails confined in a small glass container certainly press the opening of the tube against the glass as they walk about and the name Collembola refers to the adhesion idea (*kolla*=glue and *embolos*=peg), but no conclusive evidence has yet been obtained on the function of the tube.

The third and fourth abdominal segments are concerned with the springing action that gives the group its common name. The forked springing organ is formed by the partial fusion of the appendages of the fourth abdominal segment and is known as the furcula. When not in use, it is folded forward under the abdomen and held in place by the appendages of the third abdominal segment which again are partially fused and are known as the hamula or retinaculum. When the animal is disturbed the hamula releases the furcula whose muscles then contract and pull it backwards and downwards on to the ground. The force of this action is sufficient to drive the whole insect forwards through the air. This springing organ is well developed in most springtails but is small or absent in a few genera. Jumping is not, of course, the usual method of locomotion because the insects often live in confined spaces. They walk or run jerkily among the leaf litter, with the antennae continuously on the move seeking out passage ways and food.

There are usually six to eight instars in the springtail's life span, although the insects reach sexual maturity before they reach maximum size. The changes that take place during the life history are so slight that we can say metamorphosis is absent. Under normal conditions there are probably several generations per year.

Springtails can be collected in abundance from leaf litter by the usual methods (p. 32), although their jumping activities make picking up with a moist brush rather difficult.

The British springtails so far discovered number about 300, and the main groups can be identified with the following key:

Key to the Main Groups of British Springtails

1. Body more or less elongate   2
   Body more or less globular   3

2. Pronotum similar to other terga and
   quite visible from above: cuticle granu-
   lar or tuberculate   Superfamily Poduroidea
   Pronotum reduced and often invisible
   from above: cuticle with hairs or scales   Superfamily Entomobryoidea

3. Antennae shorter than head   Family Neelidae
   Antennae longer than head   Family Sminthuridae

The superfamily **Poduroidea** contains generally very small springtails with slaty colouring. The legs and antennae are relatively short. Many members of this group occur on and around water, for example the small black *Podura aquatica*. The three families within this group are not easily separated.

The superfamily **Entomobryoidea** contains larger springtails with relatively long appendages. These insects are very common in leaf litter where their brown and mottled colouring makes them difficult to see even on the examination table. There are four families.

The families **Neelidae** and **Sminthuridae** contain the globular springtails. These families are easily separated by antennal length, those of the Neelidae being very small. The insects prefer vegetation to leaf litter and some species may become minor pests at times. The yellowish *Sminthurus viridis* has established itself in many countries and frequently damages clovers, peas, and other crops. It is often called the Lucerne Flea.

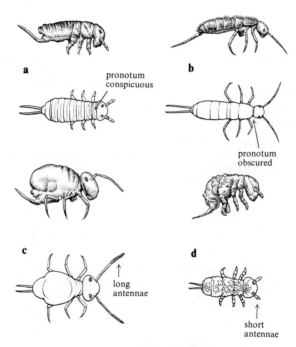

The four major groups of springtails: **a,** Poduroidea; **b,** Entomobryoidea; **c,** Sminthuridae; **d,** Neelidae

THE PTERYGOTE INSECTS

The sub-class Pterygota contains all the winged insects and it is a far larger division than the Apterygota. Although pterygote means 'with wings', the sub-order does include many wingless creatures, including the fleas and lice. The reason for their inclusion is that they are clearly descended from winged ancestors. Most of them have lost their wings during their evolutionary history as a result of adaptation to parasitic life or to life under the ground.

Order Ephemeroptera – Mayflies

Recognition features Small, medium, and large sized insects with two or three long 'tails' and one or two pairs of delicate wings. The hind wings, when present, are always considerably smaller than the front pair. Antennae short. Usually found in the vicinity of water.

The stoneflies, caddis flies, and lacewing flies are the only other insects with which the mayflies might be confused but the short antennae of the mayflies should distinguish them. Other useful distinctions are: the large hind wings of the stoneflies: the few cross veins of the caddis flies: and the similarity of the two pairs of wings in the lacewing flies. In addition, a feature that can only be seen in life, the mayflies are quite unable to fold their wings over their bodies: the wings are always held vertically over the body when at rest, a position unknown in these other insects except when just emerged from nymphal or pupal skin.

Most of our mayflies are rather small insects, less than 12mm across and, apart from the entomologist, the fisherman probably knows them better than anyone. In fact, the fisherman is probably better at recognising them than many entomologists, although he may use names such as Claret Spinner and Blue-winged Pale Watery Dun instead of the *Leptophlebia vespertina* and *Centroptilum pennulatum* of the entomologist. The reason for the angler's interest is that the mayflies spend almost all of their lives in the water and are extremely important items in the diet of many fish. Mayflies, in fact, are the models for many of the angler's artificial flies and are therefore often called 'fishing flies'.

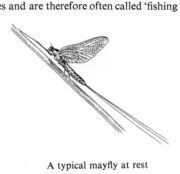

A typical mayfly at rest

Despite their common name, the mayflies are by no means confined to the month of May and one species or another can be found throughout the summer. They are all weak fliers and, except when carried by the wind, they are rarely found far from water.

The adult mayfly has a very slender body and delicate transparent wings. The hind wings are always considerably smaller than the front pair and may be absent altogether. As would be expected in an insect in which the front wings are dominant, the mesothorax is the largest thoracic region, the pro- and meta-thoracic segments being rather insignificant.

None of our species can be called colourful, the dominant colours being brown and yellow. The wings of some species appear to have a metallic sheen when light hits them at certain angles, but the colours fade after death and identification by colour is not at all easy.

Mayfly classification depends primarily on the wing venation but there are problems here too because the veins are often so faint as to be almost invisible. A good lens and suitable lighting, however, will allow one to make out most of the veins. When at rest, the mayflies hold their wings vertically for they are quite unable to fold them back along the body.

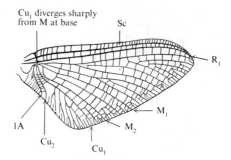

The venation of the front wing of *Ephemera* (family Ephemeridae)

The front legs of male mayflies are relatively long and are used to hold the female during pairing. Otherwise, the legs are weak and slender and used only for holding on to vegetation. The 'tails' consist of a pair of long filamentous cerci, with or without a central filament. Among the British mayflies, the number of tails is constant for individual families, though one or more may be damaged or missing in a particular individual.

The compound eyes are quite large and well developed but the antennae are small. Adult mayflies do not feed and their mouth-parts are reduced and quite ineffective.

Mayflies are unique among insects in moulting after attaining the winged state. Final instar nymphs stop eating and after a short while they climb up a plant stem, or more usually swim or float to the water surface. Here, within a few seconds, the nymphal skin splits and a winged insect emerges. In contrast to most freshly-emerged insects this one can fly right away, although the direction of its flight is largely governed by air currents. This winged insect is not the mature insect, however: it is the sub-imago (the fisherman's dun) and it is rather dull in colour. This is due to a very fine covering of hairs, which are thought to assist emergence from the nymphal skin by preventing wetting. The sub-imagos that reach a suitable place to rest moult within a few hours (in some species it is only minutes) and turn into the shinier mature imagines, known as spinners to the fishing fraternity.

The spinner's life is a short one and is responsible for the name Ephemeroptera (Greek *ephemeros* = living a day). Many species live for less than a day in the adult state: they emerge in the evening and are dead by morning. Others may live for up to a week. During this brief aerial existence the insects ensure the continuance of their species by mating and laying eggs. The males swarm in large numbers, 'dancing' up and down over and around the water. Any female that comes near the swarm is seized by a male and mating takes place in the air. The eggs are usually laid within an hour or so, although bad weather may delay it for several hours. The eggs are dropped singly or in batches into the water, but some species may descend into the water to lay their eggs on submerged plants, and, having fulfilled their purpose, the 'spent gnats' are eagerly devoured by fishes. Bats, swallows, and dragonflies also take their share of mayflies before they fall into the water.

Most of our mayfly species are widely distributed but each has its preferred habitat and the nymphs are admirably adapted to their particular niches. We can recognise cylindrical burrowing forms, rather rugged forms that crawl on the vegetation, streamlined swimmers, and flattened forms that cling tightly to stones in fast streams. Clear, fresh water, moving or still, is more likely to hold mayflies than stagnant ponds with lots of organic materials.

The nymphs are basically herbivorous, feeding on plant debris and algae, although some are believed to take animal food as well. They breathe by means of plate-like tracheal gills that grow out from the sides of the abdomen. There are usually seven pairs of these gills and they contain tiny tracheae that are continuous with those of the rest of the body. Oxygen diffuses into them from the water. All of our mayfly nymphs have three 'tails', even those in which the adults have no median filament.

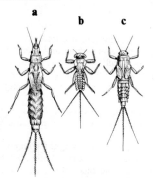

Three types of mayfly nymphs: a, *Ephemera*; b, *Ecdyonurus*; c, *Ephemerella*

The short adult life is preceded by a much longer nymphal development. *Ephemera danica* takes two years to mature, but most of our mayflies complete their life cycle in one year and some, particularly in the warmer regions, have two broods in one year. Up to 27 moults have been recorded for mayfly nymphs.

Eight families are represented in the British Isles, comprising 46 species. They are illustrated on Plate 1.

*A Key to the Families of British Ephemeroptera**
1. Insects with three 'tails'   2
   Insects with two 'tails'   5

2. Hind wings present   3
   Hind wings absent: insects under 12mm across   Caenidae, p. 62

3. Insects more than 30mm across   Ephemeridae, p. 62
   Insects less than 30mm across   4

4. Vein Cu_2 of front wing midway   Leptophlebiidae, p. 62
   between Cu_1 and A_1
   at base, or nearer to
   A_1

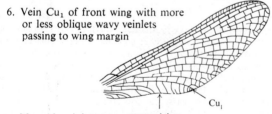

Cu_2 midway between →
Cu_1 and 1A

   1A →   ← Cu_1
        Cu_2

   Vein Cu_2 of front wing nearer   Ephemerellidae, p. 62
   to Cu_1 than A_1 at base

   Cu_2 very close →
   to Cu_1
        1A ⌐ Cu_2 ↑   ⌐ Cu_1

5. Hind wings small (less than 1/5th of front wings) or
   absent   Baetidae, p. 62
   Hind wings larger (about 1/3rd of front wings)   6

6. Vein Cu_1 of front wing with more   Siphlonuridae, p. 62
   or less oblique wavy veinlets
   passing to wing margin

                                                 ↑
                                              Cu_1

   No such veinlets   wavy veinlets   Ecdyonuridae, p. 62

Care must be taken when using this key to ensure that the correct number of 'tails' is known. Broken stumps will be present where 'tails' have been lost accidentally.

* The Potamanthidea, with one rare species – *Potamanthus luteus* – has been omitted from the key. The species is similar to the Ephemeridae, but it has no brown wing markings (Pl. 1). It is more common on the Continent.

The **Ephemeridae** contains the largest of our mayflies, typified by *Ephemera danica* (the angler's 'drake') which has dark brown wing markings. The nymphs are burrowers and these species are therefore found principally in slow moving or still water where the mud accumulates. The nymphal gills are rather feathery and are bent over the abdomen in response to the burrowing habit.

The **Caenidae**, typified by the genus *Caenis*, are all very small mayflies that have lost the hind wings. The front wings are fringed posteriorly with small hairs and the venation is reduced, there being only a few cross veins, arranged in a vague zig-zag line across the wing. The nymphs are slow-moving bottom-dwelling forms and at least partly carnivorous. They can be recognised by the enlarged second gill that forms a protective cover over those behind it.

The families **Leptophlebiidae** and **Ephemerellidae** contain eight medium-sized species between about 10 and 25mm across. The two families can be separated by wing venation (see key) but the species are otherwise superficially very similar, with clear or smoky brown wings and brown or yellow bodies.

Members of the **Baetidae** are divided into four genera: *Baetis* and *Centroptilum* with hind wings, and *Cloeon* and *Procloeon* without. They are all under 25mm across. The nymphs are swimmers but whereas the first two genera prefer running water, the latter two are more often found in ponds and canals, or even in water butts.

The **Siphlonuridae** are confined largely to the hilly regions of the north and west where the nymphs frequent lakes and rivers. The only common species is *Siphlonurus lacustris* which is 25mm or more across.

Members of the **Ecdyonuridae** vary from 10 to 35mm across and are fairly widely distributed, although commoner in the hillier regions where the streams are faster and the lakes are clearer. The nymphs are of the flattened type, adapted to clinging to stones in the river bed.

Five further families occur on the continent. The families are **Palingeniidae**, **Polymitarcidae**, **Oligoneuriidae**, **Ametropodidae**, and **Isonychidae**. The latter is still regarded by some people as a sub-family of the Siphlonuridae. All are illustrated on Plates 1 and 2. *Palingenia longicauda* has rather smoky wings and is the largest European mayfly. *Ephoron virgo* is also readily identified by its white cloudy wings. The members of the family **Oligoneuriidae** can be recognised at once by their very few wing veins.

Collecting and Preserving

Searching waterside vegetation can be very productive. Mayflies generally do not fly readily and are reasonably easy to capture. A soft net material is necessary for taking them in flight to avoid damaging the delicate wings. Emerging duns can be scooped from the water with a piece of muslin stretched over a wire frame. Nymphs collected from the water and kept in a properly arranged aquarium may be expected to provide duns and spinners at a later date. By keeping careful records of the nymphs and the adults to which they give rise, the collector can add to our knowledge of these insects for relatively little is known of the nymphs of many species.

Specimens for collection may be killed in the normal way and the larger ones pinned and set like butterflies. The smaller ones, however, are extremely fragile and are best preserved in alcohol or as whole mounts on microscope slides.

Mayfly colours rapidly deteriorate and specimens should be brought home alive if the colours are to be used for identification. Many species can be identified by colour or venation alone, but it is often necessary to examine the genitalia to separate closely related species and a microscope is obviously necessary. If this sort of examination is intended, the specimens must be preserved in alcohol.

Order Odonata – Dragonflies

Recognition features Long, slender-bodied insects. Two pairs of wings with an intricate network of veins. Very large compound eyes. Antennae short and inconspicuous.

It is unlikely that the dragonflies will be confused with any other insects, although the ant-lions of Europe (Pl. 14) are rather similar.

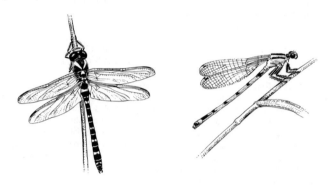

A dragonfly (*left*) and a damsel fly at rest

Like the mayflies, dragonflies spend the early part of their lives in water and few stretches of permanent water are without them, although the majority of species favour still or slow moving water. Many of the adults, however, are very strong fliers and are by no means confined to the vicinity of water. Despite such names as 'horse-stinger' – given to them perhaps on account of their large size, swift flight, and the rustling of the wings as they swoop about – dragonflies are harmless and certainly have no sting. In fact, they do a great deal of good in keeping down mosquitoes and other small flies which make up the bulk of their food.

The colours of dragonflies, produced by pigments and/or structural effects, are some of the most striking in the whole animal kingdom. In life, many of our species can be recognised by their colour alone but colour is not always a good guide. For one thing, colours fade after death and preserved specimens, unless specially treated, never really retain the colours of the living insect. Females frequently differ in colour or pattern from the males and, above all, the insects change colour as they get older: freshly emerged, or teneral, specimens are much paler than older ones. An interesting feature of several species is the gradual development of a powdery bloom or pruinescence on the surface of older specimens, particularly the males. This bloom is whitish or powdery blue and can completely alter the appearance of a specimen in two or three days.

The British dragonfly fauna comprises about 42 species, with two or three others now believed to be extinct. They fall easily into two sub-orders, the ZYGOPTERA (=similar wings) or damsel flies (Pl. 2), and the ANISOPTERA (= unequal wings) or true dragonflies (Pl. 3). The wings of the damsel flies are all more or less alike, with a narrow 'stalk', whereas among the true dragonflies the hind wings are broader than the front pair.

Dragonflies are generally day-flying insects and they rely almost entirely on sight for carrying on their daily lives. In many species, the head appears to consist of little but the compound eyes which may have up to 30,000 facets. The eyes of the true dragonflies generally meet or almost meet on top of the head. The hemispherical eyes of the damsel flies are smaller and are set widely apart on the sides of the broad head, giving the head and body a resemblance to a tiny hammer. The head is able to swivel round on the slender neck, giving the insects all-round vision. The large number of facets makes the eyes extraordinarily sensitive to movements in the surroundings and allows the insects to see and catch small insects in full flight. It also makes the faster dragonflies extremely difficult to catch. The antennae, seat of the senses of touch and smell, are poorly developed. The mouth-parts are of the biting type and well developed for a carnivorous diet, the mandibles being strongly toothed (Odonata means toothed).

The prothorax is small and distinct but the other two thoracic segments are welded together into a very prominent pterothorax, in connection with the strong powers of flight of many species. The pterothorax has undergone distortion during evolution so that the leg-bearing ventral surface is tilted forwards and the wing-bearing dorsal surface is tilted backwards. The prominent 'shield' in front of the wings is actually formed by the upward extension of the episterna (sides) of the second thoracic segment. In this way, the second and third pairs of legs are brought forward close to the front legs and are all available to form the 'basket' that scoops the dragonfly's prey from the air and holds it while the jaws get to work. The legs are also used for clinging to supports but the insects do not walk.

The basic wing venation is the same in both sub-orders although not all entomologists agree on the naming of the veins. The system used here is based on the

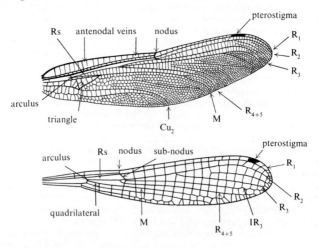

Front wings of a dragonfly (*top*) and a damsel fly, showing the main features of the venation

work of Tillyard and Fraser. Somewhere along the front edge of the wing (costa) there is a small 'kink' and a prominent cross vein called the nodus. Towards the tip of the wing there is a dark area called the pterostigma, or simply the stigma. The radius and media arise as a single vein from which vein R_1 is given off and runs to the wing-tip. Between the wing base and the nodus, vein R_1 is joined to the costal margin by a number of antenodals. Those that run straight across the sub-costa to the wing margin are said to be complete, the others incomplete. At the junction of R_1, vein $R+M$ bends sharply backwards and, together with a small cross vein behind it, forms the arculus. R_s and M separate here, R_s sending three branches to the wing margin. Supplementary veins may occur between these branches. Just beyond the arculus there is in the damsel flies a somewhat rectangular cell called the quadrilateral. In the anisopterans, this area is divided into two triangular cells, the triangle and supratriangle. This region is important in identification. There are numerous cross veins, generally developed to a greater extent in the anisopterans than in the damsel flies. Additional or supplementary longitudinal veins are also present.

The resting damsel fly holds its wings vertically over the body or partly spread, whereas the true dragonflies always rest with wings outspread. The wings work independently in flight and the insects are very manoeuvrable, even able to hover and fly backwards.

The abdomen is relatively long and slender in all dragonflies, although the anisopterans are somewhat stouter in general than the damsel flies. There are 10 recognisable segments and some vestiges of the eleventh. All males bear a well-developed pair of appendages on segment 10 and the males are unique among insects in having special reproductive organs on segments 2 and 3 of the abdomen. An ovipositor is present in segments 8 and 9 in the females of certain species.

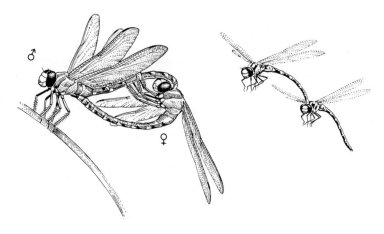

(*Left*) the mating position of dragonflies, with the male clasping the neck of the female. (*Right*) the tandem position of paired dragonflies

Before pairing the male transfers sperm from the genital opening on segment 9 to the special organs on segments 2 and 3. He then sets off in search of the female and grasps her by the neck with the aid of his 'claspers' on segment 10. The female then curves her body round until the tip of her abdomen touches the male's reproductive organs and collects the sperm. A mated pair often fly together in what is known as the tandem position with the male towing the female. In some species, particularly among the damsel flies, the eggs are laid while the male still holds the female's neck. The zygopterans and some anisopterans lay their eggs in the tissues of water plants, usually putting their abdomens below the water surface in order to make contact with a suitable plant. The ovipositor is used to make a slit and the eggs are inserted. Other dragonflies simply scatter their eggs by skimming over the water and dipping the tip of the abdomen into the water at intervals.

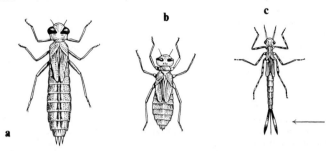

Nymphs of Odonata: **a** and **b**, dragonflies; **c**, damsel fly, distinguished by the external gills at the hind end

The nymphs that hatch from the eggs breathe by means of tracheal gills – thin-walled plates containing tracheae. Those of the dragonflies are concealed within the rectum but those of the damsel flies are developed by modification of the cerci and a central projection from the end of the body. There is therefore no difficulty in distinguishing nymphs of the two sub-orders. Those of the Anisoptera are stouter than the zygopteran nymphs but otherwise they are of similar shape.

All dragonfly nymphs, like the adults, are carnivorous and the lower lip (labium) is cleverly modified for catching food. It is greatly elongated and hinged in the middle. The palps are modified as movable claws at the end of the labium and the whole arrangement is called the mask because when not in use it is folded back under the head and conceals the rest of the face. When food is sighted the mask is thrust forwards and the prey is impaled on the claws.

The head of a dragonfly nymph showing the mask at rest (*left*) and in use to catch a worm

Apart from the development of the wings and the gradual enlargement of the eyes there is little visible change during nymphal life. The length of the nymphal life depends to a great extent on the prevailing temperatures and the availability of food, but almost all of our damsel flies complete their life cycles in one year. Among the true dragonflies the life cycle may take anything from one to five years and possibly even longer. There are usually between 10 and 15 moults during the nymphal life.

When a nymph is about to moult into a mature, winged dragonfly, it crawls up a suitable stem, usually near to the shore. After a short period of rest, the skin splits and out comes the adult's head and thorax. Another rest follows before the abdomen is pulled clear of the nymphal skin. The wings and body then expand to their full size. Many dragonflies emerge early in the morning, while it is still dark, and the early riser can see them hanging to their supports. As soon as they are warmed by the sun the newly emerged insects fly away, leaving only the cast nymphal skin as evidence of the transformation.

SUB-ORDER ZYGOPTERA

These are very slender and delicate insects with weak powers of flight. Their movement appears to be more of a silent drift from reed to reed than an active flight. They are to be found resting on the vegetation around the water for most of the time and are quite easy to collect by sweeping a net through the reeds.

Four families are represented in Europe and all are found in the British Isles. They can be separated with the following key.

A Key to the Families of European Zygoptera (Pl. 2)

1. Wings coloured: 5 or more complete antenodals   Agriidae, p. 67
   Wings colourless: less than 5 complete antenodals   2

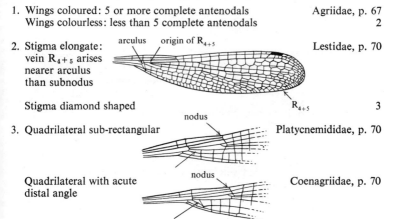

2. Stigma elongate: arculus   origin of R_{4+5} Lestidae, p. 70
   vein R_{4+5} arises
   nearer arculus
   than subnodus

   Stigma diamond shaped R_{4+5} 3

3. Quadrilateral sub-rectangular   nodus   Platycnemididae, p. 70

   Quadrilateral with acute   nodus   Coenagriidae, p. 70
   distal angle

Our two members of the **Agriidae** are the beautiful *Agrion splendens* and *A. virgo* with brilliant metallic blue or green bodies. Their wings are less abruptly narrowed than those of other damsel flies and also differ from them in being col-

Plate 1   MAYFLIES – Order Ephemeroptera

Delicate insects with long 'tails': hind wings much smaller
than front wings or even absent: usually near water.   p. 58

Family **Ephemeridae**   p. 62
Fairly large insects in which veins M and Cu_1
of front wing diverge strongly at base: wings
mottled; British species with 3 'tails'
1. *Ephemera danica* Müller × 1½   Front wing of
                                        Ephemera

Family **Potamanthidae**   p. 61
Veins M and Cu_1 of front wing diverge strongly at base:
wings clear
2. *Potamanthus luteus* (L.) × 2

Family **Siphlonuridae**   p. 62
Vein Cu_1 of front wing with oblique veinlets running to
margin: British species with 2 'tails'
3. *Siphlonurus lacustris* Eaton × 2

Family **Ecdyonuridae**   p. 62
Two pairs of intercalary veins between Cu_1 and Cu_2 of
front wing: 2 'tails'
4. *Ecdyonurus dispar* (Curtis) × 2

Family **Caenidae**   p. 62
Small insects without hind wings: British species with 3 'tails'
5. *Caenis macrura* Stephens × 4

Family **Ephemerellidae**   p. 62
Vein Cu_2 of front wing very close to Cu_1 at base
6. *Ephemerella ignita* (Poda) × 2½   Front wing of
                                            Ephemerella

△ Family **Isonychidae**   p. 62
Vein Cu_2 of front wing parallel to hind margin
for most of length
▲ **7.** *Isonychia ignota* (Walker) × 2½

Family **Baetidae**   p. 62
Small insects with hind wings very small or missing: 2 'tails'
in British species
8. *Cloëon dipterum* (L.) × 4
9. *Baetis rhodani* (Pictet) × 2½

Family **Leptophlebiidae**   p. 62
Base of Cu_2 in front wing mid-way between Cu_1 and
A_1 or close to A_1: British species with 3 'tails'
10. *Leptophlebia vespertina* (L.) × 2½   Front wing of
                                                Leptophlebia

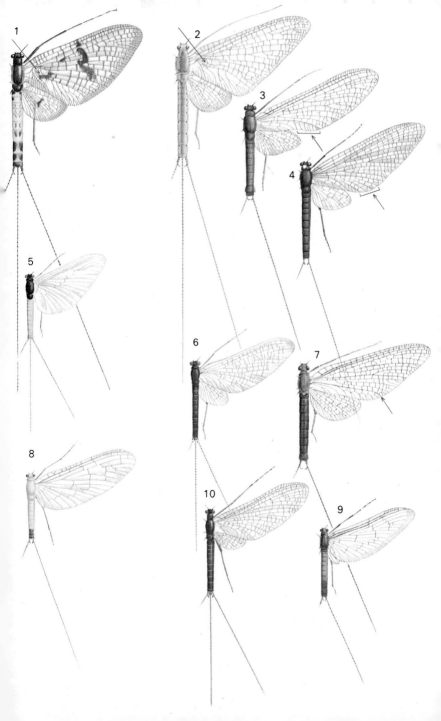

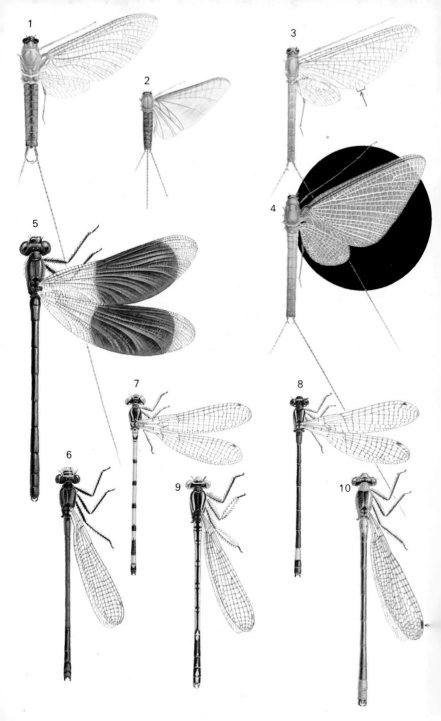

△ Family **Palingeniidae**   p. 62
    Veins M and Cu_1 of front wing diverge sharply: very large
    insects with only 2 'tails'
▲ **1.** *Palingenia longicauda*   (Ol.)

△ Family **Oligoneuriidae**   p. 62
    Wings with very few veins
▲ **2.** *Oligoneuriella rhenana* Imhoff

△ Family **Ametropodidae**   p. 62
    Hind wing very oval: one pair of intercalary veins between
    Cu_1 and Cu_2 of front wing
▲ **3.** *Metrotopus norvegicus* Eaton $\times 3\frac{1}{2}$

△ Family **Polymitarcidae**   p. 62
    Veins M and Cu_1 of front wing diverge sharply: no inter-
    calary veins on hind margins of wings: white wings
▲ **4.** *Ephoron virgo* (Ol.) $\times 3\frac{1}{2}$

DAMSEL FLIES AND DRAGONFLIES – **Order Odonata**

Long-bodied insects with large eyes and very short bristle-
like antennae.   p. 63

DAMSEL FLIES – SUB-ORDER ZYGOPTERA

Front and hind wings alike

Family **Agriidae**   p. 67
    Numerous antenodal veins
5. *Agrion splendens* (Harris) $\times 1\frac{1}{2}$

Family **Coenagriidae**   p. 70
    2 antenodals: quadrilateral with acute distal angle
6. *Pyrrhosoma nymphula* (Sulzer) $\times 1\frac{1}{2}$
7. *Coenagrion puella* (L.) $\times 1\frac{1}{2}$
8. *Ischnura elegans* (van der Linden) $\times 1\frac{1}{2}$

Wing base of *Coenagrion*   —— quadrilateral ——   Wing base of *Platycnemis*

Family **Platycnemididae**   p. 70
    2 antenodals: quadrilateral rectangular
9. *Platycnemis pennipes* (Pallas) $\times 1\frac{1}{2}$

Family **Lestidae**   p. 70
    2 antenodals: stigma elongate
10. *Lestes sponsa* (Hansemann) $\times 1\frac{1}{2}$

oured. The female demoiselles have only a yellowish colour on the wings but the males, when seen at certain angles, reflect a brilliant blue sheen. Both species are widely distributed although *splendens* is absent from Scotland.

The **Lestidae** are represented in Britain by two members of the genus *Lestes*. Both have a metallic green colour and a strong tendency to pruinescence in the males. They frequent the still water of bogs and marshes where the female lays her eggs on water plants well below the surface. The genitalia are prominent in both sexes. Only *L. sponsa* is at all common.

We have only one member of the **Platycnemididae** – the White-legged Damselfly, *Platycnemis pennipes*. This blue and green species, found only in the southern half of England, is easily recognised by the enlarged white tibiae of the middle and hind legs. The species is confined to running water and the eggs are laid on floating vegetation.

Our remaining 12 damsel flies all belong to the **Coenagriidae** and are mainly red or blue with a variable amount of black, more in the females than the males. These insects frequent various habitats but are rarely found in swift streams. *Coenagrion puella* is a common representative.

SUB-ORDER ANISOPTERA

These dragonflies are considerably more robust than the damsel flies and are much faster fliers. Adults are often found several miles from water and many species seem to have a regular 'beat', hawking up and down a particular stretch for hours on end. The stiff wings frequently make a rustling sound as they fly. The five British and European families can be separated with the following key.

A Key to the Families of European Anisoptera (Pl. 3)

1. Triangles similar in both wings   2

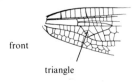

front

triangle   triangle   hind

   Triangles different in front and hind wings   3

triangle

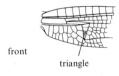
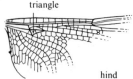

front

triangle   hind

2. Eyes in broad contact on top of head   Aeshnidae, p. 71
   Eyes widely separated: abdomen swollen   Gomphidae, p. 71
   Eyes only just touching   Cordulegasteridae, p. 71

3. Triangle of front wing with front side about as long as basal side: body metallic

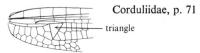

Corduliidae, p. 71

triangle

Triangle of front wing with front side much shorter than basal side

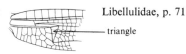

Libellulidae, p. 71

triangle

Our eight representatives of the **Aeshnidae** all have long bodies and sport blues, browns, greens, and yellows on darker backgrounds. They favour the still waters of ponds and canals where the nymphs hunt among the water weeds. The adults can be watched for hours as they fly steadily up and down a regular 'beat' along stream or hedgerow. One of the most striking aeshnids is the Emperor Dragonfly, *Anax imperator*, which has a greenish thorax and bright blue and black abdomen.

The **Gomphidae** and **Cordulegasteridae** are each represented by a single species in our islands and both species are easily recognised without looking at the wings. The green *Gomphus vulgatissimus* is confined to the southern part of England and Wales and has a characteristic swelling of the abdomen. The large *Cordulegaster boltonii* is common on moors and heathland and is easily spotted because of the bold black and gold markings. Both these species breed in running water.

Only one member of the **Corduliidae** is at all common and that is the metallic green *Cordulia linaenea* recognisable by the thick yellow hairs on the thorax. It is found near large ponds and other stretches of still water.

Members of the **Libellulidae** are shorter than most other anisopterans, rarely reaching 50mm in length, but a flattening of the abdomen makes many of them appear rather stout. Their swift, darting flight has given them the name of 'darter' dragonflies as opposed to the 'hawkers' of the Aeshnidae. Bronze and red are the dominant colours in this family but there is a strong tendency for the older males to develop the blue bloom. This is particularly noticeable in *Libellula depressa*. The 14 British species (including an infrequent visitor) are divided among four genera and favour still or slow-moving water.

Collecting and Preserving

As already mentioned, the weak-flying damsel flies can be collected quite easily by sweeping waterside vegetation, or by netting them as they fly up after disturbance. The larger dragonflies, literally with eyes in the backs of their heads, are not so easy but their habit of hawking to and fro over a certain area allows one to sit in wait and a quick upward sweep with the net from behind may be rewarded. Freshly-emerged (teneral) specimens, whether collected in the field or bred in captivity, are quite unsuitable for cabinet display as they are very soft and pale. Even if kept alive for a few days in captivity, they rarely attain their full colours.

Dragonflies intended for the collection can be killed with the usual agents but they should not be killed for a day or two after collection. They can be slipped into paper envelopes and kept cool until wanted. This treatment appears to do no harm to the insects and any that are not required can be set free. During the confinement, however, the insects get rid of most of their gut contents and this makes for quicker drying and better preservation. To save space in a cabinet they are sometimes set with wings folded but some of the detail is obscured in this way and it is better to set them with wings outspread.

It is essential to pin the insects through the pterothorax at right angles to the wings. Do not pin through the 'shield' or the wings will not lie flat. A normal setting board can be used or, alternatively, the insects can be set upside down on a flat sheet of cork or polystyrene.

Dragonfly colours fade rapidly after death but quick-drying will help to preserve them and anyone with access to a desiccator that can be connected to a vacuum pump can expect good results. Some authorities recommend slitting the abdomen and withdrawing the gut, then immersing the specimen in alcohol for several hours before drying.

Order Plecoptera – Stoneflies

Recognition features Medium-sized insects usually with two pairs of membranous wings, of which the hind pair are the larger. The soft body is somewhat flattened and this feature is often accentuated by the way in which the wings are folded flat over the body when at rest. The antennae are long and slender and there are frequently long cerci at the hind end, although these are greatly reduced in some species. Structurally, the stoneflies resemble the grasshoppers and cockroaches but there is never any great thickening of the front wings. Caddis flies and lacewing flies are probably the most likely to be confused with stoneflies but the wing venation, the cerci, and the position of the wings at rest will distinguish them. The large hind wings of the stoneflies and the resting position easily distinguish them from mayflies.

A typical stonefly showing the flattened position of the wings at rest

The stoneflies (Pl. 4) are a relatively small order with about 3,000 species, of which only 34 have been found in the British Isles. They are little known outside entomological and angling circles because of their secretive and inactive habits and because of their rather dull browns, greens, and yellows that merge in with the background.

Like the mayflies and dragonflies, the stoneflies spend their early life in the water and the nymphs are important items in the diet of fish. The adults, too, are consumed, thus making them of interest to the fly fisherman who has names for many of them and uses them as models for some of his artificial flies. The stonefly nymphs have a distinct preference for running water, only a few being found in still or slow-moving stretches. Most species and greatest numbers are found in those streams with stony or gravelly bottoms and the stoneflies are therefore found principally in the hilly regions of the north and west, although certain of the chalk streams of southern England are well stocked with them. They are very intolerant of pollution and are quite absent from stagnant water where the oxygen content is low.

Adult stoneflies live for two or three weeks which they spend crawling among the waterside stones (hence the name) or on the adjacent vegetation. Their mouth-parts are weak biting structures and many of them do not feed as adults, although some scrape algae from stones and tree trunks or take pollen from flowers. When disturbed they fly weakly and soon come to rest again.

The long, slender antennae consist of up to 80 tiny segments. The compound eyes are well developed and there are usually three ocelli. All three thoracic segments are of similar size, the prothorax being well formed. The legs are sturdy and the three-segmented tarsus ends in a strong claw which helps the insect to cling to stones.

All the wings are membranous, there being little or no hardening of the front ones which are relatively narrow. The broad hind wings are usually considerably larger than the front wings. The males of some species are almost wingless and short-winged (brachypterous) forms occur in several species, especially among those individuals living at high altitudes. The two pairs of wings are widely separated at the base and there is no wing-coupling mechanism. One of the most noticeable features, characteristic of most stoneflies, is the double 'ladder' formed by cross veins running between veins M and Cu_2 of the front wing. The

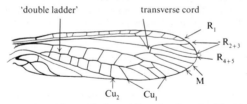

The front wing venation of a typical stonefly, showing the 'double ladder' characteristic of most families

width of the hind wing is largely accounted for by the development of the anal area, supported by numerous branches of the anal veins. There is much irregularity among the smaller cross veins, even to the extent of the two sides of one individual being different. At rest, the wings are either held flat over the body or rolled tightly around it. The name Plecoptera means 'folded wings' (Greek *plekein*=to fold) and refers to the fan-like folding of the hind wings when at rest.

The abdominal cerci are usually long, many-segmented threads but in certain families they are reduced to scarcely visible stumps. The abdomen, and indeed the whole body, is rather soft and fleshy for the sclerites are poorly developed.

Pairing in stoneflies takes place on the ground or on the vegetation and the females then either fly over the surface and dip their abdomens periodically into the water to wash off a batch of eggs, or they actually swim across the surface and lay eggs as they go. The short-winged forms simply crawl into the water or even lay their eggs at the water's edge. Each female may lay several hundred eggs.

Apart from the lack of wings, stonefly nymphs are very similar to the adults. Their flattened bodies are admirably suited to their life of clinging to stones in running water and in this respect they resemble certain mayfly nymphs. They can be distinguished from the latter, however, by the absence of the plate-like tracheal gills and by the possession of only two cerci – all our mayfly nymphs have three cerci. Even those stonefly species in which the adult cerci are reduced have two well-developed 'tails' in the nymphal stage.

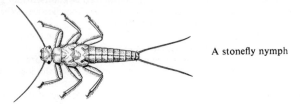

A stonefly nymph

Stonefly nymphs obtain much of their oxygen by simple diffusion through the body surface but some species have accessory gills which are like tufts of tiny hairs on various parts of the body. They are primarily vegetarians, feeding on algae and mosses growing on the stream bed but some of the larger ones are carnivorous, consuming nymphs and larvae of other aquatic insects.

Most of our stoneflies complete their development in one year but a few take two or three years. One of our larger stoneflies, *Dinocras cephalotes*, has been found to undergo 33 moults during its three-year nymphal life. Information of this sort is lacking for most stoneflies but it is likely that most species have fewer moults than this. When fully grown the nymphs move to the edge of the water and crawl out on to the land before the adults emerge. Stoneflies can be found emerging at most times of the year but most species have a fairly definite season and one can divide the insects up into spring forms, early autumn forms, and so on.

The classification of the Plecoptera is still very much in a state of flux and as yet there is no really generally accepted scheme. The following key, based on that given by Kimmins in the R.E.S. Handbook, will enable the European species to be placed in the correct family.

A Key to the Families of European Plecoptera (Pl. 4)

1. Cerci short and inconspicuous   2
   Cerci long   4

2. 2nd tarsal segment as long as the others   Taeniopterygidae, p. 75
   2nd tarsal segment shorter than the others   3

3. Apical marginal space of front
   wing with oblique cross vein

cross vein in apical space

Nemouridae, p. 75

No such cross vein   Leuctridae, p. 75

4. No obvious 'ladder' of veins in front wing: basal
   tarsal segment as long as third   Capniidae, p. 75
   Usually a clear 'ladder' of veins in front wings:
   basal tarsal segment shorter than third   5

5. R_{2+3} of front wing branched   6

   R_{2+3} of front wing simple   7

6. R_{4+5} arises at transverse cord   Perlidae, p. 78

   R_{4+5} arises distal to transverse cord   Perlodidae, p. 75

7. Anal area of hind wing small   Chloroperlidae, p. 78

   Anal area of hind wing large   Isoperlidae, p. 78

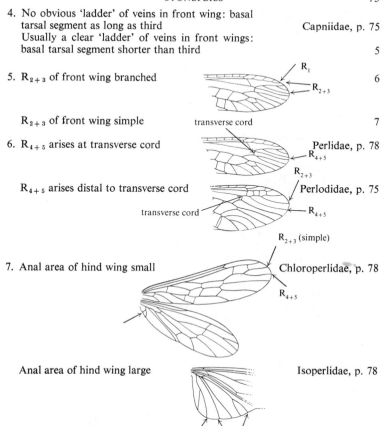

The families **Taeniopterygidae** and **Leuctridae** are often regarded as sub-families of the **Nemouridae** but modern practice is to give them family status. All three families have short, inconspicuous cerci and are brown or black in colour. They rarely exceed 12mm in length. Members of the Leuctridae are often called needle flies or rolled-winged flies because when at rest the wings are bent round the sides of the body, giving them a very slender appearance. *Taeniopteryx nebulosa*, the angler's February Red, is a rather unusual species in that it prefers muddy streams and rivers and is absent from typical stonefly areas.

The family **Capniidae** contains three small blackish stoneflies, of the genus *Capnia*. They emerge quite early in the year and are often called winter stoneflies. These insects are easily recognised because their wings lack the 'ladder' of veins found in most other families.

Our two members of the **Perlidae** – *Dinocras cephalotes* and *Perla bipunctata*

Plate 3   **DRAGONFLIES** – **Order Odonata** (Contd.)

Front and hind wings differ in shape   p. 70

Family **Aeshnidae**   p. 71
   Triangles similar in both wings: eyes touching for some
   distance
1. *Anax imperator* Leach $\times \frac{2}{3}$
2. *Aeshna grandis* (L.) $\times \frac{2}{3}$
3. *Brachytron pratense* (Müller) $\times \frac{2}{3}$

triangles

Wing bases of
Anax

front   hind

Family **Cordulegasteridae**   p. 71
   Triangles similar in both wings: eyes meet only at a point
4. *Cordulegaster boltonii* (Donovan) $\times \frac{2}{3}$

Family **Gomphidae**   p. 71
   Triangles similar in both wings: eyes widely separated
5. *Gomphus vulgatissimus* (L.) $\times \frac{2}{3}$

Family **Corduliidae**   p. 71
   Triangles dissimilar in the two wings: triangle of front wing
   with front side about as long as basal side: body metallic
6. *Cordulia linaenea* Fraser $\times \frac{2}{3}$

Base of *Cordulia*
front wing   triangle

Family **Libellulidae**   p. 71
   Triangles dissimilar in the two wings: triangle of front wing
   with front side much shorter than basal side: not metallic
7. *Orthetrum cancellatum* (L.) $\times \frac{2}{3}$
8. *Leucorrhinia dubia* (van der Linden) $\times \frac{2}{3}$
9. *Libellula depressa* L. $\times \frac{2}{3}$
10. *Sympetrum sanguineum* (Müller) $\times \frac{2}{3}$

Base of *Libellula*
front wing   triangle

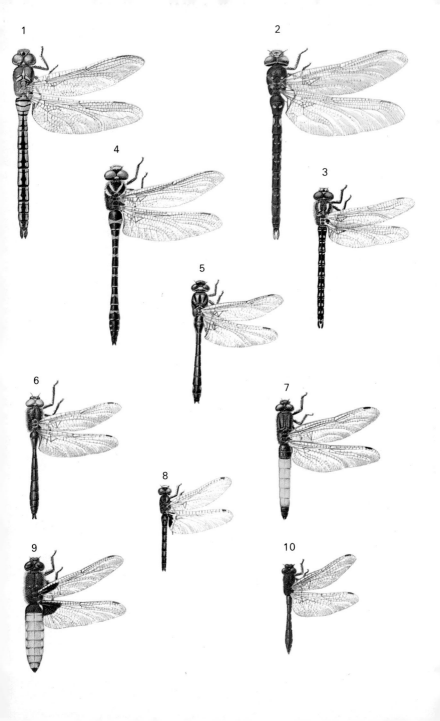

Soft-bodied insects usually found near water: hind wings larger than front wings: wings laid flat or rolled round body at rest. The insects illustrated are all females. Male stoneflies sometimes have short wings

 p. 72

Family **Leuctridae**   p. 75
 Second tarsal segment shorter than others: no oblique vein in apical space
1. *Leuctra fusca* L., showing the rolled-up position of the wings at rest $\times 3\frac{1}{2}$

Family **Taeniopterygidae**   p. 75
 All tarsal segments about equal: cerci short
2. *Taeniopteryx nebulosa* (L.) $\times 2\frac{1}{2}$

Family **Nemouridae**   p. 75
 Second tarsal segment shorter than others: oblique cross vein in apical space
3. *Nemoura cinerea* Retz $\times 3\frac{1}{2}$

Family **Isoperlidae**   p. 78
 Anal veins forked in hind wing
4. *Isoperla grammatica* (Poda) $\times 3\frac{1}{2}$

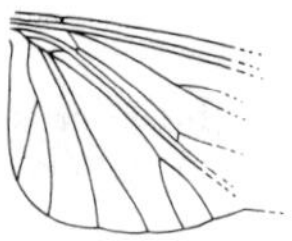

Hind wing of *Isoperla*

↑ anal veins ↑

Family **Capniidae**   p. 75
 Basal tarsal segment about as long as third: no double 'ladder'
5. *Capnia bifrons* Newman $\times 3\frac{1}{2}$

Family **Perlodidae**   p. 78
 Vein R_2+_3 branched: vein R_4+_5 arises beyond transverse cord
6. *Perlodes microcephala* (Pictet) $\times 2$

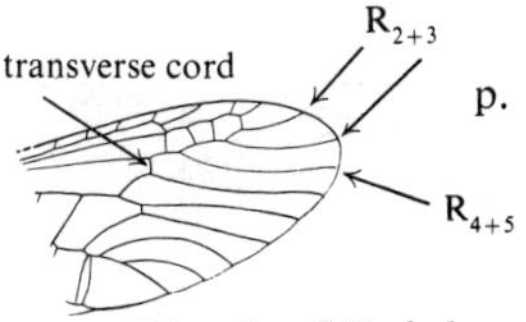

transverse cord R_{2+3} R_{4+5}

Wing tip of *Perlodes*

Family **Chloroperlidae**   p. 78
 All anal veins unbranched
7. *Chloroperla torrentium* (Pictet) $\times 3\frac{1}{2}$

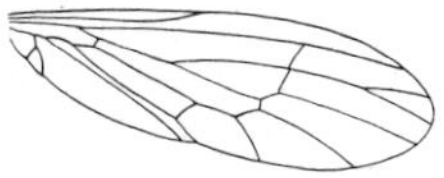

Hind wing of *Chloroperla*

Family **Perlidae**   p.75
 Vein R_2+_3 branched: vein R_4+_5 arises at transverse cord
8. *Dinocras cephalotes* (Curtis) $\times 1\frac{1}{2}$

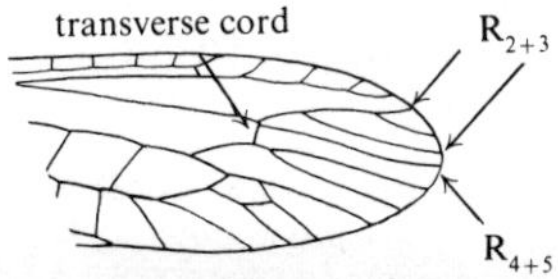

transverse cord R_{2+3}

Wing tip of *Dinocras*

R_{4+5}

– are the best known of our stoneflies for they may attain a wing span of about 50mm and are both reasonably common. To the angler, they are both known as Large Stonefly. The nymphs of these insects are carnivorous but the adults do not feed.

The remaining three families are often treated as sub-families of the Perlidae, separated by relatively minor differences in venation. The **Perlodidae** contains generally dark-coloured insects while the members of **Isoperlidae** and **Chloroperlidae** are generally greenish or yellow and go under such angling names as Yellow Sally.

Collecting and Preserving
Examination of tree trunks, walls, and so on around suitable stretches of water will provide the collector with a fair selection of stoneflies. They are easily bottled in such places because of their reluctance to fly. Turning over stones at the water's edge and sweeping waterside vegetation will also yield material for the collector.

The larger insects can be pinned and set in the normal way but the soft body soon shrivels and, although the wings remain in good condition, the genitalia and other features necessary for identification to species level are damaged or destroyed. For permanent storage and study, the insects should be preserved in spirit.

Order Orthoptera (Saltatoria) – Grasshoppers and Crickets

Recognition features Medium to large insects with a stout body, large blunt head, and conspicuous saddle-shaped pronotum. The hind legs are usually enlarged and modified for jumping. There are typically two pairs of wings of which the front ones are thicker. One or both pairs of wings, however, may be reduced or absent. The shape of these insects is so characteristic that, once known, it is impossible to confuse them with members of any other order.

A typical grasshopper, showing the enlarged hind legs used for jumping

Grasshoppers (Pl. 6) and crickets (Pls. 5 and 6) share with radio announcers the distinction of being known more by their voices than by their looks because, although these insects noisily advertise their presence, their colouring normally ensures that they remain hidden from the casual stroller. But they are not difficult to find if one listens carefully and discovers the direction of the sounds. A stealthy approach may then be rewarded with a sight of the insect quivering in full song.

There are more than 15,000 known species but the orthopterans are predominantly tropical and we have only 30 representatives, several of these being confined to the southern parts of our islands. They are quite numerous, however, and few meadows are without the familiar chirp in the summer months. Their relatively large size and the ease with which they can be kept in captivity makes them ideal insects for study and the fascination of their 'songs' adds greatly to their interest. In fact, in the warmer parts of Europe the Field Cricket is kept as a family pet on account of its song which, although perhaps less varied than that of a canary, is certainly no less pleasant.

The name Orthoptera, from the Greek word *orthos* meaning straight or rigid, refers to the rather straight front wings but it can be applied to phasmids and cockroaches as well as to grasshoppers and crickets. All these insects were, in fact, included in the same order at one time but the phasmids and cockroaches have now been moved, leaving the Orthoptera to their jumping cousins. There is now an increasing tendency to drop the name Orthoptera and to use the name Saltatoria for the present order. Saltatoria, from the Latin word *saltare*, meaning to leap, is certainly more descriptive of the crickets and grasshoppers.

The seven families of European saltatorians (some entomologists split them further and recognise more families) differ considerably from one another in structure and habits and only a very general account can be given at this point. Greater detail will be given under the individual families.

The large head is usually hypognathous, that is there is a vertical face, with the biting jaws below the rest of the head (Fig. p. 16). The compound eyes are large and most species also have two or three ocelli. The antennae vary from very short to several times the length of the body.

Behind the head, the pronotum is always large and well developed. It bends downwards at right angles and covers the sides as well as the top of the pro-thorax. In the ground hoppers, the pronotum reaches almost or quite to the end of the abdomen. Many species have reduced wings or no wings at all, but when fully developed wings are present the front ones are tougher and are sometimes called tegmina (singular tegmen). They overlap to a greater or lesser extent in the middle line and are bent downwards to cover the sides of the body as well. The hind wings are delicate membranous structures and are folded neatly under the front wings when at rest. They are generally of a drab colour, but some con-tinental grasshoppers have brightly coloured hind wings. The wing venation is fairly complete and there is normally a greatly enlarged anal area in the hind wings. One of the most noticeable features of the venation is that the costal vein of the front wing does not follow the front margin. The venation is important in classification within the families but we will not be concerned with it in this book for the families are separated by much more obvious features.

Very few of these insects are good fliers. Locusts are, of course, notable

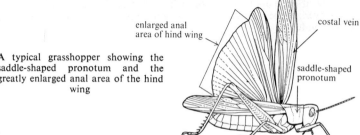

enlarged anal
area of hind wing

costal vein

A typical grasshopper showing the saddle-shaped pronotum and the greatly enlarged anal area of the hind wing

saddle-shaped
pronotum

Plate 5   CRICKETS AND BUSH CRICKETS – Order Orthoptera

Stout-bodied insects with an enlarged saddle-shaped pronotum and usually with long hind legs modified for jumping   p. 78

Family **Gryllidae**   p. 84
Antennae longer than body: tarsi 3-segmented
1. House cricket – *Acheta domestica* L. $\times 1\frac{1}{2}$
2. Field cricket – *Gryllus campestris* L. $\times 1\frac{1}{2}$
3. Wood cricket – *Nemobius sylvestris* (Bosc.) $\times 2$
4. Scaly cricket – *Mogoplistes squamiger* (Fischer) $\times 2$

Family **Tettigoniidae**   p. 85
Antennae longer than body: tarsi 4-segmented
5. Long-winged cone-head – *Conocephalus discolor* Thunberg $\times 2$
6. Oak bush cricket – *Meconema thalassinum* (DeGeer) – a silent species $\times 2$
7. Speckled bush cricket – *Leptophyes punctatissima* (Bosc.) $\times 2$
8a. Dark bush cricket – *Pholidoptera griseoaptera* (DeGeer) $\times 2$
8b. Dark bush cricket female $\times 2$
▲ **9.** *Ephippiger ephippiger* (Fiebig)
10. Great green bush cricket – *Tettigonia viridissima* L. – strident song

Family **Gryllotalpidae**   p. 84
Front legs enlarged for digging
11. Mole cricket – *Gryllotalpa gryllotalpa* (L.)

The insects illustrated are all males unless otherwise stated.

True crickets (Gryllidae) and bush crickets can also be distinguished by looking at the wings if these are fully developed. The left fore wing of the bush cricket normally overlaps the right wing, but among the true crickets it is the right wing which lies on top.

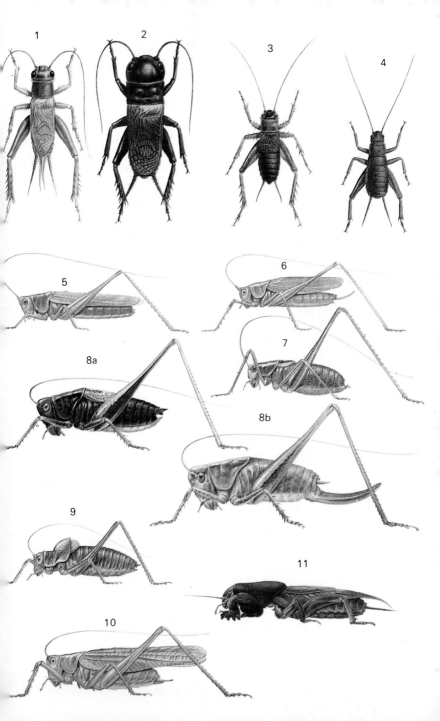

ORDER ORTHOPTERA (Contd.)

Plate 6

Family **Acrididae** – grasshoppers   p. 86
   Antennae shorter than body, but longer than pronotum
1a. Meadow grasshopper – *Chorthippus parallelus* (Zetterstedt)
  ×2
1b. Meadow grasshopper female ×2
2. Common field grasshopper – *Chorthippus brunneus* (Thunberg) ×2
3. Stripe-winged grasshopper – *Stenobothrus lineatus* (Panzer)
  ×2
▲ **4.** *Oedipoda germanica* (Latreille) ×2
5. Mottled grasshopper – *Myrmeleotettix maculatus* (Thunberg) ×2
6. Migratory locust – *Locusta migratoria* L.

Family **Rhaphidophoridae** – cave crickets and camel crickets   p. 86
   Wingless insects with very long palps
7. Greenhouse camel cricket – *Tachycines asynamorus* Adelung
▲ **8.** *Dolichopoda azami* Saulcy

Family **Tetrigidae** – ground hoppers   p. 87
   Antennae shorter than body: pronotum extends back to tip
   of abdomen
9. Common ground hopper – *Tetrix undulata* (Sowerby) ×2½

△ Family **Tridactylidae** – pigmy mole crickets   p. 87
   Very small insects with huge hind femora
▲ **10.** *Tridactylus variegatus* (Latreille) female ×2½

The insects illustrated here are males unless otherwise stated

Male and female grasshoppers may be distinguished by looking at the hind end
of the abdomen. That of the male is turned up and it resembles the prow of a
boat.

male

female

exceptions but the aerial activity of most saltatorians is confined to an extension of their leaps, for which the enlarged anal area of the hind wing is ideally suited. The poor powers of flight explain the relative paucity of grasshoppers in Britain, compared with continental Europe, for even narrow stretches of water form effective barriers to their spread. We do get quite a few foreign species brought in with the fruit and vegetables, but such insects rarely become established. One exception is the wingless Greenhouse Camel Cricket (p. 86).

The legs are well developed and carry efficient claws. The hind legs are normally considerably larger than the other two pairs and provided with powerful muscles in connection with the jumping habit. Not all species, however, jump with equal readiness, crickets and bush crickets being just as likely to crawl away as jump.

The ovipositor is normally well developed and externally visible but the male genitalia are partly concealed. The cerci vary in length, being long in the true crickets and short in most other groups, although in male bush crickets they are modified into pincers for gripping the female.

Metamorphosis in this order is very slight, the young stages being recognisable as grasshoppers almost from the very beginning. The eggs are laid under the surface of the ground, in plant tissue, or in crevices, the female's ovipositor being used to seek out or cut a suitable hole. When the eggs first hatch the young grasshopper is worm-like but this is merely a transitional stage lasting only long enough for the animal to reach the open air. There the shroud-like covering is immediately discarded to reveal the miniature grasshopper. There are normally four to six nymphal instars in the grasshoppers but the crickets undergo up to 10 or more moults before reaching the adult stage. Most of our species complete their life cycles in one year, the adults dying in autumn and leaving only eggs to survive the winter and produce the next year's insects. A few species, however, take two years to mature and pass at least one winter as nymphs. An interesting feature of all saltatorians is that in the two final nymphal instars the developing wing buds become twisted so that the front margin of the wing is uppermost and the hind wings cover the front ones.

Grasshoppers feed primarily on grass but animal material features quite largely in the diets of the crickets.

The 'song' of these insects is undoubtedly the most fascinating thing about them. It is produced by a process called stridulation which involves the rubbing of one part of the body (the 'file') over another part (the 'scraper'). The file is provided with a series of pegs or ridges that strike the scraper in turn and set up vibrations. You can imitate the action by drawing a comb over the edge of a card. The scraper is always on the wing but the file may be on the leg (grasshoppers) or on the opposite wing (crickets).

The complete passage of the file over the scraper is usually very rapid and produces a short pulse of sound (strictly speaking there are several pulses, one for each peg as it strikes the scraper, but these small pulses follow each other so rapidly that we can regard each passage of the file as producing a single pulse). This is the basic 'song-producing' mechanism in all the stridulators but the pattern of the song varies enormously. The pulses come in bursts, or chirps, of varying duration, caused by repeated passage of the file over the scraper. The Common Green Grasshopper, *Omocestus viridulus*, produces a continuous chirp for 20 seconds or more and the whole body quivers as the legs move up and down as much as 20 times a second. Very different is the song of the Common Field Grasshopper, *Chorthippus brunneus*, which produces a series of 6–10 half-second chirps, spread evenly over about 12 seconds. All of our grasshoppers have a fairly fixed song length at a given temperature and the song is repeated at irregular intervals. The crickets, however, have no such fixed song length and in warm weather they chirp indefinitely. Most of our stridulators are quiet in cool weather.

Volume and pitch also vary from species to species and one can liken the various songs, when amplified, to the sounds of motor mowers, sewing machines, motor cycles, and so on. In fact, it is usually easier to identify grasshoppers, in which there is a great colour variation, by their songs than by their appearances.

Among the crickets, stridulation is confined to the males, but many female grasshoppers can sing although their songs are normally quieter than those of the male. When in the presence of a female, many males break into the 'court-ship' song, often very different from the 'isolated male' song which is most frequently heard and which presumably serves to attract any females that happen to be in the neighbourhood.

The 'ears' with which the insects pick up the sounds are tiny membranes, at the base of the abdomen in grasshoppers and on the front legs of crickets. (Fig. p. 85).

The European families of saltatorians can be separated with the following simple key.

A Key to the Families of European Saltatoria (Pls. 5 and 6)

1. Front legs greatly enlarged and used   Gryllotalpidae, p. 84
   for digging

   Front legs not so modified: hind legs larger than
   the others and usually used for jumping   2

2. Antennae longer than the body   3
   Antennae shorter than the body   5

3. Palps very long: insects always wingless   Rhaphidophoridae, p. 86
   Palps shorter: insects often winged   4

4. Tarsi with four segments: cerci short   Tettigoniidae, p. 85
   Tarsi with three segments: cerci long pronotum   Gryllidae, p. 84

5. Pronotum extending backwards   Tetrigidae, p. 87
   and covering all or most of
   abdomen

   Pronotum not extending backwards in this way   6

6. Front tarsi with three segments   Acrididae, p. 86
   Front tarsi with two segments   Tridactylidae, p. 87*

The features of these families are so clear cut that, after a look at the plates, you will probably not need to consult this key again.

* Not found in the British Isles.

Family Gryllotalpidae – Mole Crickets (Pl. 5) The sole British member of this family – *Gryllotalpa gryllotalpa* – is one of our largest insects, with a length of 35mm or more and a very stout body. It is brown in colour and almost entirely clothed with fine hairs. The most obvious feature is the enormous development of the front legs which are strongly toothed and used for digging, for these insects spend most of their time tunnelling in the soil, hence the name mole crickets. The front wings are short but the hind wings are fully developed and extend beyond the tip of the abdomen when folded.

Our Mole Cricket favours damp ground in the vicinity of water. It seems to be rare at present and confined to the areas south of the Thames, although its subterranean habits may mean that it has escaped detection in other areas. It is widespread on the Continent.

There is no external ovipositor and the female lays 200–300 eggs loosely in an underground nest. Unlike most insects, she guards her eggs and also tends the young that hatch in two or three weeks. After a month or so the young insects leave the nest and begin to fend for themselves, taking plant roots and insect grubs. The latter make up the bulk of the diet so that the damage done to crop roots may be offset by the destruction of other insect pests. There are about 10 nymphal instars and the nymphs do not become adult until the year after hatching. Insects hatching in late summer may even spend two winters as nymphs and not reach the adult state until nearly two years after hatching.

The males stridulate like the other crickets by rubbing the wings together. The song, described as 'long bursts of a subdued churring noise', may be heard on warm summer evenings at which times the adults occasionally take to the air with rather a clumsy flight.

Family Gryllidae – True Crickets (Pl. 5) These insects are somewhat broader and more flattened than the other saltatorians, the bulk of the front wing being horizontally placed over the body instead of vertically. The front wings are also relatively shorter than in the other members of the order and the rolled-up hind wings, when present, extend beyond them. The ovipositor of the female is usually long and needle-like and the cerci of both sexes are long. The eggs are laid singly in the soil or in crevices and the nymphs follow the usual path of development, varying only in the length of time taken. They are omnivorous creatures, although vegetable material predominates in their diet.

Stridulation, which is confined to the males, is by rubbing the wings together. The wings are held up above the body a little way and a toothed ridge on the underside of the right front wing is drawn across the hind edge of the left front wing. Cricket 'songs' are prolonged and relatively musical, having a much higher pitch than grasshoppers' songs.

a, field cricket with wings raised in 'singing' position; **b,** the 'file' of the field cricket; **c,** the stridulatory pegs on the hind leg of a grasshopper

a   b   c

Our two native crickets, the Field Cricket (*Gryllus campestris*) and the Wood Cricket (*Nemobius sylvestris*) are both local insects restricted to the southern counties of England, although the Field Cricket was more widespread at one time. Both are ground-living and keep well to their respective habitats. Neither species can fly, for their hind wings are vestigial or absent. Most crickets are crepuscular insects, but these two species prefer the sunshine and they are active mainly by day.

The 'ear' of a cricket, just below the femur/ tibia junction on the front leg

'ear'

The House Cricket (*Acheta domesticus*) is not a native of our islands, although it is well established. It probably came from the warm areas of Africa and the Middle East, which explains why it is mainly an indoor insect in Europe. It is found in kitchens, bakeries, and factories where the temperature is above normal but it also exists, sometimes in enormous numbers, on rubbish dumps which are kept warm by the fermentation of refuse.

A fourth cricket, the wingless Scaly Cricket (*Mogoplistes squamiger*), is known from only one small area on the south coast and has almost certainly been introduced. It is common in coastal regions of the Continent.

Another continental species worthy of mention is the Italian cricket (*Oecanthus pellucens*). This slender, pale coloured creature sits on the vegetation at night and the male brings forth one of the sweetest of all insect songs – a bubbling sound, fairly high pitched and consisting of the phrase gri-i-i-i repeated over and over again. It is very difficult to track down the insect, however, because it alters the volume of the song at the slightest disturbance and the sound appears to come from another place. Fabre described the effect on the would-be collector as '. . . Complete confusion!'

Family Tettigoniidae – Bush Crickets (Pl. 5) These insects used to be called long-horned grasshoppers because of their very long, thread-like antennae, but the name bush cricket is much more appropriate. The insects are much more closely related to true crickets than to grasshoppers, they live among bushes rather than grass, and they crawl more than they hop. Bush crickets are separated from true crickets by having four tarsal segments and short cerci. Modern classification tends to split the bush crickets up among several families but the differences are relatively small and here we shall consider all our bush crickets as belonging to the one family.

The degree of wing development varies from species to species and only five of the 10 British species can fly. Even those that can fly rarely do so, and if disturbed they are more likely to walk away than to fly.

The male cerci are curved inwards and are used to hold the female. Their shape is useful in identification. The females are endowed with a fearsome-looking, broad-bladed ovipositor but, although it strikes terror into many people, it is quite harmless and is used solely for placing the eggs in a suitable place. This may be the soil, crevices in bark, or slits made in plant stems. The eggs are laid singly and do not hatch until the following spring or early summer. The nymphs mature in about three months, producing adults in August and September. Animal matter, particularly small insects, figures largely in the diet of these insects.

Like the true crickets, the bush crickets 'sing' by raising the wings and rubbing them together, but in these insects the left wing carries the teeth and lies on top of the right wing. The sound is very high pitched and goes on for relatively long periods.

Bush crickets are more nocturnal than grasshoppers, becoming active in the late afternoon and continuing to sing until well into the night. The pale green Oak Bush Cricket (*Meconema thalassinum*) is a common nocturnal visitor to lights in the neighbourhood of oak and lime trees. This is one of our commonest bush crickets, but the most striking species is surely the Great Green Bush Cricket (*Tettigonia viridissima*) nearly 5cm long and not uncommon in southern England, especially near the coast.

The visitor to southern Europe will hardly escape without seeing the famous 'tizi' (*Ephippiger ephippiger*). This large greenish or brown bush cricket sits on the vegetation, especially on low bushes, and uses its very short golden wings to utter a short double chirp, from which the insect gets its common French name of 'tizi'. There are several other species of *Ephippiger* in southern Europe, all possessing the raised collar-like pronotum. Unlike most of the bush crickets, the 'Tizi' is active during the daytime, This is also true of another large European bush cricket, *Decticus albifrons*. This brown and white creature is stoutly built and has a wing span of over 10 cm. It lives in very dry places and flies very well when disturbed. It is more likely to be heard than seen, however, for it produces a very shrill chirp, more like a bird than an insect.

Family Rhaphidophoridae – Wingless Camel Crickets or Cave Crickets (Pl. 6) These insects are completely wingless and rather hump-backed creatures, with extremely long antennae and a long, almost leg-like pair of palps. They are omnivorous creatures, but they prefer animal food. There are no native species in the British Isles, but an Asiatic species called *Tachycines asynamorus* has become established in various market gardening areas where there are extensive heated greenhouses. It is often called the Greenhouse Camel Cricket and, although usually regarded as an undesirable alien, it probably does more good than harm by eating other insects. There are several cave-dwelling members of the family in the southern parts of Europe, a typical species being *Dolichopoda azami*.

Family Acrididae – Grasshoppers (Pl. 6) These are the most familiar of the saltatorians, the insects that live among the grasses and serenade us in the meadows on summer afternoons. Their songs are not so highly pitched as those of the crickets, being more in the nature of buzzing sounds, but they are no less interesting.

The antennae are short and stout, in great contrast to those of the bush crickets, and there are no hearing organs on the legs: the tympana occur on the sides of the abdomen. The pronotum in this family bears a keel along the mid line. Ten of the 11 British species are fully winged and able to fly, the exception being the

The hind end of the abdomen of a male grasshopper (*left*) and a female

Meadow Grasshopper (*Chorthippus parallelus*) in which the hind wings are vestigial. The ovipositor is small and often partly concealed but the sexes may be distinguished by the shape of the hind end which is always turned upwards in the male.

As their name suggests, grasshoppers frequent grass and other low-growing vegetation but many of them have a very definite habitat preference. For example, the Large Marsh Grasshopper (*Stethophyma grossum*) is found only on peat bogs. The Meadow Grasshopper, however, is found in any grassland that is not too dry and must be our most abundant species, despite its inability to fly. The grasshoppers are almost entirely vegetarians, eating grass and a few other plants.

The eggs are laid in groups of about a dozen just under the soil or at the bases of grass tufts. When laid, they are covered with a frothy substance that hardens into a protective envelope or pod and protects them through the autumn and winter. The eggs start to hatch in spring and adult grasshoppers begin to appear in June after four nymphal instars.

Sound production in the grasshoppers involves the hind legs which carry the stridulatory pegs on their inner surface. When singing, the grasshopper moves the legs up and down, rubbing the pegs against a hardened vein on the front wings. The females of some grasshoppers can sing but the pegs on their wings are smaller than those of the male and the sound produced is much softer.

Locusts also belong to the Acrididae. They are large insects with strong powers of flight. From time to time their populations 'explode' and vast swarms emigrate from the population centres. They do an enormous amount of damage to crops at such times. Several species are centred in North Africa and the Middle East, and these often find their way to Europe. The Migratory Locust (*Locusta migratoria*) (Pl. 6) is resident in the southern part of Europe, but it does not often build up to dangerous numbers there.

Family Tetrigidae – Ground Hoppers These insects, of which we have three representatives in Britain, are found on the ground in a variety of places where the grass cover is not too extensive (this would favour grasshoppers at the expense of ground hoppers). At first sight similar to grasshoppers, the ground hoppers can be distinguished very easily by the backward extension of the pronotum which reaches the tip of the abdomen. The front wings are reduced to small scales but the hind wings are fully developed in two of our species. The Common Ground Hopper (*Tetrix undulata*) has reduced hind wings and is flightless.

Like the grasshoppers, the ground hoppers are active by day and their activity depends very much on temperature. They have no audible chirp (or hearing organs) and their predominantly brown colour makes them rather difficult to find on the ground.

The eggs are laid in batches, stuck together but not forming a pod as in grasshoppers. The batches are deposited in the ground or in moss and the young nymphs hatch within a month. They feed mainly on mosses and algae and spend the winter as nymphs or young adults.

Family Tridactylidae – Pigmy Mole Crickets This family contains about 50 species, represented in Europe by *Tridactylus variegatus*. This rather rare insect lives around the Mediterranean region and burrows in moist sandy soil. The pigmy mole crickets are all less than 10mm long, but the hind femur is relatively large.

Collecting and Preserving

Although the poor flight is to some extent offset by the jumping ability of these insects, catching them is not a difficult task. Tracked down by their songs, many species can be induced to jump or crawl into large glass tubes. A net may be used for the more active species.

Most killing agents are suitable for the saltatorians and boiling water is a useful standby as long as the insects are not immersed for more than a second or two. The insects should be pinned through the pronotum and left to dry after arranging the legs and spreading the wings if desired. As with many other large-bodied insects, the preservation of colour is difficult but rapid drying, preferably in a desiccator, should give reasonable results.

Grasshoppers and crickets are very easy to keep alive and the only equipment needed is a large glass container. An aquarium tank is ideal. A layer of moist sand in the bottom will provide a suitable medium for egg-laying and grass will provide the basic food for most of our species. A bit of fruit and bread will be welcomed by the crickets, while several of the bush crickets would appreciate a feed of aphids or other small insects. Many interesting facts about the lives of these insects can be learned by keeping them in this way.

Order Phasmida – Stick Insects

Recognition features Long slender insects with long legs and (in the European species) no wings. Biting mouth-parts are present. These insects cannot be confused with any others.

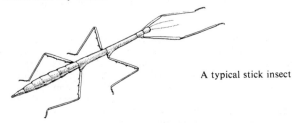

A typical stick insect

This order contains some 2,000 species and includes both stick insects and leaf insects. The latter are remarkable insects with flattened bodies and leaf-like flaps on their limbs. They look just like leaves but, as they do not occur in Europe, they do not concern us here. The stick insects are slender stick-like creatures, generally green or brown and very difficult to spot as they sit in the trees and bushes. Most members of the order are found in the tropical and oriental regions, but a few stick insects live in Southern Europe.

The head is prognathous and carries a pair of slender antennae with as many as 100 segments. All phasmids are vegetarians and they have strong biting jaws. The pronotum is small – in contrast to that of the grasshoppers and cockroaches – but the meso- and metanota are very long and between them they may account for nearly half the body length. All the legs are more or less alike and carry five tarsal segments, except where legs have been lost and regenerated. Wings are not found in the European stick insects, although many other species are winged.

When wings are present the front ones are hardened to form tegmina and they are generally quite small. The abdomen carries a pair of short cerci at the hind end.

Many species of stick insects have no known male sex, or else males are extremely rare. Reproduction is then parthenogenetic, the females laying fertile eggs without mating. The eggs are like small seeds and are usually provided with a 'lid' which comes off when the young insect hatches. The eggs are simply dropped to the ground and the female may lay several in a day. They often take many months to hatch. Apart from the increase in size, there is little change during development. When males are present they are considerably smaller than the females and much more slender.

There are several lines of thought on the classification of stick insects, but we will consider them all as belonging to a single family – the Phasmatidae. Three species occur in southern Europe. *Bacillus rossii* (Pl. 7) and *Clonopsis gallicus* are both fairly common, while *Leptynia hispanica* is less frequent. The first two species rarely produce males, but the two sexes are more or less equally represented in *Leptynia*. There are no native stick insects in the British Isles, but three exotic species have established small colonies. Two of these species are the Prickly Stick Insect (*Acanthoxyla prasina*) and the Smooth Stick Insect (*Clitarcus hookeri*). Both hail from New Zealand and probably arrived with imported plants in the first place. They are established only in the Scilly Isles and certain other places in the warmer parts of the British Isles. The Prickly Stick Insect, named from the sharp spikes on the head and thorax, has no male sex as far as is known. Male Smooth Stick Insects are common in New Zealand, but unknown in Britain. The third species is the Laboratory Stick Insect (*Carausius morosus*), which is commonly kept as a pet. It comes from the oriental region and has managed to establish itself only in greenhouses in the British Isles.

Stick insects are best preserved by pinning them through the metathorax – about half-way along the body.

Order Dermaptera – Earwigs

Recognition features Elongate brownish insects, usually with short front wings meeting in the mid-line and reaching only a short way down the body. The cerci are modified into stout pincers, strongly curved in the male. The general shape of these insects is such that they may be confused with certain of the rove beetles (Staphylinidae) but the cerci will always distinguish the earwigs.

The earwigs (Pl. 7) are a very small order with only about 1,000 known species, and the British earwig fauna is very meagre indeed, only two species being at all

A typical earwig

common. Another two species are found occasionally in the southern counties, but the earwigs are at the very limits of their range here and winter temperatures control their distribution. The insects spend the winter in the soil and our two common species, *Forficula auricularia* and *Labia minor*, are able to tolerate quite low temperatures. These species are widespread but the others, less tolerant of cold, are confined to the southern counties where cold spells are shorter and soil temperatures do not therefore fall so low. Several additional species come in occasionally with foreign produce and temporary colonies may be established in and around warehouses, but these species are unable to survive in the wild. The continental fauna is somewhat richer, and includes the large *Labidura riparia*. This insect is up to 25mm long and quite unmistakable. It used to occur in the British Isles, but is now thought to be extinct here.

Earwigs bring the shudders to many people on account of the superstition that the insects seek out a human ear and bite through the eardrum. There is no truth in this idea, although many campers' ears have been investigated by earwigs, and it seems certain that the name earwig (and similar names used in other countries) arose as the result of the occasional finding of one of these insects in the ear. Earwigs are nocturnal insects and seek out dark, narrow crevices for their daytime rest. They seem to like to feel their bodies in contact with something when at rest and this allows us to trap them with stuffed, inverted flower-pots into which they crawl after a night of petal chewing. Apart from this habit of chewing our best blooms, however, the earwigs are quite harmless. In fact, their scavenging way of life is probably useful.

The broad head carries long, slender antennae, containing up to 50 segments. The compound eyes are large but there are no ocelli. The jaws are of the simple biting type, associated with the rather omnivorous habits of the insects – flower petals, carrion, and living insects all being taken quite readily. The prothorax is well developed and clearly visible but the meso- and metathoracic segments are generally hidden by the short, veinless front wings (tegmina). The hind wings are relatively large, almost semicircular in shape, and extremely thin, having very much the texture of the skin that we shed after getting sun-burned. The name Dermaptera means skin-winged (Greek *derma* = skin) and refers to this soft texture of the hind wings.

Most of the hind wing consists of the enlarged anal area, the pre-anal part being reduced to a narrow, thickened strip. The wings are folded very elaborately under the tegmina and this thickened strip often projects a short way behind them. If you try to unfold the wings on an earwig you will realise just how

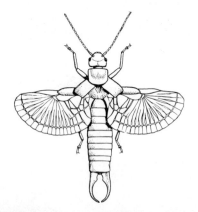

An earwig showing the delicate semi-circular wings, which are folded many times before they can be tucked under the small elytra

elaborately they are folded to get them under the small tegmina: there are about 40 thicknesses of each wing when completely folded. The Small Earwig, *Labia minor*, frequently flies but the other species rarely use their wings and one might be tempted to think that the earwig finds it too much trouble to get his wings out and then put them away again. A number of species have dispensed with wings altogether.

The abdomen ends in the characteristic forceps, strongly curved in the male and almost straight, perhaps just meeting at the tips in the female. These forceps are probably defensive structures for they are raised forward over the body scorpion-like when the insects are disturbed. There are also reports of the forceps' being used in the folding of the wings after flight.

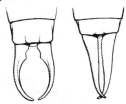

The forceps of a male (*left*) and a female *Forficula auricularia*

Insects are not noted for maternal care but the female earwig is an exception. She lays her eggs – up to 80 have been recorded, but 20–40 is more usual – in the soil and looks after them throughout the winter. Experiments under artificial conditions have shown that the female will even collect up her eggs that have been removed and scattered over the surrounding soil. The eggs hatch in early spring but the nymphs do not leave their winter quarters until they reach the second instar. They are fed and tended by the mother, even after coming above ground, until they are well able to fend for themselves and it is quite common to see such family groups in the spring.

Apart from the development of wings, there is little external change in the growing insects. The antennae increase in number of segments and the forceps gradually assume their adult form, but otherwise the nymphs look much like the adults. There are normally four nymphal instars and the earwigs reach maturity in late summer. Mating takes place before the insects seek out their winter resting places.

Our four native species (Pl. 7) may be separated with the aid of the following key:

1. 2nd tarsal segment expanded   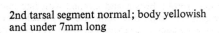   2

   2nd tarsal segment normal; body yellowish    *Labia minor*
   and under 7mm long

2. Wings projecting beyond the elytra   *Forficula auricularia*
   Wings concealed or absent   3

3. Male forceps broad at base: insects under 8mm   *Forficula lesnei*
   Male forceps slender throughout: insects over
   8 mm long   *Apterygida albipennis*

Collecting and Preserving

Our two common species are easily collected by sweeping vegetation or beating branches, or by setting traps of the type described earlier in this chapter.

The insects are best preserved by pinning. Attempts should be made to unfold the wings of at least one specimen.

Order Embioptera – Web-spinners

Recognition features Small to medium sized insects with soft brownish bodies and biting jaws. The basal segment of the front tarsus is swollen. Wings may be present in the males, but are normally absent in European species. Insects living under stones in little silken tunnels.

A typical wingless web-spinner

The Embioptera is a small and little-known group of insects, with perhaps 150 species distributed in all major regions. The insects are known as web-spinners because they make silken webs and tunnels under stones and in the soil. They live in and around their tunnels and withdraw into them very rapidly when disturbed. During the colder weather the insects go deeper into the soil. Web-spinners often live in communities of a dozen or more individuals and, although the individuals do not co-operate, their tangled webs probably help to protect them from centipedes and other predatory creatures. The silk is produced in special glands in the basal segment of the front tarsus. This segment is swollen and is a characteristic feature of the group.

The head is small, although as broad as the body, and carries typical biting jaws. These differ in the two sexes, the male having sharper ones than the female. It is likely that the male is carnivorous and the female feeds more on vegetable matter.

Female web-spinners are always wingless, and several species have wingless males too. In some species the males may be winged or wingless. When wings are present the two pairs are alike, smoky brown and clothed with fine hairs. The radial vein is greatly thickened, but the other veins are very weak. Web-spinners do not fly well, although some males come to light at night. The abdomen bears a pair of short cerci, which are generally asymmetrical in the male.

The eggs are relatively large and oval and they are laid in the tunnels. The female looks after them and the young insects for a while. Metamorphosis is more or less absent in the females, and only slight in the males.

The few European species are rarely seen and they are confined to the southern parts. Two of the commoner species are *Haploembia solieri* and *Embia amadorae*, the latter sometimes producing winged males.

Web-spinners must be preserved in alcohol because their soft cuticle becomes greatly distorted when dried.

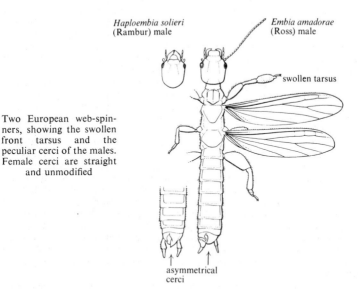

Haploembia solieri
(Rambur) male

Embia amadorae
(Ross) male

swollen tarsus

Two European web-spin-ners, showing the swollen front tarsus and the peculiar cerci of the males. Female cerci are straight and unmodified

asymmetrical cerci

Order Dictyoptera – Cockroaches and Mantises

Recognition features Small, medium, or large insects of rather flattened appearance. Usually two pairs of wings of which the front pair are leathery and held flat over the back. The antennae are long and slender. Legs long and rather spiky. A pair of rather conspicuous cerci. Cockroaches have a large shield-like pronotum extending forward and covering most of the head. Mantises do not have this shield, but can be recognised by their greatly enlarged, spiky front legs.

Cockroaches can be distinguished from the grasshoppers and crickets by the lack of jumping legs. There might be some confusion with beetles – the name 'black beetle' for the common cockroach proves this – but beetle elytra meet in the mid-line and do not overlap. Furthermore, beetles have no cerci. Some of the heteropteran bugs resemble small cockroaches, but here again there are no cerci, and the sucking beak of the bugs will always distinguish them.

A typical cockroach

SUB-ORDER BLATTODEA – COCKROACHES (Pl. 7)

The cockroaches are a mainly tropical group and most of the cockroaches seen in Britain are introduced species living only under artificial conditions. Three species, the Common cockroach or 'black beetle' (*Blatta orientalis*), the American cockroach (*Periplaneta americana*) and the German cockroach (*Blatella germanica*) are all very common here. Indeed they are common all over the world as a result of man's commercial activities. Coming originally from the warmer parts of the world (*B. germanica* is not a native of Germany), these insects find ideal homes in warehouses, kitchens, breweries, and so on where there is warmth and an abundance of food. They are all omnivorous insects, although dead animal material is probably their main food in the wild. In captivity they will readily devour their dead brothers and sisters, although they will not attack and kill each other for food.

They are nocturnal creatures and hide during the daytime in such out-of-the-way places as behind skirting boards, under floors, and in ventilating ducts. They can therefore exist unnoticed for a long time, gradually building up their numbers. The harm they do lies not so much in the material they actually eat – this consists largely of scraps – but in the contamination of other materials with a characteristic smell. Large quantities of food have to be thrown away because of this contamination. Cockroaches certainly carry disease germs but there is no regular association between any cockroach species and any particular disease.

The native cockroaches of Europe are rather small and inconspicuous insects. Three species extend into the British Isles, but do not reach beyond the southern counties of England and Wales. They live among the vegetation in a variety of habitats.

The cockroaches were at one time included in the order Orthoptera, along with crickets and grasshoppers, but they are now separated on the basis of a number of features as will be seen from the following account of their anatomy.

The 3,500 known cockroach species are sufficiently alike for us to consider them all as belonging to the single family Blattidae. There are many sub-families, regarded as separate families by some authorities, but we shall not go into the differences between them.

The cockroach head (Fig. p. 16) is hypognathous and rather primitive in structure, with few specialisations. The simple biting jaws are strongly toothed in connection with the omnivorous diet of these creatures. The antennae are long and the compound eyes are well-developed but there are rarely any ocelli – simply two pale patches believed to represent degenerate ocelli. When the insects are viewed from above, most of the head is concealed by the large pronotum which also extends laterally. The pronotum does not, however, turn down over the sides of the prothorax.

Two pairs of wings are normally present, although in some species, for example the common cockroach, the females have reduced wings. The front wings – sometimes called tegmina – are leathery in texture and overlap in the middle line to protect the underlying membranous hind wings. The typical wing venation is shown here, a notable feature being the many branches of the radius. As in the grasshoppers, there is a large anal area in the hind wing. The order name Dictyoptera means 'net-wings' (Greek *dictyon* = net) but refers more to the extinct species which had many more cross veins than the living cockroaches.

Most of our cockroach species can fly but they seem reluctant to do so and they are essentially ground-living insects. The legs are not modified for jumping but they are relatively long and slender, making the cockroaches elusive runners and very difficult to catch. The tarsi are 5-segmented (compared with 2–4 segments in the Saltatoria). The abdomen ends in a pair of short, but quite visible cerci. There is no external ovipositor.

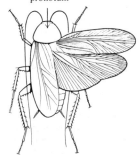

An American cockroach showing the large pronotum almost concealing the head and the complex venation of the wings

Cockroaches lay their eggs in little purse-shaped containers called oothecae and these can often be seen projecting from the female's abdomen. Most cockroaches deposit their purses soon after they are formed but *germanica* carries hers around and does not deposit it until the eggs are about to hatch. The number of eggs in a purse varies from about 12 to 50 but each species has its own range and average.

The nymphs are worm-like when they first hatch but as soon as they reach the air they shed their skins and emerge as tiny cockroaches. Metamorphosis is slight and there are between 5 and 12 moults, according to species. The nymphs take several months to mature but details of the life cycle again vary between species.

SUB-ORDER MANTODEA – MANTISES

The mantises, or praying mantises to give them their full name, are readily distinguished from cockroaches by the strongly spined raptorial front legs. They also have a long, narrow prothorax which forms a movable 'neck'. At rest, the prothorax is usually raised a little and the front legs are held folded in front of the face. The resemblance to a person in prayer has led to the common name of these insects. Many mantises are green and they are well hidden as they sit motionless among the vegetation waiting for food. Some tropical species are brightly coloured

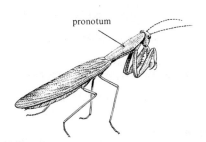

A praying mantis, showing the spiky front legs and the very long pronotum

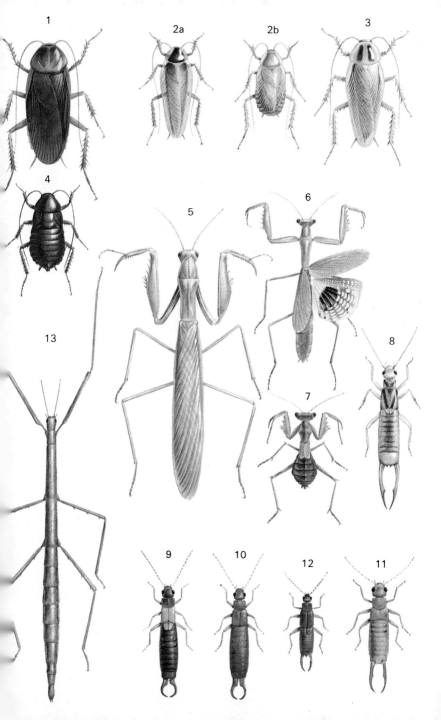

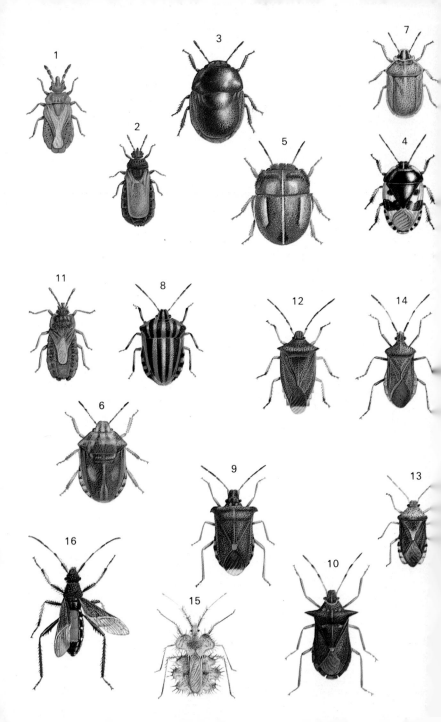

Insects with a beak or rostrum used for sucking plant or
animal juices   p. 111

SUB-ORDER HETEROPTERA

Front wings, when present, horny but with a membranous
tip: beak arising at front of head   p. 111

Aradidae. Very flat bugs with stout antennae: usually fully-   p. 120
   winged
1. Pine flat-bug – *Aradus cinnamomeus* (Panzer)   ×5

Aneuridae. Very flat bugs with front wings almost entirely   p. 120
   membranous
2. *Aneurus laevis* (Fabr.)   ×5

Cydnidae. Hind tibiae strongly spined   p. 121
3. Negro bug – *Thyreocoris scarabaeoides* (L.)   ×5
4. Pied shieldbug – *Sehirus bicolor* (L.)   ×3

Scutelleridae. Scutellum enormous, covering all of abdomen   p. 121
   and most of wings
5. *Odontoscelis dorsalis* (Fabr.)   ×5
6. *Eurygaster testudinaria* (Geoffroy)   ×2

Pentatomidae. Body generally shield-shaped: scutellum gener-   p. 121
   ally triangular: tarsi 3-segmented
7. European turtle-bug – *Podops inuncta* (Fabr.)   ×3
▲ **8.** *Graphosoma italicum* Müller   ×2
9. Forest bug – *Pentatoma rufipes* (L.)   ×2
10. *Picromerus bidens* (L.)   ×2

△ **Meziridae.** Flattened bugs similar to Aradidae but with head   p. 125
   expanded behind eyes
▲ **11.** *Mezira tremulae* Buttn   ×2

Acanthosomidae. Tarsi 2-segmented   p. 121
12. Hawthorn shieldbug – *Acanthosoma haemorrhoidale* (L.)
   ×2
13. Parent bug – *Elasmucha grisea* (L.)   ×2

Coreidae. Antennae 4-segmented: scutellum generally shield-   p. 121
   shaped: abdomen usually extending sideways beyond elytra
14. *Coreus marginatus* (L.)   ×2
▲ **15.** *Philomorpha laciniata* de Vill.   ×2

Alydidae. 4th segment of antennae long and curved   p. 122
16. *Alydus calcaratus* (L.)   ×2

and have bizarre outgrowths on the limbs and body. They bear a striking resemblance to certain flowers and they are hard to see as they sit on the blossoms.

All mantises are carnivorous insects and they use their front legs to catch food. Flies, grasshoppers, butterflies, and many other insects are eaten. The mantis shoots out its front legs at great speed and snaps them shut around the prey. The spines hold the insect firmly while the mantis devours it greedily with the aid of its strong and sharp mandibles. Even the heavily sclerotised head capsule of a wasp is no problem for a mantis – the jaws cut straight through it.

Mating in the mantises has been compared to that in spiders because the male is somewhat smaller than his mate and often ends up as her next meal. The eggs are laid in oothecae of various kinds. One common type starts off as a frothy secretion pumped out of the abdomen with the eggs. The secretion soon hardens into a tough spongy material. These oothecae are attached to the twigs and branches of plants, and a female may produce a dozen or more during her lifetime. The young mantises are worm-like at first, but they soon change into mantis-like creatures when they leave the oothecae.

Mantises, like cockroaches, are mainly tropical insects. There are nearly 2,000 species, of which only about a dozen reach Europe. Best known is *Mantis religiosa* – the original 'praying mantis'. This and two other common European species are illustrated on Pl. 7.

Collecting and Preserving
Our native cockroaches can be collected quite easily in their known haunts by sweeping low growing vegetation or by sifting leaf litter. The introduced species can be trapped with fruit or syrup when droppings and greasy marks suggest their presence. Insecticidal treatment – to be used with great care where food is prepared – usually means that the insects go back to their hideaway to die. Cockroaches are easily kept in captivity as long as warmth is provided. Food presents no problem – kitchen scraps are all that are needed. The mantises can be obtained by careful searching or by sweeping the vegetation. They live well in captivity as long as one has a supply of flies or other insects for them to eat.

The smaller cockroaches may be preserved in alcohol or staged on micro-pins. The larger ones and the mantises are best pinned through the meso- or metathorax, with the wings spread on one side.

Order Isoptera – Termites

Recognition features Small to medium-sized insects with or without wings and with biting mouths. The body is soft and pale and bears short cerci. The wings, when present, are long and narrow and the anterior veins are markedly thickened. Both pairs are alike. The insects live in colonies, with several different castes.

A winged termite

The termites are basically tropical insects and only two of the 2,000 known species are native in Europe. They are often called white ants because of their pale colour and their social life, but there are many differences between the termites and the true ants.

The mouth-parts of the termites are rather like those of the cockroaches, with tough biting jaws. Some species eat grass and fungi, but most of them feed on wood and they are extremely destructive insects. Some members of the colony get their food at second hand after it has been at least partly digested by the workers. The soldier termites and the reproductive castes are always fed in this way, and so are some of the young stages. Food is regurgitated by the workers, or else they pass partly digested faecal pellets which are consumed by the other termites. Wood is not an easily digested material, and the termites rely on an army of protozoans or bacteria in their stomachs to break down the tough cellulose. Young termites receive their micro-organisms in the food they receive from the workers.

Only the head capsule is at all hard in the termites, the cuticle of the rest of the body being soft and more or less transparent. The head is large and rather oblong or pear-shaped in the soldier castes, but small and rounded in the other castes. Compound eyes are always present in the reproductive castes, but may be greatly reduced or absent in the others, specially in species that remain below ground.

The pronotum of the thorax is clearly separated and its shape is important in the classification of the insects. The wings, when present, are all alike (Isoptera means 'equal wings') and their anterior veins are thickened. There are few regular cross veins, but the wings often carry a net-work of small veins and vein-like

The front wings of *Kalotermes flavicollis* (*left*) and *Reticulitermes lucifugus*, showing the extremely fine venation. Front and hind wings are almost identical

wrinkles. The wings normally extend well beyond the body when at rest. A pair of short cerci is present at the hind end of all termite castes.

The termites differ from the ants and other social insects in having males and females present in more or less equal numbers. All castes contain both males and females, and the colony is normally headed by a 'king' as well as a 'queen'. These are members of the primary reproductive caste and they are winged to start with. Their bodies are also more heavily sclerotised than those of the other castes. The primary reproductive termites emerge from their nests at certain seasons and have a brief aerial life on their rather weak wings. This may be sufficient to carry them away from the vicinity of their own nests and they then come to earth and break off their wings. When opposite sexes meet they excavate a small nuptial chamber and a new colony begins.

The king and queen are long-lived insects and they may live together in their colony for many years – 50 years has been quoted for some species. They mate frequently during this time and the queen may get very large – up to 10cm in length in some species – as her abdomen swells with eggs. The colony builds up slowly at first, but then speeds up. The more primitive families have only small colonies, with a few hundred individuals, but colonies of the more advanced families may contain a million termites.

As in all the social insects, the workers are the most numerous members of the colony. They look after the royal couple, tend the eggs and young, forage for food, feed the soldiers, and build and maintain the nest. The work force of the more primitive termites is composed of juvenile insects of various ages and there is no definite worker caste. The majority of these working juveniles never grow up, but they can change into soldiers or reproductive forms if necessary. Further up the termite scale we find the work being carried out more and more by the later instars only, and in the highest termite families, unrepresented in Europe, there is a distinct worker caste. These workers are still juveniles, however, and they have no wings.

Soldier castes are found in almost all genera of termites. They have large heads and their job is to defend the colony. There are two types of soldier, one with large and powerful jaws, and one with small jaws and a pointed head. The latter type eject a repellent liquid from glands in the head and this serves to keep would-be attackers at bay. The soldiers of most termite species lack functional eyes. If anything should happen to the king or the queen of a termite colony the workers are able to rear yet another caste – the supplementary reproductive. This has only small wings and it does not leave the colony. Its members are fertile, however, and they can step into the role of king or queen to ensure that the colony continues.

Young termites exhibit only a slight metamorphosis during their life, but the length of development varies from caste to caste and from species to species. The soldiers and the workers probably live for up to four years.

Termite nests vary a great deal in construction. The most primitive families simply excavate galleries in dead wood, while others make underground nests. The most advanced termites build huge mounds, partly from soil excavated from their underground chambers and cemented with saliva. These great termitaria are especially common in Africa and Australia.

The European termites belong to two families, the **Kalotermitidae** and the **Rhinotermitidae**. The former is one of the more primitive families and it is represented by *Kalotermes flavicollis*. This is a dry wood termite and it lives in dead trees, or occasionally in building timbers. It has no workers and lives in small communities of a royal pair and a few hundred working young and soldiers. The reproductives take over a year to mature, passing through several instars on the way. The soldiers, which account for about 5 per cent of the population, mature more quickly. This termite species is found along the Mediterranean coast from Portugal to Greece, and on to the Middle East.

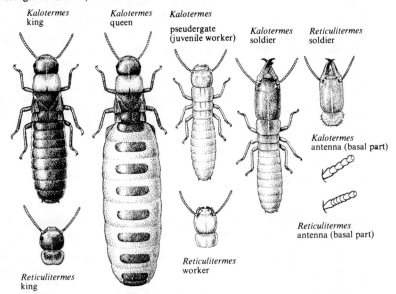

Kalotermes king

Kalotermes queen

Kalotermes pseudergate (juvenile worker)

Kalotermes soldier

Reticulitermes soldier

Kalotermes antenna (basal part)

Reticulitermes antenna (basal part)

Reticulitermes worker

Reticulitermes king

Drawings to show the differences between the castes of the two European termites

The second European species is *Reticulitermes lucifugus*, with a more distinct worker caste. It excavates galleries in trees and shrubs and in building timbers at or below ground level. It does a considerable amount of damage to old buildings. These insects travel about more than *Kalotermes* and their colonies are more diffuse. The outer branches may sever their connections with the parent colony and become self-supporting through the production of supplementary reproductives. *Reticulitermes* can survive lower temperatures than *Kalotermes* and it extends north to Bordeaux and northern Italy. An American species, *Reticulitermes flavipes*, has become established in various towns in France, and also in Hamburg. It lives only in buildings so far in Europe.

Because of their soft cuticles, termites are best preserved in alcohol.

Order Psocoptera – Psocids or Booklice

Recognition features Small or minute soft-bodied insects rarely exceeding 6mm in length. With or without wings and living in vegetation or among dried materials. Antennae generally long and filiform. Compound eyes often large and protruding from the sides of the head which itself is quite broad. The winged forms, when at rest, hold the wings steeply roof-wise over the body, a position which, with other features, gives the insect a very characteristic appearance.

The winged psocids, especially when found in large numbers, may be taken for aphids but the long antennae, broad head, and biting jaws of the psocids easily separate the two groups. They are more often confused with psyllids (p. 135) but the wing venation and mouth-parts will distinguish them. Some of the wingless psocids superficially resemble some of the lice, hence the names booklice and dust-lice, but they are in no way parasitic and are easily distinguished by the long antennae.

A typical winged psocid

This is a relatively small order of insects with only about 1,600 known species. There are about 70 British species but our fauna is swollen by another dozen or so species that exist here under artificial conditions, in warehouses and so on. The indoor species are mostly wingless or short-winged and live among dried materials such as paper, habits that have given the insects names such as booklice and dust-lice. Undisturbed books frequently harbour these psocids which feed on minute traces of mould on the paper. The insects are also found in damp houses where they feed under the peeling wallpaper. Entomological collections, too, suffer from psocid attack and many a prize specimen has been reduced to dust by these creatures.

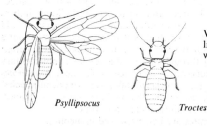

Psyllipsocus

Troctes

Winged and wingless psocids or book-lice. The swollen hind femora of the wingless *Troctes* are very character-istic of the Family Troctidae

The majority of psocid species, however, live out of doors, scraping a living from pollen grains, from algae growing on bark, and from minute fungi on leaves. The alternative name of barklice refers to the fact that many psocids live on and under bark. Old birds' nests may also harbour some psocids. Most of these outdoor species are fully winged. Economically, the psocids are unimportant, although certain species have been known to carry sheep tapeworms.

The psocid head is relatively wide and very mobile. Its width is effectively increased by the large compound eyes which protrude from the sides of the head in most of the winged forms. The eyes, however, are reduced to very small structures in the wingless Troctidae (booklice). Three ocelli are present in the winged forms. The slender antennae most often contain 13 segments although some species have 20 or more. The number of segments is used in the classification of the insects. Psocid mouth-parts are complex pieces of apparatus, the major components being the strong biting mandibles. The insects use these mandibles to scrape particles of food from the substrate and the generic name *Psocus* was coined from a Greek word meaning to grind to pieces. Psocoptera therefore means 'winged like *Psocus*'. Another name sometimes applied to the order is Corrodentia, derived from the Latin verb *rodere*, meaning 'to gnaw'.

There is a reduction of the prothorax in the winged species and the meso- and metanota are each clearly divided into scutum and scutellum. The prothorax is larger in the wingless psocids. When wings are present, there are two pairs, both membranous. The front wings are considerably larger than the hind wings and the two pairs are coupled when in flight. Flight is not common, however, most species simply scuttling away when disturbed. At rest, the wings are held roof-wise and steeply sloping over the body.

The veins are prominent, although reduced in number. The so-called pterostigma is actually a cell near the tip of the front wing and it is frequently pigmented. There is often a certain amount of other marbling on the wings. The radius with the radial sector is 3-branched and the media is also 3-branched in the front wing, although single in the hind wing. The media and cubitus are fused basally and, in the front wing, Cu usually loops around to enclose a cell known as the areola postica, which may or may not be connected with the median vein. There is a notable absence of cross veins in most species.

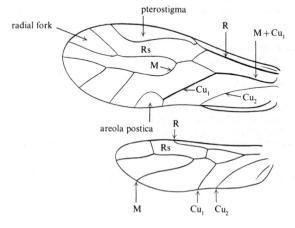

Typical psocid venation

The legs are of simple structure, well suited to running. The tarsi each have two or three segments and each bears two claws. In the family Troctidae the femora of the hind legs are broad and flat.

The majority of psocids lay small pearly eggs which may be protected by a web of silk or with an encrustation of tiny food particles or faecal matter. The nymphs usually pass through six instars before reaching maturity, and apart from increase in size and the development of wings (when present), the main external changes are increases in the number of antennal segments and in the relative size of the eyes.

On account of their small size, the psocids are difficult to identify and a low power microscope is necessary to identify some of the families with certainty. The following key, based on information provided by the late Mr J. V. Pearman, may be used to separate the British families.

Key to the Families of British Psocoptera

1. Insects totally wingless   2
   Insects with vestigial wings at least   3

2. Very small species: abdomen flattened: Troctidae
   hind femur broad

   Larger species: abdomen globose: hind
   femur slender   Epipsocidae ♀

3. Wings vestigial, not extending beyond thorax   4
   Wings fully developed   7

4. Body and winglets covered with scales   Perientomidae
   Without scales   5

5. Relatively large species with mottled coloration: abdomen humped and bearing a charac-
   teristic black band   Mesopsocidae ♀
   Not fitting this description   6

6. Winglets rounded (weakly attached and
   easily lost): maxillary palps broad at apex   Atropidae
   Winglets narrow: maxillary palps obliquely
   pointed: hind tarsi noticeably long   Psyllipsocidae

7. Wings abnormal, the   Troctidae (some ♀♀)
   front venation reduced
   to two longitudinal
   veins

   Wings normal, with greater number of veins   8

. Pterostigma and areola
postica simple forks
without pigmentation:
hind tarsi noticeably
long: (often occurs with
short wings)

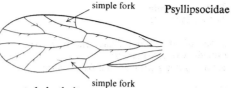

simple fork   Psyllipsocidae

simple fork

Pterostigma commonly pigmented, both it
and areola postica (if present) with curved
margins: (many females wingless or brachy-
pterous)   9

. Areola postica not present   10
Areola postica present   11

Cilia present on some veins
of front wings, at least
in basal half:
pterostigma oblong

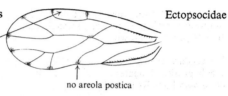

Ectopsocidae

no areola postica

Front wings without
visible cilia: pterostigma
slightly rounded distally:
membrane often dark

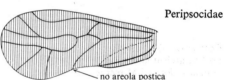

Peripsocidae

no areola postica

free pterostigma

Areola postica joined to media   12
Areola not joined to
media: pterostigma free   13

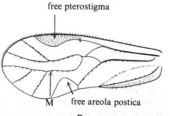

M   free areola postica

Rs

Pterostigma connected to Rs

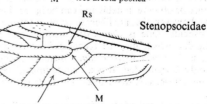

Stenopsocidae

areola postica joined to M   M

Pterostigma free   Psocidae

13. Tarsi 3-segmented   14
    Tarsi 2-segmented   16

14. Front wings without cilia: relatively large
    psocids with globular eyes   Mesopsocidae ♂
    Smaller insects with ciliated front wings   15

15. Cilia short: eyes hemispherical   Elipsocidae
    Cilia conspicuous   Philotarsidae

16. Minute species without visible cilia: ptero-
    stigma abruptly terminated and roughly
    wedge-shaped   Lachesillidae
    Larger species with ciliated wings   17

17. Insects whitish with brown streak along sides
    of thorax: areola postica nearly semi-circular   Trichopsocidae
    Insects yellow to brown   18

18. Insects dark brown: Epipsocidae ♂
    areola postica elongate:
    cross vein links Rs and M

cross vein

elongate areola postica

Colour variable: areola   Caeciliidae
postica arched and
compact: Rs and M merge

Rs+M

arched areola postica

There are a number of species that cannot be tracked down with this key
because of various departures from the basic family plan. Most of these species
are rare or obscure in habit and can be ignored in this general account. There are
a few, however, that are likely to come to the notice of anyone who starts looking
for psocids. One is *Cerobasis guestfalicus*, a small, wingless member of the
Atropidae which may be recognised by its densely speckled appearance. Another is *Reuterella helvimacula*, a member of the Elipsocidae in which the tarsi
are only 2-segmented. It is a minute insect, spending much of its time in small
communal webs on tree trunks. The male is winged but the female is totally wingless.

Only about half of these families are at all common and most of our species
belong to only four families. The majority of indoor species belong to the Atropidae, whose wings are reduced or absent, and the Troctidae, all but one of which

are wingless. The Troctidae includes the commonest of the booklice, *Troctes divinatorius*. Most of our outdoor species belong to the Psocidae and the Caeciliidae.

Collecting and Preserving
Outdoor species can be collected very easily by sweeping herbage and beating trees. Searching under loose bark or in old birds' nests is also profitable. Indoor species can be found in dim, neglected corners where there is a musty smell.

Their soft bodies dictate that psocids must be preserved in spirit if any structural detail is to be retained.

Orders Mallophaga and Anoplura – Lice

These are all small and minute insects that live ectoparasitically on birds and mammals. Their bodies are flattened and they are usually provided with strong claws, two features that enable them to cling closely to the host's body and resist all but the most vigorous scratching. In association with the flattening, the spiracles have come to lie on the dorsal surface of the body. The lice spend their whole lives on the host, although they may move from one individual to another if two hosts come into contact, and it is not surprising that wings have disappeared during the course of evolution. As in other parasitic animals, the sensory organs are poorly developed, the eyes being small or absent and the antennae short.

Lice feed either on blood or by scraping the surface of the skin and taking particles of feathers. In this way they may cause considerable irritation to the host, which must resort to almost continuous scratching when the infestation is heavy. This leads to skin damage, loss of blood, and the entry of disease germs, leading in turn to wasting and possible death of the host. Some species of lice also actively transmit certain bacterial and virus diseases. Lice are therefore of great economic importance when they infect domestic livestock and a great deal of effort is being put into finding effective control measures. Some species of lice affect a wide range of host animals but other species may be confined to one host or a group of closely related host species. The claws of some lice are so well adapted for gripping the hair of the host that they are unable to attach themselves to other hosts whose hairs are of different diameters. Some species of lice even confine themselves to certain areas of the host animal – the head and neck for example.

The evolution of lice has gone hand in hand with that of the hosts – a not unexpected situation in view of the constant association between the two. Lice are undoubtedly passed from parent to offspring in the nest and from one member of a herd or family group to another, but apart from this there will be little interchange of lice. One strain of lice will therefore tend to stay with one particular strain of host animal and the two will evolve together. To take a simple example, the lice of man and apes are much more closely related to each other than they are to those of rodents, paralleling the relationships of the host animals themselves. Lice have actually aided systematists in the determination of the relationships of some groups of birds. An oft-quoted example is that of the flamingos: these birds might appear closer to storks than to ducks but their lice suggest that they are more closely related to the ducks.

All lice are superficially similar and some entomologists place them in a single order – the Phthiraptera. Much of the similarity, however, is due to their mode of life and other entomologists, stressing differences in the mouth-parts, recognise two separate orders – the Mallophaga and Anoplura. We shall follow this arrangement here.

Order Mallophaga – Biting Lice and Bird Lice

Recognition features Small and minute wingless, fla' ɔodied parasites, mainly associated with birds. Eyes very small. Antennae wit 3–5 segments and often concealed. Biting mouth-parts.

Superficially similar to some of the wingless psocids (booklice), the true lice may be distinguished by their short antennae. Biting lice are easily separated from the sucking lice (Order Anoplura) by the general body shape and by the pro-thorax of the biting lice.

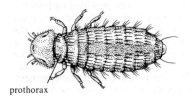

A biting louse, showing the distinct prothorax and the two claws usually present on each leg

prothorax

These parasites are found primarily on birds – hence the name bird lice – although some species infest mammals. Biting lice use their jaws to scrape the skin and chew feathers. Some species take blood, especially from wounds. The name Mallophaga actually means 'wool-eating' (Greek *mallos* = wool; *phagein* = to eat), although it has not been proved that any of the lice actually eat hair.

The largest biting lice are about 6mm long but very few reach this size, the majority being less than half as long. The flat body is quite hard and the head is generally comparatively large. There are no ocelli and the compound eyes are reduced. The antennae are sometimes concealed under the head. The large, toothed mandibles are held either vertically or horizontally. The prothorax is usually distinct from the other two thoracic segments, which may or may not be fused together. Each leg bears one or two claws with which the insects cling tightly to the host, although these lice are no sluggards when it becomes necessary to avoid capture.

The females lay something between 50 and 100 eggs which they cement to the hairs of the host. The nymphs pass through three instars before reaching the adult state, the whole process from egg to adult taking between three and four weeks in the constant temperature environment of the host's body.

About 500 species of biting lice have been recorded in Britain – some 20 per cent of the known species, although it is certain that many hundreds of species have yet to be discovered. The six British families are separated on the basis of a number of small, but distinct characteristics. The **Menoponidae** and **Philopteridae** are the two largest families and both include important poultry pests, including the Shaft Louse, *Menopon gallinae*. The family **Trichodectidae** is much smaller but it includes the very important genus *Damalinia* whose species cause much loss among sheep, goats, cattle, and other hoofed mammals in various parts of the world. None of the biting lice affects man.

Order Anoplura (= Siphunculata) – Sucking Lice

Recognition features Small and minute wingless parasites of mammals. The head is usually narrow and the eyes are reduced or absent. Antennae short. Mouth-parts modified for blood-sucking and retractable into the head when not in use. The thoracic segments are fused together and each leg ends in a strong claw. The sucking lice are distinguishable from wingless psocids by their short antennae and from the biting lice by their fused thoracic segments, there being no free pro-thorax.

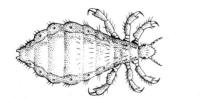

A sucking louse, showing the single claw on each leg, enlarged on the right

All sucking lice are parasitic on mammals and they all feed exclusively on blood which they obtain by piercing the skin with their highly specialised mouth-parts. These consist of a toothed proboscis and three stylets. The proboscis maintains a hold on the skin while the stylets pierce it. Muscular movements of the pharyngeal region cause the blood to flow up the channel formed by the stylets. Apart from the mouth-parts and the method of feeding, the habits and general appearance of the sucking lice are very similar to those of the biting lice.

The head is generally narrower than that of the biting lice and the thorax differs in that the segments are all fused, there being little sign of segmentation other than in the abdomen. The sturdy legs each end in a single claw, like those of some of the mammal-inhabiting biting lice. The claw is hinged in such a way that it can be drawn up tight against the tarsus to grip the host's hair. The curvature of the claw and tarsus closely follows that of the hair and the parasite gets a very firm hold.

As with the biting lice, the eggs are usually cemented to the host's hair, although the Human Louse will also attach its eggs to clothing, or even scatter them loosely. The life history is very similar to that of the biting lice.

About 25 species of sucking lice are known in Britain, although, as with all the smaller and less 'popular' orders, many more must await discovery. Our species belong to five families, one of them being found only on seals.

The best known family is the **Pediculidae**, on account of its two human-infesting species. The Human Louse, *Pediculus humanus*, exists as two distinct races – the Head Louse (*P.h. capitis*) and the Body Louse (*P.h. humanus*). The Body Louse is the larger of the two in general and the two races keep very much to their respective parts of our anatomy. The Human Louse is not much of a problem where frequent washing and changing clothes is the rule but infestation is quite common where less attention is paid to hygiene. The bite of this louse can be very irritating but more serious is the threat of disease, for *P. humanus* is the vector of several diseases, including typhus. This disease used to be a constant threat to soldiers because the conditions under which they live in wartime are very conducive to the spread of lice. Soldiers are now protected by vaccines but there is always a risk of typhus after earthquakes and similar tragedies when people are herded together, sharing sleeping accommodation and getting little chance to keep clean.

The other human-infesting louse, *Phthirus pubis*, is confined to the lower parts of the body and has not so far been found to carry any disease. Most important of the other sucking lice are those of the genus *Linognathus* which affect sheep, goats, and cattle.

Collecting and Preserving Lice

The only satisfactory way of collecting lice in any numbers is to obtain living or freshly dead host animals. Dead animals are fairly easy to search with the aid of a brush and comb. Domestic animals are fairly easy to deal with too. But living wild animals need special treatment. A quite convenient way of dealing with small birds and mammals is to put the animal's head through a slit in a piece of oil cloth and then lower the body into a jar containing chloroform fumes. The animal will struggle and in doing so will dislodge many of the parasites already disturbed by the chloroform. Such treatment does not appear to harm the animals.

The lice can be picked from the hosts or from the chloroform jar with forceps or with a brush dipped in alcohol. The insects should be preserved in spirit or, for permanent display, mounted on microscope slides after clearing slightly in potassium hydroxide. The small size of lice and the difficulty of collecting them have not helped to popularise the insects and anyone with a microscope and a good supply of animals and patience can contribute quite a lot to our knowledge of these insects.

Order Hemiptera – The True Bugs*

Recognition features Minute to large sized insects of widely different shapes and habits but all possessing piercing mouth-parts adapted for sucking the juices of plants or other animals. The needle-like mandibles and maxillae are sheathed in the labium and the whole beak or rostrum is normally held horizontally under the body when not in use. The antennae may be quite long in relation to the size of the insect, but they consist of only a few segments, usually four or five and rarely more than 10. Two pairs of wings are normally present, the front ones frequently being hardened to some extent.

The great variety of shapes and habits assumed by the bugs makes it impossible to give a general recognition pattern: the only really constant feature is the rostrum. There are, however, only three other orders with which the bugs might be confused and none of these has sucking mouth-parts. Beetles and cockroaches resemble some of the bugs but beetles can be distinguished because their elytra do not overlap and cockroaches can be recognised by their fine, many-segmented antennae. Many psocid species resemble aphids but again the many-jointed antennae of the psocids distinguish them.

The true bugs form a large order of insects with something in the region of 50,000 species, of which about 1,650 occur in the British Isles. The majority feed on plants and there are among them some very serious agricultural pests, including the aphids which not only damage the plants directly but transmit many virus diseases.

The order is divided into two quite distinct sub-orders – the Heteroptera and the Homoptera – which differ considerably in wing structure and in the position of the rostrum. These two groups are given separate ordinal rank by some entomologists.

When present, the front wing of the heteropteran is clearly divided into two regions – a tough, leathery basal area and a membranous tip – and this is respon-

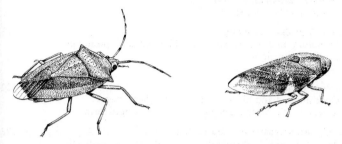

Shieldbug (*left*) – a typical heteropteran bug – and froghopper, a typical homopteran

*Among non-entomologists, the word 'bug' is often synonymous with 'insect' and even the entomologist accepts the use of the word, being quite happy with his 'bug-hunter' title. When talking about hemipterans, therefore, is is wise to talk of 'true bugs' rather than 'bugs' in order to avoid the possibility of confusion.

Plate 9   LAND BUGS – ORDER HEMIPTERA

Family **Rhopalidae**   p. 122
Front wings largely membranous, otherwise similar to
Coreidae
1. *Chorosoma schillingi* (Schummel)   ×2
2. *Rhopalus subrufus* (Gmelin)   ×2

Family **Lygaeidae**   p. 122
Generally dark insects, often marked with red: scutellum
more or less equal to or longer than commissure
3. *Megalonotus chiragra* (Fabr.)   ×4
4. *Scoloposthetus decoratus* (Hahn)   ×4
▲ **5.** *Lygaeus saxatilis* Scopoli   ×2

Family **Berytinidae**   p. 122
Legs usually very long: scutellum usually   scutellum   commissure
no more than half length of commissure
6. *Cymus melanocephalus* Fieber   ×4
7. *Berytinus minor* (Herrich-Schaeffer)   ×2

Body of *Berytinus*

Family **Reduviidae**   p. 123
Predatory and blood-sucking bugs: 3-segmented beak
curving under body at rest
8. *Reduvius personatus* (L.)   ×2
▲ **9.** *Rhinocoris iracundus* Poda   ×2
10. *Coranus subapterus* (DeGeer)   ×2
11. *Empicoris vagabundus* (L.)   ×2

Family **Piesmidae**   p. 123
Pronotum and wings with lace-like pattern: scutellum
visible
12. *Piesma maculatum* (Costa)   ×7
13. *Piesma quadratum* Fieber   ×7

Family **Tingidae** – lace bugs   p. 123
Pronotum and wings with lace-like pattern: pronotum
covering scutellum
14. *Tingis cardui* (L.)   ×7

Family **Pyrrhocoridae**   p. 122
Generally red and black or orange and black insects
15. Firebug – *Pyrrhocoris apterus* (L.) – short-winged form   ×2

Family **Stenocephalidae** – Spurge-bugs   p. 122
At least 6 veins in membrane: legs and antennae distinctly
banded
16. *Dicranocephalus medius* (Mulsant and Rey)   ×2

Family **Nabiidae**   p. 123
Predatory bugs: 4-segmented beak curving under body at
rest
17. Marsh damsel-bug – *Dolichonabis limbatus* (Dahlbom)   ×2
18. *Himacerus apterus* (Fabr.)   ×2

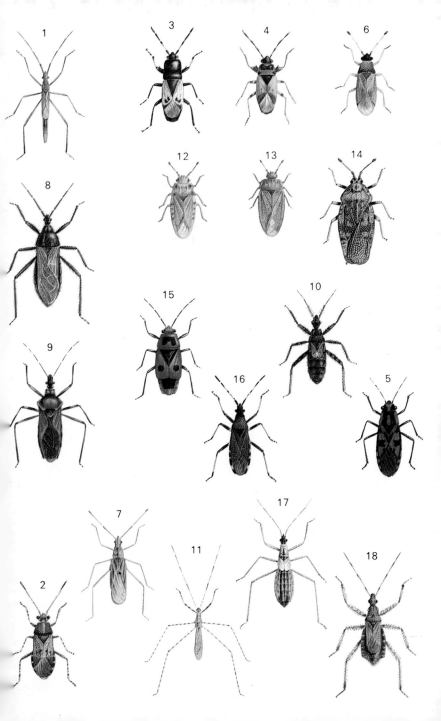

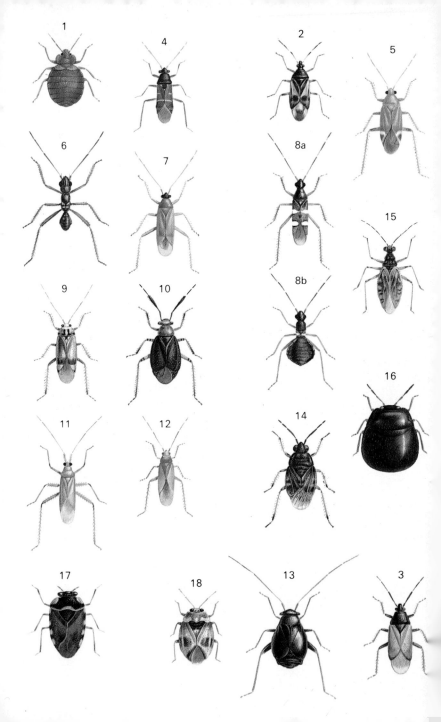

SUB-ORDER HETEROPTERA (Contd.)

Family **Cimicidae**   p. 124
    Predatory or blood-sucking bugs, often with vestigial wings.
    If wings are fully developed there is a distinct embolium and
    cuneus

1. Bed bug – *Cimex lectularius* L. ×3
2. *Anthocoris nemorum* (L.) ×4
3. *Xylocoris galactinus* (Fallen) ×6

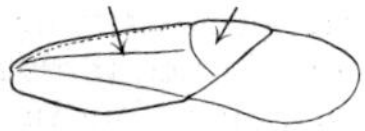

Front wing of Cimicidae

Family **Miridae**   p. 125
    Generally rather slender bugs with, in fully-winged forms,
    a distinct cuneus. Body rather soft

4. *Pilophorus perplexus* Douglas and Scott ×3
5. *Psallus varians* (Herrich-Schaffer) ×4
6. *Myrmecoris gracilis* (Sahlberg) ×3
7. *Phylus melanocephalus* (L.) ×3
8a. *Systellonotus triguttatus* (L.) – male ×4
8b. *Systellonotus triguttatus* – female ×4
9. *Lygus pratensis* (L.) ×3
10. *Capsus ater* (L.) ×3
11. *Blepharidopterus angulatus* (Fallen) ×3
12. *Amblytylus nasutus* (Kirschbaum) ×3
13. *Halticus apterus* (L.) ×6

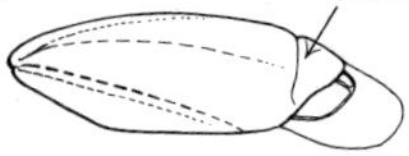

Front wing of Miridae

Family **Saldidae**   p. 125
    Large-eyed bugs usually found close to water
14. *Saldula saltatoria* (L.) ×4

△ Family **Leptopodidae**   p. 125
    Bugs found near water: similar to Saldidae, but differing
    in having the ocelli on a stalked platform
▲ **15.** *Leptopus marmoratus* (Goeze) ×4

△ Family **Plataspidae**   p. 125
    Enormous scutellum: 2-segmented tarsi
▲ **16.** *Coptosoma scutellata* Fourcroy ×4

△ Family **Ochteridae**   p. 130
    Aquatic or semi-aquatic bugs with visible antennae
▲ **17.** *Ochterus marginatus* Latreille ×3

△ Family **Isometopidae**   p. 125
    Generally tree-dwelling bugs with large eyes, ocelli, and a
    cuneus
▲ **18.** *Isometopus mirificus* Mulsant and Rey ×6

sible for the name Heteroptera (Greek *heteros* = different). It is also responsible for the name Hemiptera given to the whole order because, when at rest, the insects appear to have only half of each wing (Greek *hemi* = half). The hind wings are always membranous and both pairs are folded flat over the body when at rest. The rostrum or beak arises clearly from the front part of the head. This sub-order contains both plant and animal feeders and includes such insects as the colourful shield-bugs, mirid or capsid bugs, bed-bugs, and all those that live in or on the water.

The homopteran front wing is not divided into two regions and is either membranous or stiffened throughout (Greek *homos* = uniform). Again, the hind wings are membranous, but the wings in this sub-order are held roof-wise over the body when the insects are at rest. The rostrum arises from the posterior part of the head and often appears to spring from between the two front legs. All the members of this sub-order are plant feeders and they include the cicadas, leaf hoppers, and aphids. Apart from our one cicada, all the British homopterans are small or minute insects.

SUB-ORDER HETEROPTERA

The bodies of these insects are generally flattened and the wings are folded flat over the body when at rest. Beyond this, however, there is little uniformity of shape, as will be seen from Pls. 8 to 11. Most of our heteropterans are cryptically coloured, greens and browns being dominant, but some exhibit brilliant warning colours. Many families produce pungent secretions in special 'stink glands' near the hind legs and this secretion taints the plants on which the bugs crawl as well as giving the insects themselves an unpleasant taste. The stink glands are particularly efficient in the shield bugs which are therefore also called 'stink bugs'. Strangely enough, available evidence suggests that neither the odour nor the warning colours convey much protection against birds and other predators.

The head is rather variable in shape but is usually held horizontally and is normally clearly visible from above. Compound eyes are always present and there are two ocelli in most of our land bugs. Our water-bugs have no ocelli. The antennae never have more than five segments and in the water-bugs they are concealed under the head.

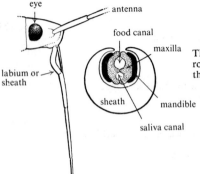

The head of a bug, showing the beak or rostrum, together with a section through the rostrum to show·the canals formed by the mouth-parts

The mouth-parts vary little throughout the order on account of the uniform feeding habits. The mandibles and maxillae are in the form of needle-like stylets and rest in the grooved labium which is known as the rostrum or proboscis. The labium is not grooved at its upper end but here the stylets are protected by the overlying labrum. At the lower end of the rostrum, the walls of the groove curve right over the stylets and hold them firmly in their sheath. The rostrum itself has a sensitive tip and is used to select a suitable feeding site; then, having guided the stylets into position it is drawn back and the stylets are plunged into the host. It has been shown that the saw-edged mandibles make the first incision and that the more slender maxillae follow them into the wound. The four stylets are arranged concentrically, with the mandibular ones surrounding the maxillary ones. The latter are held tightly together and their inner surfaces are so shaped that the central cavity is divided longitudinally into two fine canals. Food is sucked up through one and saliva is pumped down the other. The hypopharynx, which is small and insignificant in insects with biting jaws, plays an important role here because it forms part of the 'pumping chamber' which draws up the liquid food. When not in use the whole rostrum is folded back under the body, often extending beyond the base of the back legs.

The prothorax is always large and prominent in the heteropterans, the pronotum occupying most of the visible part of the thorax when viewed from above. Apart from the scutellum – the prominent triangular region between the wing bases – the mesothorax is concealed beneath the pronotum and the wings. The small metathorax is also concealed from above. In some species the scutellum is relatively huge and extends backwards so that even the wings are covered and the insects appear wingless.

Because the front wings are only partially hardened, they are called hemelytra – elytra being the name given to the hardened front wings of beetles. The hardened or cornified area is itself divided into two or more regions, the primary division being along the claval suture which separates an anterior corium from a posterior clavus – the region next to the scutellum when the wings are folded. This division is present in all winged heteropterans. A narrow strip along the anterior border of the wing is sometimes marked off as the embolium and, more commonly, a triangular region is marked off at the apex of the corium to form the cuneus. These divisions are used in the classification of the insects.

The front wing of a cimicid bug, showing the main divisions of the wing

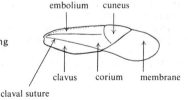

embolium   cuneus

clavus   corium   membrane

claval suture

The venation of the front wings is very indistinct but in all species it is considerably reduced. Veins R, M, and Cu are often unbranched and no veins at all may reach the membrane. The venation is also reduced in the membranous hind wings but, as it is not used in the identification of the insects, it will not be discussed any further.

Several of our bugs are quite or almost wingless and many more exist mainly as short-winged or brachypterous individuals. Polymorphism, involving both long and short-winged individuals of one species, does occur but it is rather uncommon except perhaps among the pond skaters of the family Gerridae. These aberrant individuals cannot always be tracked down with a simple key.

The legs of the heteropterans are generally unremarkable, except that the predatory species have rather thickened front legs in association with their feeding habits. In these so-called raptorial legs, the femur is toothed and the tibia closes tightly against it to hold the prey. This condition is particularly well shown by the Water Scorpion, *Nepa cinerea* (Pl. 11). Minor differences in spininess, number of tarsal segments, and so on are used in the classification of the bugs.

The abdomen varies in the number of segments visible but modifications are few. Cerci are absent from all bugs but one feature worth mentioning is the respiratory siphon or breathing tube found in the family Nepidae (p. 127).

Parts of the abdomen are sometimes modified for sound production and, although the most famous of the 'singing bugs' – the cicadas – belong to the Homoptera, a number of heteropterans stridulate modestly by rubbing legs or wings over roughened patches on the abdomen. Other parts of the body are also used for sound production, one of the best British 'singers' being *Reduvius personatus* (Pl. 9) which stridulates by rubbing the tip of its beak along a striated furrow in the prosternum.

Heteropteran eggs are very often adorned with delicate sculpturing and are frequently provided with a special detachable lid to aid the escape of the young nymph. The eggs are usually attached to plants and are often placed inside the tissues.

The young nymphs may look rather unlike the adults at first but, being members of the Hemimetabola, they change gradually, getting more like adults at each moult. The majority of heteropteran bugs pass through five nymphal instars and there are often considerable colour changes from one instar to the next. This is especially true of the change from the last nymphal instar to the adult stage. Other external changes include increases in the number of antennal and tarsal segments, alterations to the shape of the pronotum, and the development of wings. The wing buds are not usually obvious until the fourth nymphal instar. Like the adults, the nymphs feed entirely by sucking and their diet is essentially the same as that of the adult of the species. The majority of the plant-feeding bugs contain symbiotic bacteria in their digestive tracts. Their function is not fully understood. Bugs take in liquid food and there is no question of cellulose breakdown as in herbivorous mammals. An antibiotic role has been suggested for them. In many of the bugs, the symbionts are passed on to the eggs before they are laid, so that the young nymph is provided with them right from the start.

Key to the Families of British Heteropterans

The following key, modified slightly from that given in Southwood and Leston, may be used to place the British heteropterans in their families. Because of the way in which the wings develop gradually on the outside of the growing nymphs, it is sometimes difficult to distinguish between fully-grown nymphs and short-winged adult bugs. One of the best clues is in the junction between the wings and the scutellum: if it is sharp and well defined then your specimen is almost certainly an adult.

1. Antennae visible from above: generally terrestrial or living on the water surface (Geocorisae and Amphibicorisae)* 2
   Antennae small and concealed from above: insects living under water (Hydrocorisae)* 29

2. Head at least 5 times longer than broad Hydrometridae, p. 126
   Head not more than 3 times as long as broad 3

3. Antennae with 5 segments 4
   Antennae with 4 segments (apparently 8-segmented in *Coranus* but the alternate segments are very small) 8

4. Bugs 2mm long or less: scutellum not reaching middle of abdomen: living on water surface Hebridae, p. 126
   Bugs over 3mm long: scutellum reaching at least to middle of abdomen: terrestrial 5

5. Tarsi 2-segmented Acanthosomidae, p. 121
   Tarsi 3-segmented 6

6. Tibiae strongly spined: largely black or dark brown insects, often with metallic sheen Cydnidae, p. 121
   Tibiae not strongly spined, or if so, insects very hairy 7

7. Scutellum reaching end of abdomen: pronotum without lateral projections Scutelleridae, p. 121
   Scutellum not reaching end of abdomen, or if so, pronotum with lateral projections extending to near eyes Pentatomidae, p. 121

8. Underside of abdomen densely covered with fine silver hairs 9
   Underside of abdomen without such covering 11

* This three-fold division into terrestrial, surface-dwelling, and under-water bugs is ecologically useful but the true division is into the Gymnocerata (free horns) on the one hand and the Cryptocerata (hidden horns) on the other.

9. Mainly greenish insects with apical claws on front tarsi   Mesoveliidae, p. 126

Claws on front tarsi sub-apical: insects never greenish   10

10. Hind femora reaching beyond tip of abdomen: middle legs inserted nearer to hind ones than to front ones   Gerridae, p. 126

Hind femora not extending beyond tip of abdomen: middle legs inserted midway between other two   Veliidae, p. 126

11. Rostrum more or less curved and not pressed flat against body at rest: body length greater than 4.5mm   12

Rostrum pressed flat against body at rest, or if curved, body length less than 4.5mm   13

12. Rostrum with 4 segments   Nabiidae, p. 123
    Rostrum with 3 segments   Reduviidae, p. 123

13. Corium and pronotum covered with netted pattern   14

No such patterning   15

14. Pronotum projecting back and covering scutellum, or head and pronotum black: membrane not distinct   Tingidae, p. 123

Pronotum not covering scutellum: membrane distinct, with cross veins   Piesmidae, p. 123

15. Tarsi 2-segmented   16
    Tarsi 3-segmented   18

16. Bugs under 2.5mm long   Microphysidae, p. 124

Very flat bugs over 3.5mm long: antennae very robust   17

17. Front wings almost entirely membranous   Aneuridae, p. 120

Membrane not extending further forward than apex of scutellum (or wings reduced)   Aradidae, p. 120

18. Antennae with 1st and 2nd segments short and thick, less than half as long as segments 3 and 4 together: 3rd and 4th segments very thin: bugs under 3mm long   Dipsocoridae, p. 125
    Antennae not as above   19

19. Ocelli absent   20
    Ocelli present   22

20. Bugs extremely flat, brown, and wingless   Cimicidae (part), p. 124
    Not as above   21

21. Over 8mm long: scarlet and black: no cuneus if
    winged   Pyrrhocoridae, p. 122
    Under 8mm long, or if longer, not scarlet and
    black: cuneus present if winged   Miridae, p. 125

22. Rostrum 3-segmented and not flattened against
    underside of head at rest: cuneus and embolium
    present, or if short-winged, bugs under 2.5mm
    long   Cimicidae (part), p. 124
    Rostrum with 3 or 4 segments and held flat
    under head at rest: no cuneus or embolium, or
    if short-winged, usually over 2.5mm long   23

23. Rostrum 3-segmented   Saldidae, p. 125
    Rostrum 4-segmented   24

24. Membrane with 5 or less $\pm$ parallel veins: if
    short-winged, abdomen dark brown or black   25
    Membrane with 6 or more veins: if short-winged,
    abdomen green or yellowish with red or black
    markings   26

25. Scutellum distinctly shorter   commissure   Berytinidae, p. 122
    than commissure (the line
    formed where the two clavi
    meet), or if nearly as long,
    entire upper surface shiny
    and strongly punctured: legs   scutellum
    usually very slender

    Scutellum as long as or longer than commissure,
    if about as long, upper surface not entirely shiny
    or strongly punctured   Lygaeidae, p. 122

26. Antennae, tibiae, and mid and hind femora
    distinctly banded   Stenocephalidae, p. 122
    Antennae, tibiae, and mid and hind femora not
    all distinctly banded   27

27. 4th antennal segment curved: head nearly as
    wide as base of pronotum: hind femora with
    strong spines beneath near apex   Alydidae, p. 122
    4th antennal segment straight: head much
    narrower than base of pronotum, or if nearly
    as wide, hind femora without spines   28

28. Front wings with well-developed cornified
    region: deep brown or grey-brown   Coreidae, p. 121
    Front wings largely membranous: mainly
    reddish and/or black   Rhopalidae, p. 122

SERIES GYMNOCERATA (= NAKED HORNS) – BUGS WITH FREE ANTENNAE

Geocorisae: Terrestrial Bugs (Pls. 8–10)

The terrestrial bugs as a whole are essentially a tropical group and many of the British families are right on the edge of their range here: many species are found only in the southern counties. Our damp climate is more to blame than our latitude because the bugs reach further north in continental Europe. Many of our species, particularly the large ones, hibernate among grass tufts or in the upper layers of the soil where they are very prone to attack by fungi in damp weather. Winters on the Continent are often considerably colder than ours but they are also drier and the bugs survive better. It is significant that most of our ground-living bugs are found in the drier areas of the south and east – on the better-drained chalk and sandstone areas – or on sand dunes around the coasts. Our somewhat low and rather unpredictable summer temperatures, however, are probably just as important as the winter damp in denying us a richer bug fauna.

Continental Europe has a much richer bug fauna than the British Isles, but there are relatively few additional families on the Continent. The major difference is in the greatly increased number of species within the families.

Bugs of the family **Aradidae** (flatbugs) are broad and very flat insects, usually living on and under loose bark where they feed upon fungi, although the Pine Flatbug, *Aradus cinnamomeus* (Pl. 8) feeds on the sap of pine trees. The stylets are very long and slender and are coiled inside the head when not in use. Apart from the Pine Flatbug, in which the males have narrow wings and most females are brachypterous, all British flatbugs are fully winged, although flight is common only at certain times. The closely related family **Aneuridae** (barkbugs) contains only two British species. Both live under bark and may be distinguished from the aradids, by the largely membranous wings, reduced hind wings, and the fact that the head does not narrow immediately behind the eyes (Pl. 8).

The shieldbugs, so called because of their general shield-like shape, belong to four families in the superfamily Pentatomoidea. The insects are also known collectively as stink bugs on account of the particularly pungent odour produced by some of the species. The family **Acanthosomidae** (Pl. 8) differs from the others mainly in having only two tarsal segments. The Hawthorn Shieldbug, *Acanthosoma haemorrhoidale*, is a common representative whose principal food is hawthorn fruit, although leaves sustain the overwintered adults in spring. Another interesting member of this family is the Parent Bug, *Elasmucha grisea*. The female of this species, which frequents birchwoods, lays a diamond-shaped egg-mass on the birch leaves and then sits over it until the eggs hatch. Even after hatching, parent and offspring move about in a family group and the parent actively protects the young. This maternal care may reduce parasitism, especially of the eggs which are well protected under the female's body.

Members of the **Cydnidae** (Pl. 8) can be distinguished by their spiny tibiae and the generally dark, often metallic colouring. The insects feed on various low-growing plants and their eggs are generally laid in the soil. The adults also hibernate in the soil and the insects are therefore most common in sandy and chalky regions where the soil is light. *Sehirus bicolor*, the Pied Shieldbug, feeds on white dead nettle and related plants, the nymphs being found within the calyx feeding on the nutlets, while the adults feed on the leaves and stems. The Negro Bug, *Thyreocoris scarabaeoides*, is widespread on chalkland, where it lives among the leaf litter and short vegetation. It is easily recognised by the large scutellum, rounded shape, and shiny black colour.

The **Scutelleridae** (Pl. 8) is found mainly in the tropics, where some species are serious pests. The main feature is the greatly enlarged scutellum which extends backwards to the tip of the abdomen and almost completely covers the wings as well. *Eurygaster integriceps* is a serious pest of wheat in Europe and Asia but it does not reach Britain. Our commonest species is *E. testudinaria* which is found on grasses and rushes in most parts of southern England. Our two species of *Odontoscelis* – both mainly coastal – have spiny legs like those of the Cydnidae but they can be distinguished by their hairy appearance.

The **Pentatomidae** (Pl. 8) is the dominant family among the shieldbugs but it is near the edge of its range here in Britain and none of our species is numerous. They are much more numerous on the continent and it seems that hot summers are necessary for their well-being, perhaps more so than dry winters because we usually get increased numbers of these bugs the year after a good run of summers. In warmer regions, these insects cause a certain amount of damage to crops and other plants but numbers are not sufficient for them to cause any damage in Britain.

The scutellum is generally triangular and the whole body is clearly shield-shaped, more so than in the other families of the group. *Pentatoma rufipes*, found in trees over most of the country, is a typical example. *Podops inuncta*, the European Turtle Bug which is common in grassy places throughout most of southern England, differs from the rest of the family in having a large scutellum covering almost all of the abdomen. It can be distinguished from the Scutelleridae, however, by the possession of two tiny 'horns' on the front of the pronotum. *Sciocoris cursitans* is of interest on account of the very loud stridulation of the male.

Members of the **Coreidae** are collectively called squash bugs as a result of the serious damage caused by some of them to squash fruits in America. They are almost all fruit or seed feeders. Squash bugs have a broad pronotum and they are somewhat shield-shaped but they are narrower than the typical pentatomid and the scutellum is much less prominent. In most of our species, the abdomen is expanded posteriorly, giving the insects a quite characteristic shape. *Coreus marginatus* (Pl. 8.) is a common species feeding on sorrels and docks.

Alydus calcaratus, our only member of the **Alydidae**, is a very narrow insect, about 10mm long, found in coastal areas and other sandy places in the south of England. It readily takes flight and is one of the fastest of our bugs. The wings are very dark but the upper surface of the abdomen bears a bright orange area which is visible when the insect is in flight (Pl. 8). This is an example of flash coloration.

The family **Rhopalidae** (Pl. 9) is very similar to the Coreidae but is separated mainly by the ventral position of the stink glands (lateral in Coreidae). Most of the species are red and/or black and the family is typified by *Rhopalus subrufus*, a not uncommon woodland and hedgerow insect. *Chorosoma schillingi* is rather atypical on account of its narrow shape but this is associated with its life among marram and other duneland grasses and is not a fundamental difference. The front wings in this family are often largely membranous.

Pyrrhocoris apterus (Pl. 9), our sole representative of the **Pyrrhocoridae**, is found regularly only in Devon, where it feeds on tree mallow. There is, in fact, only one known permanent colony in Britain. Migrants reach us occasionally from the Continent, but confirmed records are few. Winged, brachypterous, and apterous individuals are known.

The spurge bugs of the family **Stenocephalidae** (Pl. 9) are something of a link between the coreid and lygaeid bugs. Our two species, *Dicranocephalus medius* and *D. agilis*, are both found on various spurges. The species are easily confused, although *medius* is mainly an inland species and *agilis* is confined mainly to southern and western coasts.

The ground bugs – family **Lygaeidae** (Pl. 9) – form a large group of brownish insects, narrow or somewhat oval in outline when viewed from above. They are all under about 12mm in length and many of the species are brightly marked with red. Lygaeid bugs bear many resemblances to the coreids but they can be distinguished by having only a few veins in the wing membrane. Some ground bugs also resemble the mirid bugs but the latter have a softer body and lack ocelli. The mirids also have a conspicuous cuneus.

Ground bugs feed on a wide range of plants and, although none is a serious pest in Britain, the family contains a number of economically important species. The Chinch Bug, *Blissus leucopteris*, for example, is particularly injurious to cereals in the United States. The bugs often hibernate in masses and may be found in winter by opening up tufts of grasses and rushes. Two common examples of the family are *Megalonotus chiragra* and *Scoloposthetus decoratus*, the latter being widespread on heathland.

Most members of the **Berytinidae** (Pl. 9), for example *Berytinus minor*, possess very long, slender legs – hence their common name of stilt bugs – and are quite

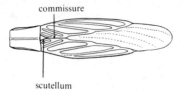

commissure

scutellum

Body of *Berytinus* showing the very short scutellum compared with the commissure. This feature is characteristic of most members of the Berytinidae, although some *Cymus* species, recognised by their shiny and strongly punctured surface, have a relatively long scutellum

unmistakable. The family does, however, contain the short-legged *Cymus* species which are superficially similar to the members of the Lygaeidae. Stilt bugs range up to about 12mm in length and are generally to be found at the base of various leguminous plants.

The beet bugs of the family **Piesmidae** (Pl. 9) are rather like the lace bugs (Tingidae) to look at but the resemblance is only superficial and confined to the lace-like pattern on the wings and pronotum. The insects are actually more closely related to the Lygaeidae. They feed almost entirely on plants of the family Chenopodiaceae – beet, spinach, and so on. The two British species, *Piesma maculatum* and *P. quadratum*, are primarily insects of salt-marshes and coastal areas where sea purslane and other chenopods grow, but they are now quite widespread in old gravel pits and similar waste land. *P. quadratum* is found over much of Central Europe where it interferes with sugar beet cultivation because of a virus disease it carries. The males of this species stridulate loudly by rubbing their wings against certain abdominal sclerites.

The lace-like pattern of a lacebug (family Tingidae)

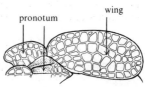

Members of the family **Tingidae**, called lace bugs on account of the delicate sculpturing of the wings and pronotum, can be distinguished from the Piesmidae because in most lace bugs the pronotum extends backwards to cover the scutellum (Pl. 9). It also extends forwards and sideways to some degree, forming the hood and the lateral margin. The wing membrane is indistinct, in contrast to the definite membrane of the piesmids. All the lace bugs are plant feeders and all are rather small, 6mm being the upper limit of length. Many of them live among moss and the majority of these are short-winged forms. The insects often have a greyish colour caused by a powdery wax layer formed on the surface. The Spear Thistle Lace Bug, *Tingis cardui*, is a widespread species found on various thistles. *Agramma laeta* is a minute insect (2.5mm) in which there is no hood and in which the pronotum does not completely cover the scutellum.

The assassin bugs – family **Reduviidae** (Pl. 9) are, as their common name suggests, predatory insects feeding mainly on other arthropods. Many of them can give a painful jab with their beaks when handled but relatively few feed regularly on mammalian blood. Mimicry is well developed among the assassin bugs, many of them resembling their prey so exactly that even the entomologist has difficulty in telling them apart. The family is a large one but most of its members are tropical, only six reaching Britain. Our commonest species is the Heath Assassin Bug, *Coranus subapterus*, which is usually brachypterous. *Reduvius personatus* lives in and around human habitations where it feeds on bed-bugs, flies, psocids, and so on. Both of these insects stridulate quite loudly by rubbing the rough tip of the curved rostrum along a ridged groove in the prosternum. The legs are relatively long in all the assassin bugs but especially so in *Empicoris* species which look rather like large mosquitoes when at rest.

The damsel bugs of the **Nabiidae** (Pl. 9) resemble the assassin bugs in several ways but they have a 4-segmented beak (assassins have only three segments) and are more closely allied to the bed-bugs (Cimicidae). These bugs are rather slender, with relatively long legs, but they are fiercely carnivorous, feeding on a variety of other insects. The Marsh Damsel Bug, *Dolichonabis limbatus*, is a widespread species, by no means confined to marshland despite its common name. *Himacerus apterus* is our only truly tree-dwelling damsel bug and, like the previous species, is usually micropterous. All our damsel bugs are some shade of brown.

The family **Cimicidae** (Pl. 10) contains the blood-sucking bed-bugs – parasites of birds and mammals – and a number of other predatory bugs. The bed-bugs are always micropterous and chestnut brown in colour. Our species may reach about 6mm in length. *Oeciacus hirundinis* lives on house martins and often finds its way into houses from the nests in autumn. It rarely feeds on man however. The true Bed-bug, *Cimex lectularius*, feeds primarily on man and is very widespread, although less common since the introduction of synthetic insecticides. The insects do not remain attached to their hosts but hide away in crevices or among clothing during the day. They come out at night for a meal of blood. Although the Bed-bug's bite may be very annoying, there is no proof that the insects regularly transmit any diseases. Related species are found on bats and various birds.

The other members of the family are usually fully winged and they are not generally blood-suckers: they feed primarily on other insects. They are often treated as a separate family but detailed investigations have shown that they are clearly related to the bed-bugs. The latter have evolved from winged predatory bugs.

One group of these insects is found mainly on flowers and leaves and its members are known as flower bugs. A typical example, and one of our commonest bugs, is *Anthocoris nemorum*. This species, in common with most of its relatives, spends the winter hibernating under bark and in similar places but can be found on flowers throughout most of the summer. It feeds on other small insects that visit the flowers. The other main division of the Cimicidae is typified by *Xylocoris galactinus* which lives in haystacks, granaries, manure heaps, and other accumulations of vegetable debris. These insects, which may be called debris bugs, feed on psocids, springtails, and other small arthropods. Flower and debris bugs may be distinguished from mirids and lygaeids found in similar places by their distinct embolium.

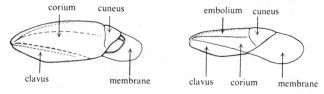

Comparison of the front wings of Miridae (*left*) and Cimicidae

The tiny bugs of the family **Microphysidae**, for example *Loricula elegantula*, are usually found among lichens and mosses on tree trunks where they are believed to feed on psocids, springtails and so on. These tiny insects are easily overlooked and it is possible that more will be added at some time to our list of seven known species.

Nearly two-thirds of the British heteropterans belong to the **Miridae** (Pl. 10) – a large family of small and medium-sized insects with relatively soft bodies. The range of habitats exploited by the members of this family is almost as wide as that occupied by the rest of the heteropteran families. Mirids are found from mountain top to saltmarsh and coastal dunes and among all types of vegetation – trees, shrubs, herbs, grasses, and almost bare ground. The majority of mirids – also known as capsids – are rather slender plant-feeding bugs but a number are at least partly predatory. Mimicry is well-exhibited by many members of the family and we have two excellent ant-mimics in the British fauna – *Myrmecoris gracilis* and the female of *Systellonotus triguttatus*. These mimics are normally micropterous and they live on heathland, frequently in association with their ant models. Although they have not been known to attack living ants, they readily feed on dead ones and larval ants probably make up a part of their diet.

The mirid bugs usually have a well-marked cuneus in the wing and this serves to distinguish them from most other bugs. The flower bugs also possess a cuneus but they have a well-marked embolium which identifies them. As to be expected among insects which live primarily among vegetation, greens and browns are the dominant colours.

Many of our mirid species are very common and can be taken in numbers by sweeping or beating herbage in summer: almost every umbellifer head supports one or more of these insects. The developing fruits and seeds are the main targets of these bugs and the family contains many species of economic importance. *Lygocoris pabulinus*, the Common Green Capsid, is a common pest of fruit trees, producing blemishes on leaves and fruit. The eggs overwinter on the trees and the young nymphs feed there for a while in spring before moving to the various herbaceous plants on which the summer generation exist. The latter insects, however, return to the trees in autumn to feed and lay eggs. Another common mirid of fruit trees is the Black-kneed Capsid, *Blepharidopterus angulatus*. This green insect, easily recognised by the black marks around the 'knee' joints, is mainly predatory and feeds on the red spider mites which themselves do so much damage to plants. It is therefore one of the better bugs to have in the orchard.

The family **Dipsocoridae**, with only three British species, is a rather specialised group believed to have evolved from cimicid-like ancestors. They are small (under 2.5mm) predatory insects found in wet places. *Cryptostemma alienum* may be found in gravel at the edges of swift streams.

Members of the family **Saldidae** (Pl. 10) are predatory bugs almost always found around the edges of water – coastal marshes, bogs, ponds, and so on. They are therefore commonly known as shore bugs. The head is rather broad and the eyes are very prominent. The 3-segmented beak and the general presence of four or five long, closed cells in the membrane will help to identify this family. Our commonest shore bug, *Saldula saltatoria*, is found around muddy ponds. Its brown pattern merges with the mud when it is at rest, but it runs, jumps, and flies when disturbed.

Among the few European families not represented in the British Isles we can mention the following: **Isometopidae**, **Plataspidae**, **Meziridae**, and **Leptopodidae**. These families have few European species, but examples are illustrated on Pls. 8–10.

Amphibicorisae: Pond Skaters and other surface-living bugs (Pl. 11)
The surface-living bugs are classified with the terrestrial ones in the Gymnocerata

because they possess free, visible antennae, in contrast to the hidden antennae of the true water bugs. The families concerned, however, form a very distinct ecological group specially adapted for life on the water surface. One of the main features is the coating of fine water-repelling hairs that clothe at least the undersides of the insects and prevent their getting wet. All are predatory insects, finding food by sight and/or by sensing vibrations in the surface film.

The **Mesoveliidae** and the related **Hebridae** are much less specialised for life on the water surface than the other skaters and retain more features of their terrestrial ancestors. For example, both families have a scutellum – absent in other skaters – and both have apical claws on their tarsi, although this feature is also shared by the Hydrometridae. The two families are represented in Britain by only three species, all under 3mm in length. *Mesovelia furcata* is green and black and is usually apterous. It spends much of its time on the floating leaves of pondweeds. *Hebrus pusillus* and *H. ruficeps* – the latter species usually with vestigial wings – are both found on mosses at the edges of streams.

Hydrometra stagnorum (Pl. 11) belongs to the **Hydrometridae**, a family characterised by great elongation of the head. The species is generally microterous and is found on still and slow-moving water throughout most of the country. Unlike most surface-dwelling bugs, the water measurers spear food through the surface film and hold it with the rostrum instead of the front legs. It

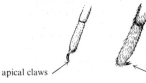

Tarsi of *Mesovelia* (*left*) and *Gerris*, showing the position of the claws. The sub-apical claws of *Gerris* allow the insect to skate more easily over the water surface

apical claws   sub-apical claws

would appear, therefore, that the elongation of the head is associated with this method of feeding. Water fleas, mosquito larvae, and other small creatures venturing near the surface make up *Hydrometra*'s food.

The family **Veliidae**, typified by the Water Cricket, *Velia caprai*, resembles the Gerridae in many ways but the middle and hind legs are relatively shorter than those of *Gerris* and the water crickets are altogether stouter. They are brownish insects, up to 8mm in length and are generally wingless. They are very common on ponds and streams where they feed on small creatures that fall on to the water. They probably also take mosquito larvae from under the surface film. The prey is held on the rostrum rather than by the legs.

The **Gerridae**, typified by the Common Pond Skater, *Gerris lacustris*, is the most advanced family of surface bugs. These are the true pond skaters or water striders, *G. lacustris* being found on almost all stretches of still, fresh water. The insects 'row' themselves across the surface at high speed by means of the long middle legs. The hind legs trail behind and act as a sort of rudder. This arrangement leaves the short front legs free to catch food in the form of small insects that fall on to the water. The claws, like those of the Veliidae, are situated just before the apex of the tarsi and the apical position is occupied by a pad of water-repellent hairs. This makes movement over the surface more efficient. *Gerris* is usually fully winged and a good flier but short-winged individuals are often found. The front wings are always homogeneous in texture, there being no distinct membrane. Although not in the British fauna, the genus *Halobates* deserves mention because it is one of the few insects that have conquered the seas. The insects are found on floating seaweed, and on the surface itself, hundreds of miles out in tropical and sub-tropical seas.

SERIES CRYPTOCERATA (= HIDDEN HORNS) – WATER BUGS (Pl. 11)

The members of this group are characterised by having the antennae concealed in pits or furrows under the head. They all live under the surface of water and the protection of the antennae is associated with this mode of life. These aquatic bugs are also known collectively as the Hydrocorisae. The families that make up the Cryptocerata are rather diverse in structure and it is not possible to pinpoint their origin from terrestrial bugs. There is, however, a clear sequence in the water bugs from the tube-breathing nepids, through bubble carrying bugs, to the plastron-breathing *Aphelocheirus*. The majority of water bugs are predatory and many can inflict a painful bite when handled.

Members of the family **Nepidae** (Pl. 11) are easily recognisable by the long 'tail' which is the respiratory tube or siphon. At intervals the siphon is pushed up through the water surface and air is thereby conducted to the abdominal spiracles. The insects possess hydrostatic receptors which help them to maintain a suitable depth in the water for the correct functioning of the breathing tube. This family is mainly a tropical one but Britain has the flat, bottom-living Water Scorpion, *Nepa cinerea*, and the slender stick-like *Ranatra linearis* which lives among the water weeds. Neither species is a good swimmer and the insects rely mainly on the crawling motion characteristic of terrestrial bugs. Both species are winged but cannot fly as the flight muscles are poorly developed. The front legs are raptorial, particularly so in *Nepa*, and well suited for catching food. *Nepa* feeds on other insects, tadpoles, and even small fish, while *Ranatra* normally takes smaller prey such as *Daphnia* and other small arthropods.

The Saucer Bug, *Ilyocoris cimicoides*, is our only member of the **Naucoridae** and is easy to identify on account of its enormous front femora projecting horn-like from the front of the head. It is a large bug, up to 15mm long, and can be found in muddy ponds in the southern half of England. The Saucer Bug is a bubble breather but it can stay under water for longer than most bugs before needing to renew its air supply.

Closely related to the saucer bug and sometimes included in the same family is *Aphelocheirus*, of which our only representative is the sub-species *A. aestivalis montandoni* (Pl. 11). It differs from the Naucoridae in having a narrower head, less highly raptorial legs, and poorly developed wings (often none at all). The main feature of *Aphelocheirus*, however, is that it is a plastron breather (p. 26). This means that it is confined to well oxygenated waters. Bubble-carrying bugs that rely on air from the surface can, of course, live in foul water with very little oxygen content.

The backswimmers – family **Notonectidae** – are among the fiercest of bugs and they are represented in Britain by four species of *Notonecta*, of which *N. glauca* (Pl. 11) is the most common. These insects swim on their backs – ventral side uppermost – using their long, hair-fringed back legs as oars. The upside-down position, together with the very long back legs, distinguishes the back-swimmers from the corixids on sight. Light, not gravity, controls the swimming position and if backswimmers are put into a tank lit only from below they will swim right-way-up. Backswimmers are bubble-breathers and must come to the

Plate 11   **WATER BUGS – ORDER HEMIPTERA**

SUB-ORDER HETEROPTERA (Contd.)

Family **Hydrometridae**   p. 126
   Head 5 times longer than broad
1. *Hydrometra stagnorum* (L.)   ×2½

Family **Hebridae**   p. 126
   Very small: antennae 5-segmented
2. *Hebrus ruficeps* Thomson   ×15

Family **Mesoveliidae**   p. 126
   Front tarsi with apical claws: usually wingless
3. *Mesovelia furcata* Mulsant and Rey   ×7

apical claw

Family **Pleidae**   p. 130
   Minute back-swimmers
4. *Plea atomaria* (Pallas)   ×7

Family **Veliidae**   p. 126
   Skating insects: legs ± equally spaced
5. Water cricket – *Velia caprai* Tamanini   ×2½

Family **Nepidae**   p. 127
   Long breathing siphon
6. Water scorpion – *Nepa cinerea* L.   ×2
7. Water stick insect – *Ranatra linearis* (L.)   ×2

Family **Gerridae**   p. 126
   Skating insects: front legs well separated from others
8. *Gerris lacustris* (L.)   ×2½

Family **Aphelocheiridae**   p. 127
   Flattened bugs with vestigial wings
9. *Aphelocheirus aestivalis* (Fabr.)   ×2

Family **Naucoridae**   p. 127
   Enlarged front femora
10. Saucer bug – *Ilyocoris cimicoides* (L.)   ×2

Family **Corixidae**   p. 130
   Cylindrical boat-shaped bugs: middle and hind legs ± equal
11. *Corixa punctata* (Illiger)   ×2

Family **Notonectidae**   p. 127
   Boat-shaped back-swimmers: middle legs much shorter than
   hind legs
12. *Notonecta glauca* L.   ×2

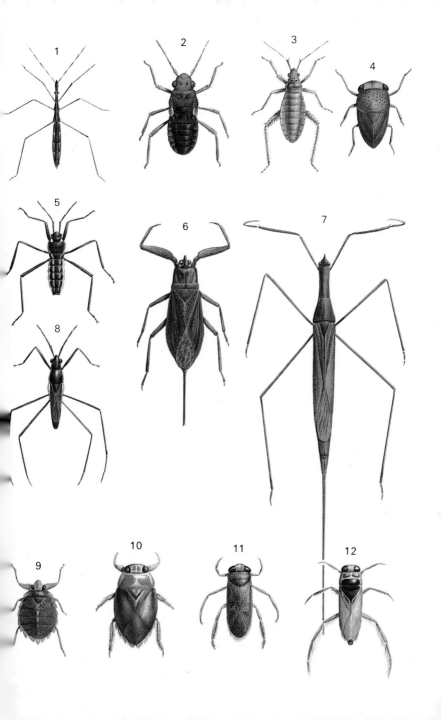

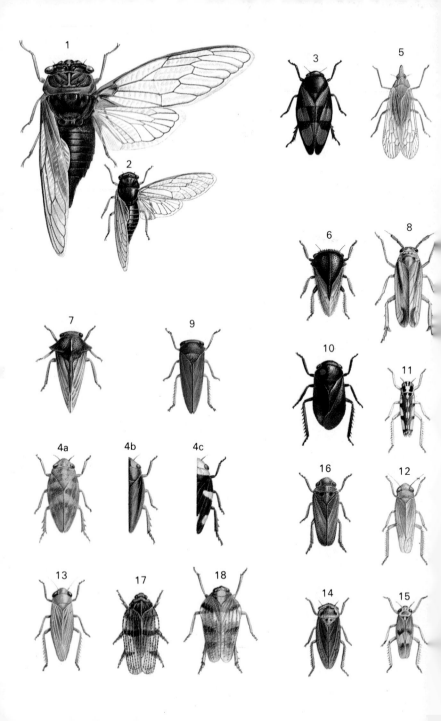

Plate 12

CICADAS AND PLANT HOPPERS – ORDER HEMIPTERA

SUB-ORDER HOMOPTERA

Front wings of uniform texture throughout – all horny or
all membranous. Beak arises from hind part of head   p. 130

Family **Cicadidae**   p. 133
Large insects with three ocelli
▲ **1.** *Lyristes plebejus* Scopoli
2. *Cicadetta montana* (Scopoli)

Family **Cercopidae**   p. 134
Hind tibia rounded, with only a few spines
3. *Cercopis vulnerata* Illiger ×2
4a. *Philaenus spumarius* (L.) ×2½
4b. and **4c.** Varieties of *P. spumarius*

△ Family **Dictyopharidae**   p. 135
Head normally with a forward projection
▲ **5.** *Epiptera europaea* L. ×2

Family **Membracidae**   p. 133
Pronotum extending back over abdomen
6. *Gargara genistae* (Fabr.) ×3½
7. *Centrotus cornutus* (L.) ×2½   pronotum

Gargara

Centrotus

Family **Delphacidae**   p. 135
Hind tibia with large movable spur
8. *Delphax pulchellus* (Curtis) ×3½

Family **Cicadellidae**   p. 134
Hind tibia angular, with one or more rows of spines
9. *Jassus lanio* (L.) ×2½
▲ **10.** *Penthimia nigra* Fabr. ×3½
11. *Eupteryx aurata* (L.) ×3½
12. *Elymana sulphurella* (Zett.) ×3½
13. *Thamnotettix confinis* (Zett.) ×2½
14. *Macropsis scutellata* (Boheman) ×3½
15. *Macrosteles variatus* (Fallen) ×3½

Family **Tettigometridae**   p. 133
Front wings distinctly pitted
16. *Tettigometra impressopunctata* Dufour ×3½

Family **Cixiidae**   p. 132
Large membranous wings with well defined veins
17. *Cixius nervosus* (L.) ×2½

Family **Issidae**   p. 133
Front wings horny and covered with network of fine veins:
front wings bulge noticeably at shoulder
18. *Issus coleoptratus* (Fabr.) ×2½

surface quite frequently to renew their air supply. Tadpoles, small fish, insects, and other arthropods are all consumed by *Notonecta* which should not, therefore, be kept in a mixed aquarium. The tank should also be covered, for the insects are strong fliers.

The name 'water boatmen' is widely used for both Notonectidae and Corixidae, although most authors now favour 'backswimmers' for the former. Take care, therefore, when meeting the name 'water boatmen'. Some authors retain the name for the notonectids and use 'lesser water boatmen' for the corixids.

Plea atomaria (Pl. 11), our only member of the **Pleidae**, is closely related to the backswimmers and, like them, it swims on its keel-shaped back. Its small size (under 3mm) distinguishes it.

The **Corixidae** or water boatmen (Pl. 11) differ from the other water bugs in being largely herbivorous, feeding on plant debris and unicellular algae from the bottom of the pond. This material is scooped up with the flattened front tarsi and then sucked in through the short, blunt rostrum. The corixids, typified by *Corixa punctata*, are superficially similar to the backswimmers but they do not swim on their backs and the dorsal surface is much flatter. The hind legs are used for swimming and are fringed with hairs, but they are relatively shorter than in the backswimmers and little longer than the middle legs. Water boatmen spend much of their time on the bottom of the ponds, rising only to renew their air supply. Except in the small *Micronecta*, the scutellum is completely covered by the wings. The insects generally fly well – by day and night – although some individuals have reduced flight muscles and cannot take to the air. Male water boatmen produce a courtship 'song' by rubbing their hairy front legs against a ridge on the side of the face.

The family **Ochteridae** is not found in Britain, but it is represented on the Continent by *Ochterus marginatus* (Plate 10). This family differs from the other water bugs in that the antennae are not concealed. About 20 species are known, all small oval insects which lead predatory lives along the margins of ponds and streams.

SUB-ORDER HOMOPTERA (Pls. 12 and 13)

The members of this sub-order are a rather diverse collection of insects bearing little resemblance to the heteropteran bugs. Only the striking similarities in their mouth-parts link these two groups together. The homopterans themselves, ranging from the large cicadas on the one hand to minute aphids and scale insects on the other, would probably be split into several orders were it not for their mouth-parts. As it is, two distinct divisions or series are recognised within the sub-order; the *Auchenorrhyncha* (cicadas and hoppers) with short, bristle-like antennae, and the *Sternorrhyncha* (aphids and others) in which the antennae are long and thread-like.

The head of the homopterans is usually strongly deflexed or hypognathous so that the mouth-parts come to lie below and behind the eyes, thus appearing to arise from the back of the head. Among the Sternorrhyncha, the rostrum actually appears to come from between the front legs. Apart from this more posterior position, however, the homopteran mouth-parts are very like those of the heteropteran bugs (p. 115).

Compound eyes are usually present and clearly visible, although they often have only a few facets. Two or three ocelli are also usually present and many aphids possess accessory eyes or ocular tubercles. The antennae generally have four or five segments, although psyllids have 10 and some male scale insects have 25 segments. The form of the antennae is an important guide to the identification of some of the families.

Whereas the prothorax of the heteropteran bugs is large and conspicuous, that of the homopterans is generally small, forming little more than a 'collar' behind the head. The exceptions to this are the tree hoppers (family Membracidae) in which the pronotum extends backwards and upwards to form a 'hood'. The meso- and metanota are usually well-developed but the mesoscutellum is never as conspicuous as it is in the heteropterans.

It is in the wings that the two sub-orders of bugs differ most noticeably: the front wings of the homopterans are never divided into leathery and membranous areas. They may be membranous, as in the aphids, or tough and leathery, as in some hoppers, but they are always uniform in texture. At rest, the wings are generally held roof-wise over the body, whereas those of the heteropterans are folded flat. The venation is fairly complete in the cicadas and hoppers but very reduced in the other families. Female scale insects and certain generations of aphids are regularly wingless but most other homopterans are fully winged.

Most cicadas and hoppers possess broad, sabre-like ovipositors with which they place their eggs in crevices or in slits cut specially in the plant tissues. Aphids and most other sternorrhynchans, however, have no ovipositor and the eggs are simply laid on the plant surface. Homopteran eggs are far less ornate than those of the heteropterans and the nymphal life is more variable, there being from three to seven instars in the various families. Viviparity and parthenogenesis occur regularly among aphids. The majority of our species overwinter as eggs.

All homopterans are plant feeders and the sub-order contains some very serious pests, especially among the aphids and leaf hoppers. These insects weaken the plants by taking large amounts of sap and many also inject toxins which destroy chlorophyll and reduce the plants' food-making activities. Some produce blockages in the food-conducting phloem tubes of the plants so that regions beyond the injury wither and die. The greatest importance of these insects lies, however, in their ability to transmit viruses. Leaf hoppers are not serious pests in Europe but aphid-borne viruses cause huge losses annually. The virus particles pass down through the rostrum and infect each new plant on which the insect feeds. The wise potato grower selects 'seed' potatoes from Scotland or some other cooler region. The aphids are less common there and so the potatoes are less likely to carry viruses at the time of planting.

An interesting habit displayed by many homopterans, notably the aphids and other sternorrhynchans, is the production of a sweet secretion called honey dew. This is exuded from the anus – although it was once thought that the paired 'horns' on the aphid abdomen were responsible – and consists largely of excess sugars derived from plant sap. It is this substance that makes greenfly and other aphids so attractive to ants. Honey dew – often produced so copiously that it can be seen falling from aphid-infested trees – is also responsible for the sooty appearance of plants in late summer. Nothing is wasted in Nature and a black fungus utilises the dried honey dew as a food material.

Waxy substances are also produced by many homopterans from glands on the abdomen. In the form of waxy powders or strands, the secretions help to keep the insects dry in what is often a very wet habitat. The abdominal cornicles of aphids produce a waxy fluid which apparently acts as a protection against predators.

The following key may be used to place most of our homopterans in their correct families, although the aphids and scale insects are taken only to their superfamilies. Further information is given on these groups later but differences between the sexes and/or generations makes accurate identification a specialist task, beyond the scope of the present book.

With the exception of our one rare cicada, all the British homopterans are small insects, the majority being under 5mm long. Detailed study therefore necessitates the use of a microscope.

Key to the Families of British Homoptera

1. Antennae very short, with terminal arista: rostrum clearly arising from head: tarsi 3-segmented. Series Auchenorrhyncha   2
   Antennae longer: rostrum (if present) appears to arise between front legs: tarsi with 1–2 segments. Series Sternorrhyncha   9

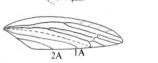

pronotum

2. Pronotum extended backwards over ab- domen   Membracidae, p. 133

   Pronotum not so extended   3

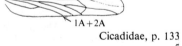

3. Veins 1A and 2A do not unite   4
   distally: middle coxae short and together

   2A   1A

   Veins 1A and 2A unite distally: 6
   middle coxae larger and apart

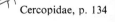

   1A + 2A

4. Insects about 20mm long: 3 ocelli   Cicadidae, p. 133
   Insects smaller: 2 ocelli or none   5

5. Hind tibiae rounded and bearing only a few spines   Cercopidae, p. 134

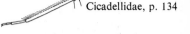

   Hind tibiae angular and bearing   Cicadellidae, p. 134
   one or more rows of spines

6. Posterior tibiae with large movable spur   Delphacidae, p. 135

   No such spur, although several smaller fixed ones are often present   7

7. Wings more or less membranous, with strongly defined veins   Cixiidae
   Front wings more or less horny, with less distinct veins   8

8. Front wings distinctly pitted (1 British
   species, Pl. 12)   Tettigometridae
   Front wings not pitted: costa swollen
   basally and wings bearing many reticulate
   veins (1 British species, Pl. 12)   Issidae

9. Tarsi with 2 segments of about equal
   length: insects always fully winged and
   with well developed legs: antennae with
   7–10 segments   10
   Adults often wingless and legs sometimes
   greatly reduced: tarsi (when present) with
   1 segment or else 2 segments of which
   basal one is small: antennae with 1–13
   segments   11

10. Front wings rigid and with prominent
    veins   Psyllidae, p. 135
    Front wings soft and whitish, with reduced
    venation   Aleyrodidae, p. 136

11. Tarsi, when present, usually 1-segmented
    and bearing a single claw: females always
    wingless, males with or without wings but
    never with more than 1 pair   Superfamily Coccoidea, p. 138
    Tarsi usually present and having two seg-
    ments and paired claws: winged or wing-
    less and often bearing little tubes on the
    abdomen   Superfamily Aphidoidea, p. 136

The only British cicada (family **Cicadidae**) is *Cicadetta montana* (Pl. 12), a rather
rare insect found only in the New Forest – although it occurs much further north
on the Continent. Several more species are found in Continental Europe.
Cicadas are easily recognised by their large size – *C. montana* reaches about
20mm in length – and by the two pairs of transparent, membranous wings which
are held roof-wise over the body when at rest. The majority live on trees of one
sort or another, although *C. montana* is believed to feed largely on bracken. Young
cicadas are subterranean creatures and have greatly enlarged front legs with
which they burrow through the soil from one root to another. They spend several
years feeding on plant roots – one American species takes 17 years – before
emerging as adult insects. Despite this long period of development, the nymphs
pass through only seven instars.

Adult cicadas sit on trees or among other vegetation and the males give out
their shrill, monotonous 'whistle' which is produced by two small membranes
called *tymbals*. These are situated in two resonating cavities, one on each side of
the abdomen, and they are vibrated rapidly by the action of tiny muscles. The
noise is emitted almost continuously and it is a relief to leave an area where
cicadas are numerous. This method of sound production is almost unique among
insects. Similar organs are found in certain leaf hoppers but they do not produce
anything like the same volume of sound as the cicadas.

The family **Membracidae** is characterised by the backward extension of the pronotum to form a sort of 'hood' over the rest of the thorax and abdomen (Pl. 12). This is mainly a tropical family whose members live largely in trees. They are commonly called tree hoppers and they show many examples of protective resemblance. The 'hood' of the thorn hopper, for instance, is shaped and patterned like the prickles on the insect's food plant and it is not easy to pick out the insect. *Centrotus cornutus* and *Gargara genistae*, both rare insects, are the only British membracids.

Members of the **Cercopidae** (Pl. 12) are known mainly through the nymphal habit of living in a mass of froth or spittle. Their common names therefore include 'spittle bugs' and 'cuckoo-spit insects'. They are also known as frog hoppers from their leaping ability and the vaguely frog-like appearance of some of the adults. The froth which surrounds the nymphs protects them from drying up and also gives them some degree of protection from predators. It is produced by the nymphs themselves by forcing air into a fluid exuded from the anus. *Philaenus spumarius* is our commonest frog hopper but the dull brown adult is less well known than the red and black *Cercopis vulnerata*. The nymph of the latter species lives underground.

The family **Cicadellidae** (Pl. 12), also known as **Jassidae**, contains the leaf hoppers, so called because they are usually found on leaves. This is a large family, with over 250 British species, and many workers divide it into several smaller families. They are generally small and often brightly coloured although, as to be expected, greens are the dominant colours. The leaf hoppers resemble small, narrow frog hoppers but can be distinguished by the very broad hind coxae, which extend almost to the sides of the abdomen, and by the one or more rows of small spines on the hind tibiae. The tibiae are also more angular than those of the frog hoppers. Leaf hoppers are extremely numerous insects and large numbers can be beaten from almost any bush or tree in summer. Grasses and other herbage are also well stocked with them, although each species has a fairly restricted range of food plants. Interesting series of leaf hoppers can be taken

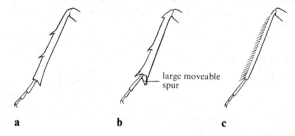

large moveable spur

a   b   c

Hind legs of homopteran bugs, showing the different arrangement of the spines in three families: **a**, Cercopidae; **b**, Delphacidae; **c**, Cicadellidae

from different habitats. For their size, the leaf hoppers jump extremely well. They also fly readily.

Leaf hoppers cause a great deal of damage to crops in the warmer parts of the world but they are not serious pests in this country, although *Eupteryx aurata* is commonly found on potatoes. By removing sap and destroying chlorophyll, the leaf hoppers produce a characteristic pale blotch around the feeding injury.

With a severe attack, these blotches join up and the whole leaf appears pale. Many species also produce honey dew.

The remaining families of the Auchenorrhyncha (Pl. 12) belong to the superfamily **Fulgoroidea** and were at one time all included in a single family. Many of these insects resemble the leaf hoppers but they differ in that veins 1A and 2A unite distally. There are other smaller differences, notably the origin of the antennae below the compound eyes in the Fulgoroidea. The four British families

Y-shaped vein
formed by fusion

2A   1A

Front wings of Delphacidae (*left*) and Cercopidae, showing how veins 1A and 2A unite to form a Y-shaped vein in the Delphacidae and other families of the Fulgoroidea, but not in the frog hoppers and leaf hoppers

within the Fulgoroidea are separated by relatively minor differences (see key). Collectively called plant hoppers, these insects feed on all parts of plants although none is a really serious pest. The **Delphacidae** is the largest family of the group and contains about 70 British species. Its members can be recognised by the large apical spur on the hind tibiae. A typical species is *Delphax pulchellus*.

Three further families occur on the Continent: the **Derbidae**, with two Mediterranean species, the **Achilidae**, and the **Dictyopharidae**. The latter includes the relatively large *Epiptera europaea* (Pl. 12), which extends into Germany. One tropical family worthy of mention is the **Fulgoridae**, many of whose members possess a relatively enormous head and are known as lantern flies.

Members of the family **Psyllidae** (Pl. 13) are minute insects, 2–3mm long as a rule, bearing a strong resemblance to miniature cicadas. They are quite numerous insects, found particularly on trees. Many species stick to one particular kind of tree – a glance at a check list of species will reveal Alder Psyllid, Birch Psyllid, and Apple Psyllid among many others – and several are responsible for gall formation. The shape and resting attitude of the insects are quite characteristic but the most diagnostic feature of these insects is the venation of the front wings. Veins R, M, and Cu_1 are all fused basally so that most of the veins appear to come from a central stalk. There are no cross veins. The front wings are rather thicker than the hind wings and may or may not be mottled. Psyllids do not fly well but, for their size, they are excellent jumpers, being propelled by the enlarged hind legs. The common name for these insects is jumping plant lice.

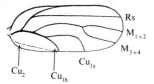

Rs
M_{1+2}
M_{3+4}
Cu_{1a}
Cu_2 Cu_{1b}

The venation of the front wing of a psyllid

There are five nymphal instars and the life history is very easy to follow by opening a series of red-veined leaf galls from ash trees (Pl. 13). These are caused by *Psyllopsis fraxini* and can be found wherever ash is common. The eggs hatch as the buds open and the nymphs start to feed on the leaves. Their activity causes the leaf to swell and roll and the veins turn to red. Inside this gall, the psyllids continue to feed and grow. The flat greenish nymphs, their stages recognisable by the increasing number of antennal segments, are covered with fluffy wax threads and look like tiny pieces of cotton wool. From June onwards the brownish adults can be seen in the galls, amid masses of tiny balls of fluid. This fluid is honey dew exuded from the anus but the droplets are coated with wax from special abdominal glands and this prevents the insects from getting sticky. Another common psyllid is *Psylla mali* – the Apple Sucker – which does a considerable amount of damage by attacking the growing points and flowers of apple trees.

The family **Aleyrodidae** (Pl. 13) is easily recognisable because its members are covered with a fine white waxy powder, giving them their common name of whiteflies. All are tiny insects with wing spans ranging up to about 5mm and, because of the opaque wings, they resemble minute moths. The wing venation is always greatly reduced. The life histories of these insects show a departure from that of the typical bug, there being something in the nature of a pupal stage. The flat, oval nymph – perhaps more correctly called a larva – is active in the first instar but legs and antennae degenerate after the first moult and the next two stages are spent motionless, often protected by the cast skins of a waxy secretion. The insect continues to feed throughout this period and then enters the 'pupal' stage. It feeds during the early part of this stage but then stops while the adult appendages develop inside the body.

Whiteflies are most abundant in tropical regions but several species are found in Britain, both out of doors and in glasshouses. These species include *Aleyrodes proletella*, the Cabbage Whitefly, and the introduced *Trialeurodes vaporariorum* or Greenhouse Whitefly. Both these species do considerable damage to crops.

The superfamily **Aphidoidea** (Pl. 13) contains a vast number of species arranged in an ever-growing number of families. Generally known as aphids, plant lice, greenfly, or blackfly, these insects feed mainly on the leaves and tender young shoots of plants. Their immense reproductive abilities make many of them serious pests.

Aphids are all minute insects, the majority being 2–3mm in length. The body is typically pear-shaped, with a narrow head and bulbous abdomen. Greens and browns are the dominant colours. The wings, when present, are usually clear and membranous, the front ones being much larger than the hind ones. The venation is reduced but fairly constant in all aphids: the most obvious feature is a broad vein running near the costal margin. This broad vein is believed to represent all the principal veins fused together for the only other veins are branches from this main one. At rest, the wings are usually held roof-wise over the body, occasionally flat or vertically upwards. Polymorphism is very common among aphids, however, and wingless forms occur in most species.

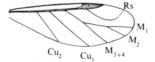

The venation of the front wing of an aphid

Although greatly reduced in certain genera, the paired abdominal cornicles are the most characteristic features of aphids and will usually serve to distinguish aphids from other insects. The tubes, once thought to exude honey dew, are the openings of specialised wax glands. The fluid produced is thought to protect the aphids to some extent from predators but, luckily for mankind, it seems to have little effect on ladybirds, lacewings, and hoverfly larvae all of which eagerly devour the aphids. Many aphid species also produce fluffy or powdery wax in dermal glands. The Woolly Aphid, *Eriosoma lanigerum*, often found on apple trees, provides a good example of this.

Aphids pass through several generations in a year and their annual cycle involves a sequence of several different forms. The basic cycle is as follows. The aphids overwinter as eggs laid on the host plant in the previous autumn and the eggs hatch in spring to produce wingless, parthenogenetic female individuals known as stem-mothers or fundatrices. When mature, these stem-mothers reproduce without mating and, moreover, they are viviparous, bringing forth a few active young each day. The insects of the new generation differ slightly from the stem-mothers and a few winged forms may occur. Several generations of these parthenogenetic females are produced during the summer, winged forms, which spread the species from plant to plant, usually alternating with a number of wingless generations. As autumn approaches, the aphids produce both male and female offspring. The females are oviparous and lay the overwintering eggs after mating. The occurrence of parthenogenesis in several successive generations, together with the production of large numbers of almost sessile individuals, is responsible for the rapid build-up of aphid colonies.

Numbers are, however, kept in check by the predators mentioned above and by various braconid and chalcid parasites. The condition of the plant host also affects the aphid population by affecting the numbers of young produced and also by determining whether winged or wingless forms are produced.

Superimposed on the basic life cycle there is often a pattern of migration. A few species of aphids are able to live on a wide variety of plants and the winged individuals distribute themselves at random through the vegetation. Other species, however, are more restricted in their diet and some require a regular alternation of hosts. It is in this latter group – typified by the Black Bean Aphid, *Aphis fabae* – that regular migration occurs. The eggs of *A. fabae* are laid on the spindle tree (*Euonymus europaeus*) or on *Viburnum* or *Philadelphus*. This aphid is almost unique in having three primary hosts – most aphids have only one. The stem-mothers produce a generation of wingless offspring but the following generation are the migrants and they are almost all winged. They fly to the summer hosts, which include beans, spinach, docks, and so on, where they reproduce parthenogenetically and viviparously, giving rise to the black masses so common on these plants. These summer generations may be winged or wingless, the winged ones spreading the species throughout its summer hosts. Migration back to the trees takes place in September and October. Winged parthenogenetic females fly there and bring forth the wingless sexual females. The males are winged and are produced on the summer hosts, reaching the trees under their own power. Eggs are laid after mating and the cycle starts again. The insects can also go on breeding asexually throughout the year in suitable situations.

Myzus persicae, a common potato pest in summer, is another migratory aphid. Its primary winter host is the peach, although in Britain it will also pass the winter on various herbaceous plants. The greyish green cabbage aphid, *Brevicoryne brassicae*, is non-migratory, spending its whole life on cruciferous plants and often causing severe damage to cabbages.

Most of the aphids mentioned so far belong to the principal family, the **Aphididae**. Closely related to this family, and only recently separated from it, is the **Pemphigidae**. This family is of interest mainly on account of the gall-forming activities of some of its members. *Pemphigus bursarius* is responsible for the little pouch-like swellings on the petioles of poplar leaves (Pl. 13). Other families of note are the **Adelgidae**, whose members are confined to conifers, and the **Phylloxeridae**, which includes a serious vine pest, *Viteus vitifolii*. The latter two families lack cornicles and the Phylloxeridae have the added distinction that the wings, when present, are folded flat over the body when at rest.

The scale insects or mealy bugs of the superfamily **Coccoidea** (Pl. 13) are very atypical insects, indeed the females are hardly recognisable as insects at all for they are often wingless and legless. The antennae are also greatly reduced. These females remain motionless, attached to the host plant by the rostrum which is just about the only external feature that links them with the rest of the insect world. They are covered with a hard or waxy scale, or with a mass of waxy threads. These coverings are secreted by the insect and are responsible for the common names given to the group. Male scale insects are more normal in appearance, usually winged and not unlike small midges – a resemblance that is heightened by the fact that the hind wings are reduced to small halteres. The scale insects can be distinguished, however, by their atrophied mouth-parts and by the presence of one or more terminal processes on the abdomen. Male scale insects are, in fact, rarely seen and the classification of the group at present depends almost entirely on the characters of the females.

Scale insects are extremely prolific, parthenogenesis and viviparity being quite common. A single female may produce 1,000 eggs or young and, with perhaps six generations in a year, this could theoretically lead to more than 30 million scale insects. The eggs are usually protected with a wax scale or they may be kept under the body of the parent until they hatch. First instar nymphs are responsible for the dispersal of the insects for, apart from the adult males, only they are mobile. Legs are often lost after the first instar and the nymphs are then sessile, attached only by their mouth-parts.

A wide variety of plant hosts is attacked by scale insects, although some species are restricted to one or two closely related plants, and scale insects include some of the most important insect pests in the world. The female scales often occur in such numbers that the host trees are killed. In their natural homes, they are kept down by parasites and predators but they are so easily transported on plant material that many species now have a world-wide distribution. Freed from their natural controls, many have become serious pests. Others have become pests simply through the increased cultivation of their host plants.

The scale insects native to Britain are not of great importance but a number of exotic species have become established in glasshouses and other artificial situations. An example is the Citrus Mealy Bug, *Planococcus citri* (Pl. 13), a serious pest of citrus fruits in America. The mealy bugs (family **Pseudococcidae**) are among the least specialised of the Coccoidea: the females retain their legs and a certain amount of mobility. Segmentation is clearly visible and the mealy bugs look, at first sight, not unlike small woodlice. An example of a European scale insect that has become a pest in America is the Oyster Scale, *Lepidosaphes ulmi*.

This hard-scaled species (Pl. 13) causes great damage to various deciduous trees, including many orchard species.

The control of scale insects is a rather difficult matter because, under their scales, the female insects are protected from most sprays. Fumigation with cyanide was used widely in the United States but many scales have now become resistant to cyanide and other methods have to be employed. One of the most successful examples of biological control involved the Cottony Cushion Scale, *Icerya purchasi*. Introduced into America from Australia, this scale became a serious pest in the citrus-growing regions. It is kept in check in Australia by a ladybird beetle, *Rodolia cardinalis*, and, in an attempt to control the scale in America, large numbers of these beetles were transported. They became established and quickly reduced the *Icerya* population.

Coccids, however, are sometimes useful insects. Shellac, cochineal, and various waxes are all obtained from species of scale insect. The manna of bible stories is believed to have been the syrupy honey dew exuded by certain species of coccid: in warm, dry climates it quickly solidifies into sugar lumps as the water evaporates.

Collecting and Preserving Bugs

Beating, sweeping, and detailed examination of herbage are the best methods of collecting the terrestrial bugs. Water bugs can be taken fairly easily with a small water net but the surface dwellers are more difficult. They can sometimes be attracted with greenfly scattered over the water surface and then careful wielding of the net may result in a few captures.

Many bugs, especially the mirids, are very delicate creatures and must not be shaken about in large containers either before or after dispatch. Small tubes with a few specimens in each are best for collecting these insects.

The heteropteran bugs, together with most of the auchenorrhynchans, are best preserved in the dry state. Carding can be used when the specimens are required simply for display but this method conceals the rostrum and other useful identification guides. Pinning is a more satisfactory method. The ventral surfaces of the thorax and abdomen are particularly important in specific identification and when pinning – through either the scutellum or hemelytron – take care to leave one side undamaged. The smaller bugs may be mounted on points in the usual way.

Aphids are best preserved in spirit because their soft bodies soon shrivel when dried. They can be put straight into collecting fluid in the field. Winged specimens are normally necessary to ensure correct specific identification. Other sternorrhynchans may also be preserved in spirit, although practice enables one to display psyllids and whiteflies suitably on pins or points. Female scale insects not required for detailed anatomical study can simply be dried on a part of the host plant. Otherwise, they should be kept in spirit and examined microscopically.

Order Thysanoptera – Thrips

Recognition features Minute dark insects with very slender bodies and usually with two pairs of narrow, fringed wings. Commonly found in flowers.

The nature of the wings, or the narrow, flattened shape of the wingless thrips will distinguish them from all other insects.

Unless you happen to be an ardent flower-sniffer, your first meeting with a thrips is quite likely to be when one gets in your eye, for these tiny insects are rarely noticed unless they intrude into our lives in this way. They live on the vegetation, under loose bark, in leaf litter, and so on where their small size and dark colour conceal them very effectively. Few flowers are without thrips, however, during the summer months and examination of a dandelion will usually reveal a dozen or more of these insects deep down among the florets. The thrips feed by piercing plant cells with their mouths and drawing sap. A few are said to suck the juices of other insects and some live on fungi and decaying material, but the majority feed on living plant tissues and, although the individual thrips are so small, they exist in such large numbers that some species are agricultural pests. One such pest is the Pea Thrips, *Kakothrips robustus*, which is responsible for the mottled silvery appearance of pea pods. The insects pierce and scrape the outer cells to get at the sap and the collapsed cells give the surface its silvery appearance. When the thrips attack the flower or the early stages of the pod, the latter becomes deformed and there is a considerable loss of the crop. Other species damage wheat and ornamental flowers. In addition to the direct damage done by the thrips, some species are able to transmit plant diseases. The damage is offset to some extent, however, by the pollinating services carried out by the insects as they wander among the flowers.

The head carries a pair of small but prominent compound eyes and, in winged thrips, three ocelli. The antennae are rather short and are placed close together on the front of the head. They contain between 6 and 10 segments. The piercing mouth-parts are unusual in that they are not symmetrically developed. The short beak is composed mainly of the upper and lower lips, while the piercing stylets are derived from the maxillae and the left mandible. The right mandible is missing. The stylets pierce the plant tissue and the sap is sucked up through the hollow of the beak.

The prothorax is distinct but the meso- and metathoracic segments are completely fused. The wings, when present, are very narrow, with few or no veins. They are fringed on both front and hind edges with relatively long bristles which more than double the effective width of the wing. The name Thysanoptera (Greek *thysanos* = a fringe) simply means 'fringed wings'. The wings are coupled by tiny hooks on the hind wings. In view of their small size and the delicate structure of the wings, the thrips are surprisingly good fliers and many of them take to the air on warm, still days. This is when they get in our eyes and hair and, despite their small size, they can be a source of considerable irritation. These flying thrips are often called thunder flies or thunder bugs because of their association with thundery weather. Many species are wingless but wing development is very variable – even within a single species there may be wingless, short-winged, and fully-winged individuals.

A thrips, showing the feathery nature of the wings

Eggs are laid on or in plant tissues, some females having well-developed saw-like ovipositors which are used to slit the plants before depositing the eggs. The first two nymphal instars are quite normal, resembling the adults but without wing pads After the second moult wing pads appear but the insect is now in a short non-feeding quiescent stage called the *prepupa*. This is followed by a pupal stage, sometimes with the intervention of a second prepupa, before the adult thrips appears. Although there is this unusual resting phase during development, we cannot say that the thrips undergo a complete metamorphosis because the early nymphs, although often called larvae, are very similar to the adult insects. Many species hibernate as adults in neglected corners, old birds' nests, and so on.

Some 3,000 species of thrips are known, of which about 160 are British. The three families to which our thrips belong may be separated with the aid of the following simple key and, at least, a strong lens.

1. With a saw-like ovipositor, or with the abdomen bluntly rounded   2

    ovipositor

No ovipositor, abdomen tubular at tip   Phlaeothripidae

2. Body flattened: wings narrow and pointed   Thripidae
   Body not flattened: front wings broader and rounded   Aeolothripidae

Members of the **Phlaeothripidae** have stouter bodies than most other thrips and the majority of them are fungus-feeders or predators. Relatively few cause any damage.

The other two families contain most of the injurious species. The broad-winged **Aeolothripidae** often have coloured bands on the wings and are therefore called banded thrips. Most of our species, however, belong to the **Thripidae**. In both these families the ovipositor of the female is very conspicuous, jutting out from the underside of the abdomen. The ovipositor curves downwards in the Thripidae and upwards in the Aeolothripidae.

Collecting and Preserving

Beating and sweeping vegetation are the best methods of obtaining thrips, although it is not always possible to know exactly which plant the insect came from when this method is used. Flower-frequenting thrips can be picked up quite easily with a moistened brush. When out of alcohol one day the writer used a particularly pungent after-shave lotion in a collecting tube: the brush had only to touch a flower and out came the thrips. Ordinary alcohol has not had the same effect. Litter inhabiting thrips can be obtained in the normal way.

Spirit-preservation and slide-mounting are the only satisfactory ways of dealing with these small insects.

Order Neuroptera – Alder flies, Snake flies, and Lacewing flies

Recognition features Small, medium, and large soft-bodied insects generally brown or green in colour. Two similar pairs of flimsy wings covered with a delicate network of veins and held roof-wise over the body when at rest. Antennae long and slender. Compound eyes usually large.

The members of this order should be distinguished from other insects by the netted wings and the long antennae. Some of the brown species resemble caddis flies but the latter are much more hairy and have very few cross veins. The 'tails' and small antennae of mayflies easily distinguish them from the Neuroptera.

A typical lacewing fly at rest

These insects undergo a complete metamorphosis during their life histories and in this respect they are more advanced than those dealt with so far in this book. The order is, nevertheless, an ancient one and it contains some of the most primitive living endopterygotes. About 4,500 species are known at present, of which 60 are on the British list.

The green lacewings (Pl. 15) are the best known British members of the order, being attracted to light and frequently finding their way into houses. The smaller brown lacewings often come with them but the diurnal alder flies and snake flies generally have to be sought among the herbage. They are all predatory insects and the lacewings are important allies of the gardener on account of the hordes of greenfly and other small insect pests they destroy.

There are considerable differences, particularly in the young stages, between the alder flies and snake flies on the one hand and the other Neuroptera on the other. For this reason, many entomologists place them in two separate orders but here we shall adhere to Imms' classification and deal with them all in one order. The alder flies and snake flies then fall into the sub-order **Megaloptera** and the lacewings into the sub-order **Planipennia**. Snake flies are easily recognised by their long prothorax which can raise the head above the rest of the body in the manner of a snake about to strike. The alder flies lack this long prothorax but their wing venation and generally stouter appearance will distinguish them from the lacewings.

All adult Neuroptera have biting mouths, although some of them rarely seem to feed. The antennae are long and slender, the individual segments being more conspicuous (moniliform condition) in some families than in others (filiform condition). Compound eyes are always present and are especially well developed in the ant-lions and the fast-flying ascalaphids. Ocelli may or may not be present.

The prothorax, already noted as being long in the snake flies, is more or less square in the alder flies and appears to merge with the head. That of the lacewings, however, generally tapers towards the front and the back of the head is rounded so that there is more of a 'neck' in these insects. The meso- and metathoracic segments are both well developed and the two pairs of wings are generally very similar. The venation is fairly complete, although in the green lacewings (family Chrysopidae) there is a secondary reduction of the main veins by fusion.

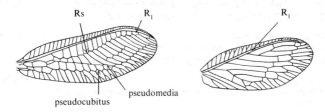

The venation of a green lacewing (family Chrysopidae) (*left*) and a brown lacewing (Hemerobiidae), showing the forked veins at the margins and the reduction of the longitudinal veins in the green lacewings (p. 150)

There are usually numerous fine accessory veins and the name Neuroptera (Greek *neuron*=nerve) refers to this nerve-like network. The name was originally used by Linnaeus for all insects with delicate, netted wings – including the exopterygote dragonflies and mayflies – but as entomological knowledge increased, Linnaeus' large and heterogeneous group was gradually split into several orders until the name became restricted to the insects considered in this chapter.

There is a simple type of wing-coupling, consisting of a small jugal lobe on the front wing and sometimes a frenulum on the hind wing (Fig. p. 21). The insects, however, are mostly weak fliers, travelling with a slow drifting motion, although the wings beat quite rapidly.

A long ovipositor is present in female snake flies but abdominal appendages are otherwise absent in our adult Neuroptera.

The larvae are rather shuttle-shaped and have three pairs of well-developed legs. The abdomen carries a number of bristles but true appendages are absent except in the aquatic larvae, in which the appendages form tracheal gills.

Neuropteran larvae, like the adults, are entirely carnivorous but the fundamental differences between the larvae of the two sub-orders is that those of the Megaloptera have biting jaws whereas those of the Planipennia have sucking mouths. But the sucking mouths of the lacewings are of a very unusual type and many of them have such powerful-looking mandibles that one might be excused for thinking that they are biting jaws. Each mandible, together with part of the corresponding maxilla, forms a tube which is sunk into the body of the victim. The lacewing larva then sucks the juices of its prey, as if through two tiny drinking straws.

The internal anatomy of the lacewing larva is interesting in that part of the hind intestine is closed and there is no through passage from the digestive region to the anus. This is, of course, associated with the liquid diet of the larva. The small amount of solid taken accumulates in the digestive tract and is not voided until the insect reaches adulthood.

Plate 13 PSYLLIDS, APHIDS, AND SCALE INSECTS
Order Hemiptera

SUB-ORDER HOMOPTERA (Contd.)

Superfamily **Psylloidea**

Family **Psyllidae**
Femora thickened: front wings tougher than hind wings   p. 135
1. *Psyllopsis fraxini* (L.) × 10 and gall on ash leaf

Superfamily **Aphidoidea**   p. 136
Tarsus with two claws: wings, when present, transparent and
all of same texture: abdomen usually with cornicles

Family **Aphididae**   p. 136-8
At least four oblique veins in front wing: cornicles usually
distinct
2. Cabbage aphid – *Brevicoryne brassicae* (L.) × 10
3. Black bean aphid – *Aphis fabae* Scopoli × 10
4. Peach and potato aphid – *Myzus persicae* (Sulzer) × 10

Family **Pemphigidae**   p. 138
At least four oblique veins in front wing: antennae shorter
than body: cornicles very small and generally invisible
5. Woolly aphid – *Eriosoma lanigerum* (Hausmann) × 10
6. *Pemphigus bursarius* (L.) × 10 and gall on poplar petiole

Family **Adelgidae**   p. 138
Only three oblique veins in front wing: no cornicles
7. *Adelges abietis* (L.) × 10 and gall on spruce

Family **Phylloxeridae**   p. 138
Wings, when present, held flat over body at rest: antennae
3-segmented
▲ **8.** *Viteus vitifolii* (Fitch) – the common wingless form: winged
specimens are extremely rare in Europe × 30

Superfamily **Aleyrodoidea**
Family **Aleyrodidae**   p. 136
Wings opaque, usually white
9. *Trialeurodes vaporariorum* (Westwood) × 10

Superfamily **Coccoidea**   p. 138
Males with only one pair of wings: females wingless and
often living under a protective scale: tarsi with only one
claw
10a. Mussel scale – *Lepidosaphes ulmi* (L.) – male × 30
10b. Mussel scale – female × 4
11. Cottony cushion scale – *Icerya purchasi* Maskell × 4
12. *Planococcus citri* (Risso) – a serious pest of oranges in
southern Europe × 4

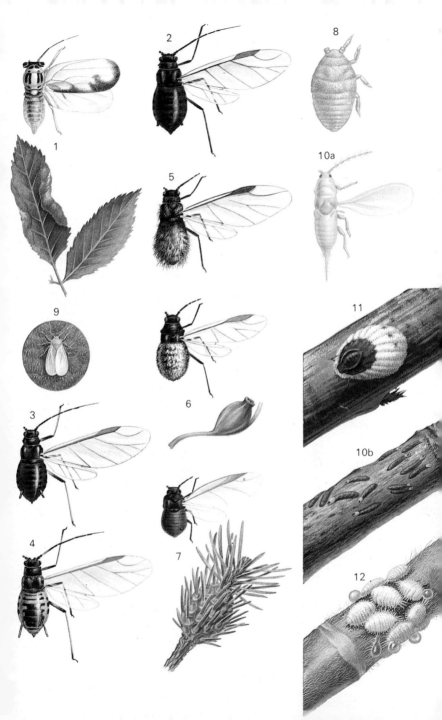

Insects with complex wing venation, the veins tending to fork as they approach the wing margin: antennae usually relatively long   p. 142

△ Family **Myrmeleontidae** – ant-lions   p. 151
    Large insects with long bodies: antennae short and thickened at end
▲ **1.** *Palpares libelluloides* L. × 1½

△ Family **Nemopteridae**   p. 151
    Hind wings ribbon-like
▲ **2.** *Nemoptera coa* L. × 1½

△ Family **Ascalaphidae**   p. 151
    Long, clubbed antennae
▲ **3.** *Ascalaphus libelluloides* Schaeff × 1½
▲ **4.** *Ascalaphus macaronius* Scopoli × 1½

△ Family **Mantispidae**   p. 151
    Front legs raptorial
▲ **5.** *Mantispa styriacus* Poda × 2

This insect might be mistaken for a praying mantis (p. 95), but its netted wings should easily distinguish it. The remarkable similarity in the front legs of the two groups of insects has been brought about because they both feed in the same way.

A Praying Mantis

△ Family **Dilaridae**   p. 151
    Male antennae strongly feathered: female with long ovipositor
▲ **6a.** *Lidar meridionalis* (Hagen) – female × 3
    6b. *Lidar meridionalis* – male × 3

Our alder flies and snake flies have only one generation per year but most of our lacewings have two, or even three generations. Three larval instars are usual and there is a prepupal stage – little more than a shrunken and inactive larva – prior to pupation. In the summer generations the prepupal stage is very short but the autumn generation usually overwinters in the prepupal stage. Pupation always takes place on land even in those species with aquatic larvae. The pupae of the planipennians are enclosed in a silken cocoon, the silk being produced not from the salivary glands but from specially modified excretory tubules which have acquired an opening into the hind gut. The silk is thus extruded at the anus. The pupae of the megalopterans are naked.

A Key to the Families of European Neuroptera

* Denotes families not found in the British Isles.

1. Hind wings long and ribbon-like — Nemopteridae*, p. 151
   Wings not like this — 2

2. Front legs raptorial — Mantispidae*, p. 151
   Front legs not raptorial — 3

3. Small insects covered with white powder — Coniopterygidae, p. 147
   Insects not like this — 4

4. Prothorax elongate, forming a 'neck' — Raphidiidae, p. 147
   No such 'neck' — 5

5. Antennae thickened or clubbed at tip — 6
   Antennae not thickened or clubbed at tip — 7

6. Antennae over half the length of front wings — Ascalaphidae*, p. 151
   Antennae less than half the length of front wings — Myrmeleontidae*, p. 151

7. Antennae feathery in male: female with ovipositor — Dilaridae*, p. 151
   Antennae not feathery: no visible ovipositor — 8

8. Veins forking conspicuously at wing margins — 9
   Veins not forking conspicuously at wing margins — Sialidae, p. 147

9. Large insects with speckled wings — Osmylidae, p. 150
   Insects not like this — 10

10. Vein Sc joining distally with R_1 — Sisyridae, p. 150

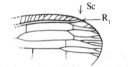

Vein Sc not joining R_1
(beware of cross veins) — 11

11. Medium-sized insects, usually green, with fili-
form antennae and few longitudinal veins   Chrysopidae, p. 150
Small grey or brown insects with moniliform
antennae and several longitudinal veins   Hemerobiidae, p. 150

SUB-ORDER MEGALOPTERA

The alder flies – family **Sialidae** – are easily distinguished from other neuropterans
on account of the venation which shows no signs of forking at the wing margins.
It is true that the coniopterygians also lack this feature but they cannot be
confused with the much larger, smoky-winged alder flies. We have only two alder
flies, of which *Sialis lutaria* (Pl. 15) is the commoner.

The eggs are laid around the waterside in batches of 200 or more and the larvae
fall or crawl into the water where they feed on other insects. Both of our species
live in still or slow-moving water and the larvae are provided with seven pairs of
feathery tracheal gills on the abdomen. There is also a terminal filament of
similar appearance. Pupation takes place in the soil and the pupa works its way
to the surface before the imago emerges. The life cycle takes about a year, the
winter being spent in the larval state. The adults are to be found in May and June.

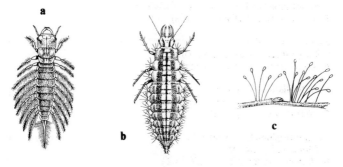

a, the larva of an alderfly, showing the feathery gills on the abdomen; **b,** a green
lacewing larva; **c,** the stalked eggs of a green lacewing

The snake flies – family **Raphidiidae** – are completely terrestrial, the larvae
living mainly under the bark of trees. The female has a long ovipositor with which
she places her eggs in suitable crevices in the bark. We have four species – all in
the genus *Raphidia* (Pl. 15) – and the adults are most likely to be taken from oaks
and pines during the summer months, although they are not common insects.

SUB-ORDER PLANIPENNIA

The members of the family **Coniopterygidae** differ considerably from the other
Neuroptera in appearance, being very small and covered with white, waxy
powder. They are often found in groups and look more like whiteflies (p. 136)
than typical lacewings. These insects resemble the megalopterans in retaining a

Family **Chrysopidae**   p. 150
Reasonably large insects, with only a few longitudinal veins
1. *Chrysopa septempunctata* Wesmael   ×2½
2. *Nathanica capitata* (Fabr.)   ×2½

Family **Sisyridae**   p. 150
Vein Sc meets vein R_1 near wing tip:
costal veinlets rarely fork
3. *Sisyra fuscata* (Fabr.)   ×4

Wing tip of *Sisyra*

Family **Hemerobiidae**   p. 150
Vein Sc does not meet vein R_1: costal
veinlets nearly all fork in front wing
4. *Hemerobius humulinus* L.   ×4

Wing tip of *Hemerobius*

Family **Coniopterygidae**   p. 147
Small insects with white powdery wings
5. *Conwentzia psociformis* (Curtis)   ×6

Family **Osmylidae**   p. 150
Large insects with spotted wings
6. *Osmylus fulvicephalus* (Scopoli)   ×6

Family **Sialidae** – alder flies   p. 147
No marked forking of veins at wing margin
7. *Sialis lutaria* (L.)   ×2½

Family **Raphidiidae** – snake flies   p. 147
Elongated prothorax
8. *Raphidia notata* Fabr. male   ×2½

SCORPION FLIES – Order Mecoptera

Head prolonged into a 'beak' with jaws at lower end

Family **Panorpidae**   p. 152
Wings normally blotched: male abdomen turned up in
scorpion fashion
9. *Panorpa communis* L. male   ×2½

△ Family **Bittacidae**   p. 152
Legs extremely long and slender, ending with a single claw
▲ 10. *Bittacus italicus* Müller   ×2½

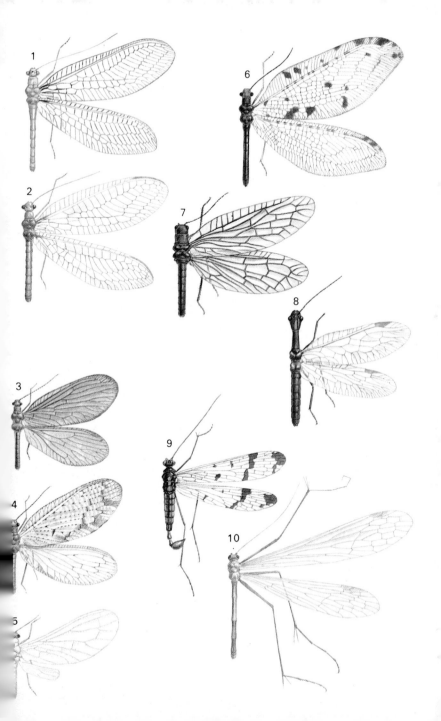

BUTTERFLIES – Order Lepidoptera

Wings covered with tiny scales which give the pattern   p. 154

Family **Danaidae**   p. 171
   Large butterflies with scale-less antennae: antennal club
   often small: front legs incompletely formed
*1. Monarch – *Danaus plexippus* (L.)

Family **Papilionidae**   p. 175
   Large butterflies with all legs fully developed: hind wings
   often with 'tails' and with only one anal vein

2. Swallowtail – *Papilio machaon* L.
▲ **3.** Apollo – *Parnassius apollo* L.

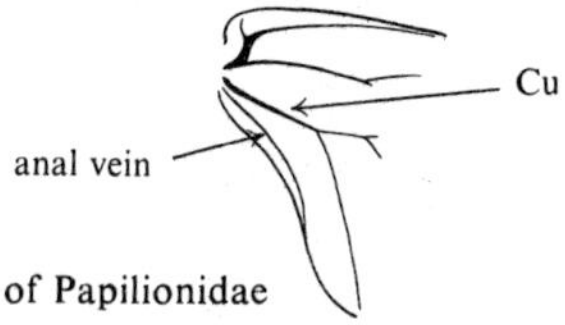

Cu

anal vein

Base of hind wing of Papilionidae

Family **Satyridae**   p. 171
   Front legs useless for walking: anterior veins of front wing
   swollen near base

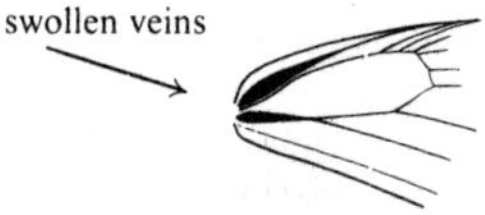

swollen veins

4. Gatekeeper – *Pyronia tithonus* (L.)   Base of front wing of Satyridae
5. Ringlet – *Aphantopus hyperantus* (L.)
6. Marbled White – *Melanargia galathea* (L.)

△ Family **Libytheidae**   p. 174
   Very long palps
▲ **7.** Nettle-tree butterfly – *Libythea celtis* Laicharting

*The Monarch does not occur regularly in Europe but mig-
rants arrive spasmodically from America and the Canaries

forked sub-costal vein, although the venation in general is reduced. Only seven species are known in Britain at present but these tiny insects are easily overlooked or assumed to be something else and it is quite possible that more will be discovered. Our commonest species, *Conwentzia psociformis*, is easily recognised by the narrow hind wings (Pl. 15).

Our largest neuropteran is *Osmylus fulvicephalus* (Pl. 15) – our only representative of the family **Osmylidae**. With a 50mm wing span and mottled wings, it is a beautiful and unmistakable insect. The larvae live near water, hiding among moss and stones, and the adults are found mainly near shady streams. It is a local insect, although widely scattered, and is on the wing from May to July.

Although rather different in appearance, the **Sisyridae** are closely related to the last family. The larvae are aquatic and live entirely on freshwater sponges. They have seven pairs of abdominal gills. The adults are found near water during the summer. *Sisyra fuscata* (Pl. 15) is the commonest of our three species, all of which are small and brownish. They are quite similar to the Hemerobiidae but the costal veinlets are fewer in number and rarely fork.

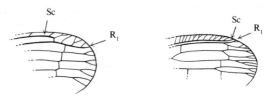

Wing tips of *Sisyra* (*left*) and *Hemerobius*, showing how vein Sc meets vein R_1 in the Sisyridae but not in the Hemerobiidae

The **Hemerobiidae** is the largest of our neuropteran families, with 29 small brown or greyish species, often very hairy. There is fusion of veins R and Rs (Pl. 15) and this feature, together with the forked costal veinlets, separates the family from the Sisyridae. All our genera possess a frenulum.

The most familiar of our neuropterans are certainly the green lacewings of the family **Chrysopidae**. The body and wing veins are generally a delicate shade of green and the prominent eyes have a brilliant metallic appearance – hence the alternative name of golden-eyes for these insects. The main feature of the wing is the reduction of the longitudinal veins. Rs is present as a zig-zag vein but its various branches fuse with those of the media and cubitus to form two composite veins – a straight pseudomedia and a zig-zag pseudocubitus (Fig. p. 143). As well as the green species of *Chrysopa* (Pl. 15), we have two brown species of *Nathanica*, but these are fairly large insects and the venational features just mentioned easily separate them from the Hemerobiidae.

Unlike the other lacewings, the chrysopids lay their eggs at the ends of threads of mucus so that each egg has a slender stalk. The stalks may or may not coalesce. Another interesting habit of some green lacewings is that the larvae cover themselves with the drained skins of their victims, thus resembling just another piece of rubbish.

One of the commonest of green lacewings is *C. carnea*. This often enters buildings in the autumn and, unlike most other species, it hibernates as an adult, assuming a pinkish tinge in the process.

The Continental Neuroptera

The continental insect fauna as a whole is considerably richer than that of the British Isles, but there are surprisingly few additional families on the Continent. The Neuroptera is exceptional because, although it is a fairly small order, we find five extra families when we cross the Channel. Four of these families are very different from our own Neuroptera, and two of them will almost certainly come to the attention of travellers in southern Europe.

Members of the **Ascalaphidae** (Pl. 14) are swift-flying insects with long, clubbed antennae. There are several European species, mainly in the south but extending northwards to Paris and even beyond. Most of the species are diurnal and they catch other insects as they dart to and fro. The larvae have sharply toothed mandibles and they hunt their prey among the leaves and stones on the ground.

The ant-lions of the family **Myrmeleontidae** are superficially like dragonflies because of their long wings and their long, narrow bodies. They are easily distinguished, however, by their stout clubbed antennae (Pl. 14). The name ant-lion refers to the larva, particularly to that of *Myrmeleon formicarius*. This lives in sandy soil and excavates a little pit. It buries itself at the bottom, leaving only its strong jaws above the sand. Small insects fall into the pit and cannot climb up the loose sandy sides. The ant-lion seizes them and sucks them dry. Most ant-lions feed in this way, although not all species make pits. Adult ant-lions fly in the sunshine with a very lazy rising and falling motion, rarely moving very far at one go. The insects are found mainly in the tropics, but several genera live in Europe and one species even reaches Finland.

Members of the family **Nemopteridae** are easily recognised by their long, ribbon-like hind wings (Pl. 14). They generally fly at dusk and 'dance' up and down rather like mayflies. The larvae may be found among debris in outbuildings and caves, where they feed on various small insects. Several species occur in southern Europe, but they are not normally common.

The mantis flies of the family **Mantispidae** are easily recognised by their large raptorial front legs (Pl. 14). These are very much like those of the praying mantis (Pl. 7), but the wings of the two insects are quite different. Most of the mantis flies live in the tropics, but a few species reach southern Europe. *Mantispa styriaca* is widely distributed around the Mediterranean, although not common in France. It has a very strange life history, for the larvae seek out the egg cocoons of wolf spiders and enter them to prey on the young spiders. Adult mantis flies catch a variety of insects with their front legs.

The family **Dilaridae** is related to the Hemerobiidae and its members are less striking than those of the previous four families. They are medium-sized insects with rounded and somewhat hairy wings, but they can be identified by the feathery antennae of the male and by the long ovipositor of the female. *Dilar meridionalis* (Pl. 14) is a fairly common species in Spain and southern France.

Collecting and Preserving
As to be expected from the habits of these insects, the best way of collecting them is by beating and sweeping the vegetation – in the neighbourhood of streams for those species with aquatic larvae. Many species also come to light.

Crushed laurel leaves is one of the best killing agents as this does not harden the delicate insects. Specimens can be set in the normal way but quick drying is necessary to preserve the greens. The soft bodies shrivel considerably on drying and any specimen needed for anatomical work must be preserved in spirit.

Order Mecoptera – Scorpion flies

Recognition features Minute and medium-sized insects in which the head is produced downwards into a 'beak' with the biting jaws at the lower end. Two similar pairs of wings are usually present and the tip of the male abdomen is frequently turned up, giving the insects their common name.

The 'beak' makes these insects quite unmistakable.

A typical scorpionfly (*Panorpa* sp.), showing the beak and the upturned tail of the male

This is a small group of insects with only about 300 known species but, like the Neuroptera, it is a very ancient group. In fact, the oldest known fossil endopterygotes – some 250 million years old – were mecopterans and it is believed that the butterflies and moths, caddis flies, two-winged flies, and fleas all evolved from mecopteran-like ancestors. Some of the present-day Australian scorpion flies appear to have survived with little change since Permian times and qualify for the title 'Living Fossils', along with the coelacanth and other famous examples.

Only four species are found in Britain and, although quite common, they are not numerous insects. Three of our species belong to the family **Panorpidae**, in which the terminal segments of the male abdomen are carried scorpion-fashion above the body – hence the common name given to the whole order. Despite their name and appearance, however, the insects are quite harmless.

Our three *Panorpa* species (Pl. 15) are fully winged but spend much of their adult lives crawling on vegetation in shady places: they are real hedgerow insects. They are largely carnivorous but seem loath to attack living prey and live mainly on dead insects and other carrion. They have also been known to nibble at bird droppings and on more than one occasion to take an interest in human sweat. Vegetable matter is not ignored and over-ripe gooseberries appear particularly attractive to these insects in the writer's garden.

Our fourth scorpion fly is the minute, wingless Snow Flea, *Boreus hyemalis*, a member of the family **Boreidae**. Less than 3mm long, this insect feeds on the mosses among which it lives. The adult is to be found in autumn and winter and has often been seen when snow is on the ground, a feature which, added to the jumping ability of the insect, is responsible for its common name.

A third family of scorpion flies is found on the Continent. This is the **Bittacidae**, whose members are recognisable from their very long slender legs. The males do not have the upturned abdomen, and the insects look very much like crane-flies. The tarsi are prehensile and the insects spend most of their time hanging from

Boreus, the snow flea

Bittacus hanging by its front legs and waiting to catch a passing fly with its hind legs

plants by their front legs. They catch small insects with the tarsi of the hind legs. There are two species in southern Europe, *Bittacus italicus* (Pl. 15) being quite common.

Although the common name for a member of this order is scorpion fly only the males of the family Panorpidae have the up-turned abdomen and the diagnostic feature of the family is the 'beak', formed largely from the clypeus, labrum, and labium. The slender, toothed mandibles are carried at the lower end. The filiform antennae have 40 or 50 segments and the compound eyes are well developed. Three ocelli are normally present, although *Boreus* has none.

In *Panorpa* the two pairs of wings are very similar and carry a variable amount of dark mottling (Pl. 15). They are relatively long and narrow (Mecoptera is derived from the Greek *mekos* = length) but, apart from an unbranched Cu_1, the venation is complete – clearly indicating the primitive nature of these insects. There is a simple wing-coupling mechanism consisting of jugal and humeral lobes and a few bristles (Fig. p. 21) but flight is very weak and the insects rarely fly far. The wings of *Boreus* have little claim to be wings at all, being reduced to two pairs of bristles in the male and one pair of scales in the female.

The ninth abdominal segment of *Panorpa* males is considerably swollen and, as already described, raised above the rest of the abdomen. The female abdomen tapers considerably, although in living specimens the last four segments are normally telescoped inside each other. *Boreus*, however, has a well-developed ovipositor. In both sexes, there are tiny cerci at the apex of the abdomen. The shapes and relative sizes of the abdominal segments are useful in identifying the species of *Panorpa*.

The eggs are laid in the soil and the *Panorpa* larva bears three pairs of thoracic legs and eight pairs of abdominal prolegs. It lives as a scavenger in the soil and leaf litter and pupates in a cavity in the soil. The pupa is of the exarate type and moves to the surface in preparation for the emergence of the adult. *Bittacus* has a similar life history. The larva of *Boreus* is of the curved scarabaeiform type, with no abdominal legs. Like the adult, it lives among mosses and pupates there or in the soil just below.

Collecting and Preserving
Beating and sweeping in suitable places between May and August may produce all three of our *Panorpa* species but *Boreus* will have to be searched for in the autumn. The winged forms can be set in the usual way but *Boreus* is best preserved in spirit.

Order Lepidoptera – Butterflies and Moths

Recognition features Minute to large insects usually possessing two pairs of membranous wings which, together with the body, are more or less covered with tiny scales. The mouth-parts are composed mainly of the maxillae which normally form a long sucking tube (proboscis), coiled under the head when not in use. Mandibles are usually absent but may be vestigial or, rarely, functional.

Apart from a few wingless female moths and some of the clearwings, whose wings are nearly naked and which therefore resemble the Hymenoptera, the butterflies and moths are easily recognisable, even by the non-entomologist. The only likely confusion is between some of the smaller moths and caddis flies but the scales and the proboscis will identify the moth upon closer examination.

A butterfly in its typical resting position

The butterflies (Pls. 16–18) and moths (Pls. 19–27) form a very large order of insects with more than 100,000 known species. Some 2,300 – only about 70 of them butterflies – occur in the British Isles but not all of these are resident in our country. Despite the size of the order, its members are very uniform in both appearance and habits. With the exception of members of the family Micropteri-gidae (p. 179), the adult insects, if they feed at all, are all liquid feeders, imbibing nectar and other juices through the proboscis. The larvae, on the other hand, all possess biting jaws and feed almost exclusively on plant material. Some of the best-known exceptions to this are the clothes moths whose larvae find sustenance in dry hair and other keratin-containing animal material.

The order is economically very important, mainly because of the damage caused by the larvae to our crops and other plants. On the credit side, some species are effective in keeping down weeds – the success of the moth *Cactoblastis cactorum* in controlling prickly pear cactus in Australia springs to mind – while a number of others provide us with silk. The aesthetic value of many butterflies should also be considered: although not making up for the damage caused by their larvae, they do at least brighten our fields and gardens. While pleasing our eyes, these insects are also performing a very useful service by pollinating the flowers.

'What is the difference between a butterfly and a moth?' This is a very common question but one which is not easy to answer. The division of the order into butterflies and moths is really an artificial division: there is the same degree of difference between hawk moths and butterflies as between hawk moths and geometer moths. The differences between butterflies and one group of moths may not hold true when we consider another group of moths. The popular idea of butterflies as brightly coloured day-flying insects and moths as dull, night-fliers is quickly dispelled by a look at the Dingy Skipper butterfly (Pl. 18) – admittedly day-flying but very dull – and the brightly coloured, day-flying Speckled Yellow moth (Pl. 27). As far as the European Lepidoptera are concerned, however, there is a convenient way of distinguishing butterflies from moths. All the butterflies have knobbed or clubbed antennae. Those of the moths are of various shapes but none of them is clubbed. The nearest approach to the clubbed appearance is in the burnet moths and here, if still in doubt, we can turn to another feature. The front and hind wings of the burnets are coupled with a stout spine (the frenulum) projecting from the base of the hind wing. Butterflies never have such a device. The British butterflies are so few in number, however, that the enthusiast will soon recognise them all on sight.

The head of a butterfly or moth is relatively large and much of its surface is occupied by the two compound eyes, each with several thousand facets. There are often two ocelli but these are generally concealed among the scales and hairs of the head. The antennae vary enormously, ranging from the tiny points of the Swift moths to the huge feathery organs of some male emperor moths (Saturniidae) capable of detecting a female a mile or more away. The antennae are usually covered with scales.

The mouth-parts almost always take the form of a sucking tube called the proboscis. This is composed of the maxillae which are grooved on the inner side and hooked together so that the grooves form a canal through which the insect draws nectar and other liquid food. When not in use, the proboscis is coiled neatly beneath the insect's head. This coiling is possible because each half of the tube is hollow and composed of numerous horny rings separated by membrane. Muscles inside each half are attached to the rings and the contraction of these muscles coils up the proboscis as a whole. When the insect wishes to feed again – stimulated by the scent of food, or by picking up its 'taste' with the feet – the proboscis is extended.

A butterfly showing how the proboscis is uncurled and used to suck nectar from a flower. The enlargement shows how the proboscis is formed from the two maxillae, which are joined together to form a canal

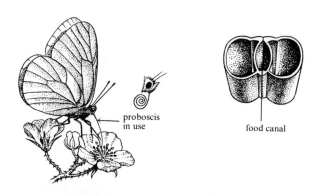

proboscis
in use

food canal

Plate 17   **BUTTERFLIES** – **Order Lepidoptera** (Contd.)

Family **Nymphalidae**   p. 171

Front legs useless for walking: antennal club usually very clear

Front legs of male (left) and female Nymphalidae

1. Silver-washed Fritillary – *Argynnis paphia* (L.)

2. Pearl-bordered Fritillary – *Clossiana euphrosyne* (L.)

3. Small Tortoiseshell – *Aglais urticae* (L.)

4. Red Admiral – *Vanessa atalanta* (L.)

5. Purple Emperor – *Apatura iris* (L.)

6. Comma – *Polygonia c-album* (L.)

7. White Admiral – *Limenitis camilla* (L.)

8. Peacock – *Inachis io* (L.)

Family **Nymphalidae** (Contd.)   p. 171
> Front legs useless for walking: antennal club usually very clear

*1. Camberwell Beauty – *Nymphalis antiopa* (L.)

Family **Hesperiidae**   p. 178
> Antennae widely separated at base and gradually thickening to form club: club often hooked at tip

2. Grizzled Skipper – *Pyrgus malvae* (L.)
3. Large Skipper – *Ochlodes venatus* (Bremer and Grey)
4. Dingy Skipper – *Erynnis tages* (L.)

Family **Nemeobiidae**   p. 174
> Front leg of male useless for walking: front leg of female fully formed. Only one European species

5. Duke of Burgundy Fritillary – *Hamearis lucina* (L.)

Family **Lycaenidae**   p. 174
> All legs functional, although males may have claws missing on front legs: small or medium-sized butterflies, often metallic in colour

6. Purple Hairstreak – *Quercusia quercus* (L.)
7. Chalkhill Blue – *Lysandra coridon* (Poda)
8. Small Copper – *Lycaena phlaeas* (L.)
9. Common Blue – *Polyommatus icarus* (Rottenburg)

Family **Pieridae**   p. 175
> All legs functional: 2 anal veins in hind wing: usually white or yellow

Base of hind wing of Pieridae — Cu — anal veins

10. Orange-tip – *Anthocharis cardamines* (L.)
11. Clouded Yellow – *Colias crocea* Geoffroy
12. Brimstone – *Gonepteryx rhamni* (L.)
13. Small White – *Pieris rapae* (L.)

*Casual immigrant to British Isles from the Continent

The proboscis reaches a considerable length in some moths – 15cm or more in the Convolvulus Hawk moth and even longer in some tropical species – and enables them to draw nectar from deep-throated flowers. But there are other species in which it is short or even absent. In the Common Vapourer moth, for example, the two maxillae do not link up, while in the Swift moths they are virtually absent altogether. Obviously, these insects cannot feed as adults. Some have even lost their mouths.

The rest of the mouth-parts are generally poorly developed. In the majority of Lepidoptera, the mandibles are completely absent. Only in the pollen-feeding Micropterigidae are they at all functional. The labium, too, is small, although its palps are developed to some extent and held in front of the face.

In the more primitive members of the order the prothorax is clearly obvious, but in the higher groups it is reduced to a small collar-like ring behind the head. The mesothorax is always the largest of the thoracic segments and carries a well-developed rounded scutellum. Overlying the base of each front wing and forming a sort of 'shoulder-pad' there is an arched, triangular sclerite called a tegula. Tegulae are found in many insects but they are particularly large in this order, although often buried among the 'fur' of the hairier species. The metathorax is always very much smaller than the mesothorax and is tucked in behind it, partially concealed. There is little to note about the legs other than the reduction of the front pair in certain families of butterflies.

Among the more primitive Lepidoptera, the two pairs of wings are of similar size and shape but in most other groups the front wings are noticeably longer. The name Lepidoptera means 'scale wings' (Greek *lepis* = scale) and refers to the tiny overlapping scales that clothe the wings. These scales also cover most of the

The overlapping scales of a butterfly's wing

body. The scales are secreted by hypodermal cells and each fits into a minute socket in the wing membrane. The scales are, in fact, modified hairs. Typically they are broad and flat but many are long and narrow and clearly show their relationship to hairs. Unmodified hairs are also found to a greater or lesser extent, particularly on the thorax and the base of the wing.

The scales are hollow and generally contain pigments responsible for the colours of the wings. The surface of the scale is generally delicately sculptured with longitudinal ridges, sometimes less than 1/1,000mm apart. When they are as close together as this, the ridges interfere with light reflection and produce striking iridescent colours which often change when you look at the insect from a different angle. Special scent-discharging scales called androconia are found in some male Lepidoptera. They are connected to scent glands in the wing membrane and the scent passes up through the hollow scale and into the air. Its dispersal is aided by the tiny plumes on the scales. Androconia may be scattered, or grouped into visible patches as in hairstreak butterflies (Pl. 18).

Wing venation is most fully developed in the Micropterigidae where both pairs of wings are alike and retain most of the primitive venation. The venation tends to be reduced in other members of the order and cross veins are always rare. One of the most noticeable features among the higher Lepidoptera is the large cell $R+M$ which comes into being through the disappearance of the basal part of the media. This large cell is often called the discal cell but it does not correspond with cells of the same name in other orders. One of the key veins is Cu_2. This vein is generally present in both wings of the primitive Lepidoptera but it disappears, first from the front wing then from the hind wing, as we move up the line to the more advanced insects.

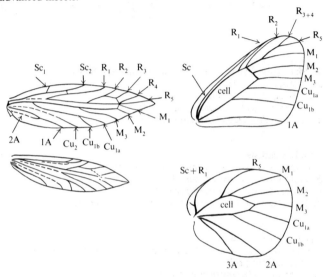

The venation of *Micropterix* (*left*) and a butterfly, showing the reduced venation in the higher families of Lepidoptera. Notice the large cell in the butterfly wing (not to scale)

The wing venation of butterflies and moths is not readily visible because of the covering of scales. A small stiff paint brush can be used to remove a few scales here and there if it is necessary to look at small areas of venation. A few drops of alcohol or ether dropped on to the wings will show up the veins for a few seconds without causing permanent damage to the specimen. Permanent preparations to display wing venation can be made by the following method. Remove the wings and wet them in alcohol (90%). Dip them into dilute hydrochloric acid for about 15 seconds and then immerse in bleach. This will clear the colour from the wings. When the wings are clear transfer them to water and then to 90% alcohol for 30 seconds. Transfer them then to pure alcohol for a further 30 seconds and then mount them on microscope slides in Euparal. If the veins are particularly delicate they can be stained with chlorazol black to make them show up.

The wing-coupling apparatus in its simplest form consists of a small lobe, the fibula, at the base of the front wing and a few spines on the front of the hind

Plate 19   MOTHS – **Order Lepidoptera** (Contd.)

Family **Hepialidae**   p. 179
  Ahtennae very short: venation very similar in two wings:
  prominent jugum on front wing

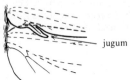

Base of wings showing jugum
overlapping on to hind wing — jugum

1. Map-winged swift – *Hepialus fusconebulosa* (DeGeer)
2a. Ghost swift – *Hepialus humuli* (L.) – male
2b. Ghost swift – female
3. Common swift – *Hepialus lupulina* (L.)
4. Gold swift – *Hepialus hecta* (L.)

Family **Cossidae**   p. 181
  Large moths with no large cell in front wing
5. Goat moth – *Cossus cossus* (L.)
6. Leopard moth – *Zeuzera pyrina* (L.)
7. Reed leopard – *Phragmataecia castaneae* (Hübner)

Family **Limacodidae**   p. 181
  A small family of varied appearance: no large cell in front
  wing and no proboscis
8. Triangle – *Heterogenea asella* (Schiff.)
9. Festoon – *Apoda avellana* (L.)

Family **Sesiidae** – clearwings   p. 184
  Very narrow front wings nearly devoid of scales
10. Hornet clearwing – *Sesia apiformis* (Clerck)
11. Currant clearwing – *Synanthedon tipuliformis* (Clerck)
12. Fiery clearwing – *Bembecia chrysidiformis* (Esper)
13. Red-belted clearwing – *Conopia myopaeformis* (Borkh.)

Family **Zygaenidae**   p. 181
  Metallic insects with clubbed or toothed antennae and a distinct frenulum
14a. Six-spot burnet – *Zygaena filipendulae* (L.) – typical form
14b. Six-spot burnet – yellow form
15. Mountain burnet – *Zygaena exulans* (Hoch.)
16. Common forester – *Procris statices* (L.)
17. Transparent burnet – *Zygaena purpuralis* (Brünn.)
▲ 18. *Zygaena fausta* (L.)

Family **Phaloniidae**   p. 183
Wings squared off at ends and almost rectangular: vein
Cu_{1b} of front wing arises from distal part of cell
1. *Agapeta hamana* (L.) × 1¼
2. *Aethes cnicana* (Westwood) × 1¼

Front wing of Phaloniidae

Family **Tortricidae**   p. 183
Wings squared off at ends and almost rectangular: vein
Cu_{1b} of front wing arises near centre of cell
3. *Cacoecimorpha pronubana* (Hübner) × 1¼
4. *Tortrix viridana* L. × 1¼
5. *Cydia pomonella* (L.) × 1¼
6. *Croesia bergmanniana* (L.) × 1¼

Front wing of Tortricidae

Family **Pterophoridae** – plume moths   p. 182
Slender moths with narrow wings usually divided up into
2, 3, or 4 feathery plumes: legs long and spiky
7. *Pterophorus pentadactylus* (L.) × 1¼
8. *Agdistis bennetii* (Curtis) × 1¼

Family **Alucitidae**   p. 187
Wings each divided into 6 slender plumes
9. *Alucita hexadactyla* (L.) × 1¼

Family **Pyralidae**   p. 182
Mainly small moths with relatively narrow front wings:
vein $Sc + R_1$ of hind wing fused with vein Rs beyond the cell:
hearing organs on abdomen (Fig. p. 182)
10. *Eurrhypara hortulata* (L.) × 1¼
11. *Pyrausta purpuralis* (L.) × 1¼
12. *Ostrinia nubilalis* (Hübner) × 1¼
13. *Nymphula nymphaeata* (L.) × 1¼
14. *Pyralis farinalis* (L.) × 1¼
15. *Galleria mellonella* (L.) × 1¼
16. *Scoparia dubitalis* (Hübner) × 1¼
17. *Crambus pratellus* (L.) × 1¼
18. *Crambus pinellus* (L.) × 1¼
19. *Nephopteryx palumbella* (Fabr.) × 1¼
20. *Ephestia kuehniella* (Zeller) × 1¼
21. *Nephopteryx semirubella* (Scopoli) × 1¼

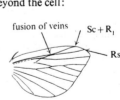

fusion of veins $Sc + R_1$

Rs

Hind wing of Pyralidae

wing. The fibula rests on top of the hind wing and is held in place by the spines. This arrangement is found in the Micropterigidae and some other primitive families (Fig. p. 164). In the Swift moths the fibula is replaced by a longer lobe called the jugum (Fig. p. 21). This also rests on top of the hind wing but there are no spines to hold it in place.

The most advanced form of wing-coupling in this order, found in most of the larger moths, involves an outgrowth from the 'shoulder' of the hind wing. This outgrowth is called the frenulum and consists, in the male, of a stout bristle. The female frenulum usually consists of several more slender bristles held loosely together, and in weak fliers it may be considerably reduced. In both sexes, the frenulum passes obliquely forwards under the front wing where it is held in place by the retinaculum. This is normally in the form of a hook on the underside of vein Sc in male insects, but in females it consists of a group of stiff hairs (Fig. p. 21). Butterflies and some moth families exhibit a simpler form of coupling in which the frenulum is lost and the wings are held together simply by a large overlap.

Many moths carry hearing organs at the base of the abdomen. These organs are thin-walled swellings on each side of the insect. They are particularly well-seen in the geometer moths in which they are associated with the first abdominal spiracle. Some moths, however, bear their 'ears' on the metathorax.

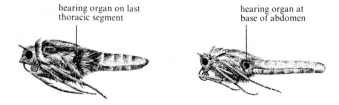

hearing organ on last thoracic segment

hearing organ at base of abdomen

The bodies of a noctuid moth (*left*) and a geometrid moth, showing the position of the 'ears'. The openings are in much the same place, but the membrane is on the thorax of the noctuid moths and on the abdomen of the geometrids

Lepidoptera all pass through the four stages: egg, larva, pupa, and imago, although there is some variation in the length of the life cycle. The eggs are usually laid in groups ranging from two or three – as in the Puss moth and the Duke of Burgundy Fritillary – to several hundred as in the Lackey moth. The total number of eggs laid by a female varies from about 50 to more than 1,000, according to their size. The female uses the 'tasting' organs on her feet and elsewhere to make sure that she lays her eggs on the right food plant. Otherwise the tiny caterpillars could well die before they find a suitable plant. Some Swift moths, however, whose larvae feed on the roots of grasses and other plants, simply drop their eggs among the herbage. Two or three weeks is the usual duration of the egg stage, except, of course, in those species which lay in late summer and pass the winter as eggs.

The larva eats its way out of its egg shell when ready and often consumes the rest of the shell after hatching. It is typically an eruciform larva, i.e. a caterpillar, with a well-developed head, three pairs of true thoracic legs, and usually five pairs of fleshy prolegs on segments 3–6 and 10 of the abdomen. The prolegs bear a ring of minute hooks at the end that enable the caterpillar to maintain a firm hold of its support. The power of these hooks is well known to anyone who has tried to remove an unwilling caterpillar from a twig.

All caterpillars possess a pair of silk glands which are highly modified salivary glands. Each gland is tubular and the total length of the coiled tube may be several times the length of the body in some of the silk moths. The ducts of the two glands join and open to the outside at the spinneret on the labium or lower lip. Each duct is also connected with an accessory gland. The silk is produced as a fluid material and is forced out through a spinneret. The secretions of the accessory glands are somewhat tacky but quick-drying and they help the silk thread to adhere to the surroundings and also help it to harden quickly. Caterpillars put silk to several uses, including the formation of the protective 'tents' and life-lines referred to below, but the major use is in the formation of the cocoon which surrounds the pupa of many moths.

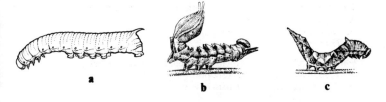

a, a fairly typical caterpillar (hawkmoth); **b**, Lobster moth larva; **c**, hooktip moth larva

Some caterpillars feed on the flowers or the developing fruits of their food plants, a few bore into the stems and roots, but the vast majority feed on the leaves and use their strong jaws to carve each leaf methodically down to the tough midrib. A number of the smaller species, including many of the pigmy moths (Nepticulidae) which are the smallest of them all, actually live inside the leaves, tunnelling their way between the upper and lower surfaces. Insects living in this way—not all of them are Lepidoptera—are called **leaf miners.** One of our commonest is *Nepticula aurella* whose whitish tunnels (Fig. p. 180) can be found in bramble leaves nearly everywhere. Many of these leaf-mining caterpillars have no legs.

Feeding is almost a non-stop activity for caterpillars, apart from a day or two of rest at each moult, and growth is rapid. The number of moults varies between three and nine but the majority of species undergo either four or five moults. Larval life may be as short as three weeks or, in those species hibernating as larvae, as long as nine months. In exceptional cases, for example, the wood-feeding Goat and Leopard moths, the larval life may exceed three years.

Caterpillars feeding exposed on the foliage of plants are naturally open to attack by birds and other enemies and we therefore find many protective devices and behaviour patterns among caterpillars. Some species spin silken 'tents' and hide in them, while others roll leaves or spin them together to make hideouts. Several species escape from enemies by attaching a silk thread to their leaf and simply falling off, paying out a 'life-line' as they fall. When the danger is past, they merely climb back up the thread. Many caterpillars rely on camouflage:

Plate 21　　**MOTHS** – **Order Lepidoptera** (Contd.)

Micropterigidae. Small metallic moths with functional jaws　　p. 179
1. *Micropterix calthella* (L.)　×2

fibula

Eriocraniidae. Small, metallic; no functional jaws　　p. 179
2. *Eriocrania purpurella* (Haworth)　×2
'eye-cap'　　*Eriocrania*

Nepticulidae. 1st antennal segment forms　　p. 180
'eye cap': strong frenulum in ♂♂
3. *Nepticula aurella* Stainton　×2　　Head of *Nepticula*

Elachistidae. Pointed hind wings; well marked cell in hind wing　　p. 185
4. *Elachista bisulcella* Duponchel　×2

Tineidae – clothes moths. Often with silvery or golden sheen　　p. 186
5. *Tinea pellionella* (L.)　×2
6. *Tineola biselliella* (Hümmel)　×2
7. *Trichophaga tapetzella* (L.)　×2

Plutellidae. Greyish or brownish: antennae forward at rest　　p. 185
8. *Ypsolophus mucronellus* (Scopoli)　×2
9. *Plutella maculipennis* (Curtis)　×2

Incurvariidae. Metallic; fibula (♀) or strong frenulum (♂): often　　p. 180
with extremely long antennae: mainly day-flying
10. *Adela viridella* (Scopoli)　×2
11. *Nemotois degeerella* (L.)　×2

Yponomeutidae. Often boldly patterned: wings relatively broad　　p. 185
12. *Ethmia bipunctella* (Fabr.)　×2
13. *Yponomeuta padella* (L.)　×2

Oecophoridae. Usually with a tuft of hair at base of antennae　　p. 185
14. *Depressaria pastinacella* (DeGeer)　×2
15. *Dasycera sulphurella* (Fabr.)　×2
16. *Hoffmannophila pseudospretella* (Stainton)　×2

Gelechiidae. Upturned palps: curve on hind wing margin　　p. 184
17. *Sitotroga cerealella* (Olivier)　×2

Gracillariidae. Very small: narrow wings: front raised at rest　　p. 185
18. *Phyllonorycter alnifoliella* (Duponchel)　×2

Glyphipterygidae. Rather square wings: large ocelli: often metallic　　p. 185
19. *Glyphipteryx haworthana* (Stephens)　×2

Psychidae. ♂♂ sparse wing scales, feathery antennae: ♀♀ wingless　　p. 186
20. *Sterrhopteryx fusca* (Haworth)　×2

Coleophoridae. Narrow pointed wings almost all fringe　　p. 185
21. *Coleophora alticollella* Zeller　×2

Cosmopterygidae. Narrow, often brightly coloured wings　　p. 185
22. *Chrysoclista linneella* (Clerck)　×2

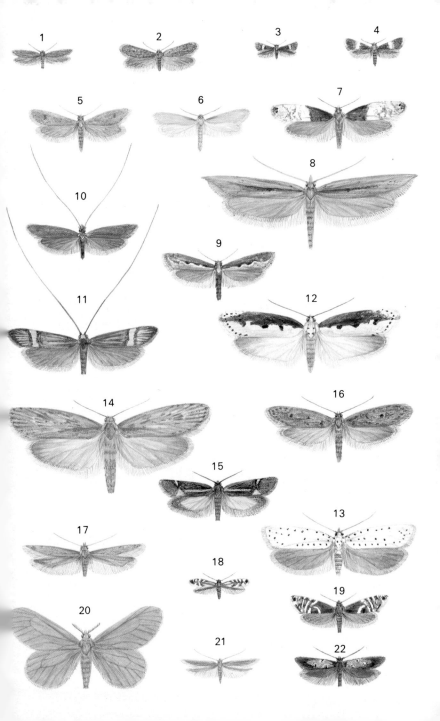

Family **Notodontidae**   p. 187
   Stout moths with relatively narrow wings: front wings often
   bear tuft of hairs on hind margin: vein M_2 of front wing not
   close to M_3 at base

Front wing M_2

                                                           M_3

1. Swallow prominent – *Pheosia tremula* (Clerck)

2. Buff-tip – *Phalera bucephala* (L.)

3. Iron prominent – *Notodonta dromedarius* (L.)

4. Puss moth – *Cerura vinula* (L.)

5. Pale prominent – *Pterostoma palpina* (Clerck)

6. Sallow kitten – *Harpyia furcula* (Clerck)

7. White prominent – *Leucodonta bicoloria* (Schiff)

8. Processionary moth – *Thaumetopoea processionea* L.

△ Family **Amatidae** (=**Syntomidae**)   p. 188
   Vein $Sc+R_1$ absent from hind wing: moths often metallic
▲ **9.** *Syntomis phegea* L.

Family **Arctiidae**   p. 188
   Generally stout moths with bright colours: vein M_2 of front
   wing close to M_3 at base: vein $Sc+R_1$ usually arises near
   middle of cell in hind wing

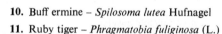

                                                           M_2

                                                           M_3

                                                           $Sc+R_1$

10. Buff ermine – *Spilosoma lutea* Hufnagel   cell

11. Ruby tiger – *Phragmatobia fuliginosa* (L.)

12. Rosy footman – *Miltochrista miniata* (Forster)

13. Common footman – *Eilema lurideola* (Zincken)

14. Garden tiger – *Arctia caja* (L.)

15. Cinnabar – *Callimorpha jacobaeae* (L.)

greens and browns are the dominant colours and the insects therefore blend in with the leaves and twigs. Longitudinal and oblique stripes often add to the effect by resembling leaf veins or shadow effects. A number of caterpillars take this camouflage a stage further and not only merge with the background but actually resemble some part of it. The outstanding examples are the caterpillars of various geometer moths. These slender brownish caterpillars bear a number of wart-like growths that resemble buds and when they sit motionless they are easily passed over as leafless twigs.

It might be thought that the brightly coloured caterpillars of Cinnabar moths and Large White butterflies are just asking to be eaten but they are, in fact, rarely taken by birds. Both have a very unpleasant taste and the bold colours and patterns serve to warn their enemies. Young birds will attack the caterpillars but they soon learn to associate the colours with unpleasantness and they leave the insects alone after that. Many other distasteful insects – ladybirds, wasps, and so on – have evolved similar warning coloration and a large number of 'tasty' insects have taken advantage of it through mimicry (p. 258). The commonest warning coloration patterns involve black with red or yellow.

Birds, lizards, and other enemies rarely take very hairy caterpillars and so the larvae of the tiger moths, ermines, and tussocks can afford to show themselves. Many insect hairs have irritant properties which add to their repellent effect and it is as well to avoid handling hairy caterpillars if possible, although the effects vary from person to person.

These protective devices are often carried over into the adult state. The Cinnabar moth (Pl. 22) is brightly coloured and the tiger moths (Pl. 22) are both colourful and hairy, while a great many other moths can sit undetected on a tree trunk. A strange example of protective resemblance in adults is afforded by the Chinese Character moth (*Cilix glaucata*) which spends the daytime sitting on leaves and looking very much like a bird dropping.

When fully grown and ready to pupate, the caterpillar stops feeding and seeks out a suitable site for pupation. It is at this time that caterpillars are often found walking 'purposefully' across roads and pavements. The place selected depends on the habits of the species and may be in the soil, among mosses or leaf litter, or attached to the food plant. The site must be suitable for the caterpillar to change into the pupa and also for the emergence of the adult insect. The soil, for example, must not be too heavy because, even if the caterpillar could burrow in, the freshly-emerged, soft-bodied moth would not be able to get out. Wood-boring caterpillars make their way towards the outside before pupating just under the surface. The adult moths then have to break through only a paper-thin layer to reach the air.

It seems probable that the formation of a cocoon is a fairly primitive feature that has been or is being lost in several families, notably most of the butterflies. In its typical development, the cocoon is spun up among the leaves of the food plant, in a bark crevice, or among leaf litter. Having found itself a suitable site, the caterpillar begins to extrude its silk and, by continuously moving its head and twisting its body this way and that, it completely envelops itself with silk. The density and thickness of the cocoon varies enormously, reaching its greatest development in the cultivated silk moth *Bombyx mori*, whose cocoon contains more than half a mile of unbroken silk as well as the numerous smaller strands around the outside. The cocoon of the Puss moth (*Cerura vinula*) (Pl. 22) is worth mentioning because of its extreme hardness. The caterpillar combines silk with saliva and particles of wood to make its cocoon and it is extremely difficult to squash a well-made Puss moth cocoon between the fingers. The caterpillar instinctively makes one end of the cocoon fairly thin and the moth, aided by a softening fluid, is able to escape without too much trouble.

Many moths pupate in the soil and these do not make much of a cocoon. The caterpillars hollow out a chamber for themselves and bind the walls with saliva and perhaps a few strands of silk. The pupa lies freely in this chamber.

Succinct (*left*) and suspended pupae

silken girdle

Among our butterflies, the only ones to make recognisable cocoons are the skippers (family Hesperiidae), which spin up among the grasses and other plants on which they feed. Most of our other butterflies pupate without any protection at all. Some of these pupae, including the tortoiseshells, fritillaries, and most of the browns, hang upside down on the food plant or other convenient support. The caterpillar spins a little silken pad before pupating and the suspended pupa – or chrysalis as the butterfly pupa is often called – grips this with its cremaster, a small hooked structure at the tail end. In the other method of pupating, used primarily by the white butterflies (Pieridae), the chrysalis remains upright. It is still attached to a pad of silk by the cremaster but it has an additional support in the form of a silk girdle or 'safety belt' slung from the twig or leaf on which it sits. Pupae supported in this way are called succinct.

Having suitably concealed or attached itself, the caterpillar begins the change into a pupa. Internal changes have, of course, been going on for some time but visible changes now occur. The body gets shorter and flatter and the skin becomes rather wrinkled. The creature looks rather dead. But then the skin splits and reveals the shining skin of the pupa. The pupa begins to wriggle and gradually the old larval skin is shrugged off. In those pupae that rest in a cocoon or earthen chamber, the larval skin often remains loosely attached to the tail end but the butterfly chrysalis, not without some danger to itself, manages to free itself completely. By deft manipulation of the hooks of its cremaster, the chrysalis 'steps out' of the old skin. Failure to hook up again correctly could mean death but casualties seem rare.

The eyes, proboscis, antennae, legs, wings and so on can all be seen in outline in the pupa, although in most species they are all inside the main body of the pupa. This kind of pupa is called the obtect pupa (Fig. p. 28).

The majority of our species hibernate as pupae and the pupal stage may therefore be as long as 10 months with single brooded species. The Duke of Burgundy Fritillary (Pl. 18), for example, emerges in early June after pupating in August. On the other hand, double-brooded species and species that hibernate as eggs or larvae may have only a very short pupal stage in spring or summer. Many species have two broods per year and a few, notably the Small Copper butterfly (*Lycaena phlaeas*) (Pl. 18), may have three. Individuals of the third brood, which is often only a partial emergence, are usually noticeably smaller than their parents.

Some of our butterflies hibernate as adults. Familiar examples are the Peacock and the Brimstone which can often be seen as early as February, drawn from hiding by a warm sun.

The general uniformity of the Lepidoptera means that we must rely on quite small details to sub-divide the order. Details of the venation are particularly important in separating the families but, because such details are usually obscured by the scales, it is often quicker to identify a species by its general appearance (using illustrations or a reference collection) than to track down its family with a key. For this reason, no family keys are attempted here but a simplified artificial key to superfamilies is provided. Each superfamily is then described, together with its principal families, although systematists are continually moving families from one superfamily to another and the make-up of the superfamilies is not by any means agreed. It is hoped that the following key, together with the descriptions and illustrations, will help to place most of our Lepidoptera in their correct families. The superfamilies adopted here are in general those given by Imms, but with some modifications suggested by Mr J. D. Bradley in the light of current ideas.

Simplified Key to the Superfamilies of European Lepidoptera

1. Insects with clubbed antennae: hind wing without
   a frenulum (Butterflies)   Papilionoidea, p. 171
   Insects with tapering antennae, or if clubbed a
   frenulum is present (Moths)   2

2. Adults with functional mandibles: insects very
   small   Micropterigoidea, p. 179
   Adults without functional mandibles   3

3. Fibula or jugum present, or else venation greatly
   reduced   4
   No fibula or jugum: venation well developed   7

4. Front and hind wings alike: fibula or jugum
   well developed: no frenulum   5

   Venation reduced and different in   6
   front and hindwings: fibula
   present, but rudimentary in
   males in which there is a   frenulum
   strong frenulum

5. Insects under 25mm in wing span: fibula and
   costal spines present   Eriocranioidea, p. 179
   Insects 25mm or more across: long jugum present   Hepialoidea, p. 179

6. Insects rarely more than 6mm
in wing span: 1st antennal
segment enlarged to form an
'eye-cap'

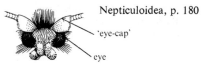

Nepticuloidea, p. 180

'eye-cap'

eye

Insects at least 8mm across: no 'eye-cap': anten-
nae sometimes very long   Incurvarioidea, p. 180

7. Wings entire   8
Wings each broken up into 2–4 plumes   Pyraloidea, p. 182
(Family Pterophoridae)
Wings each broken up into 6 plumes   Copromorphoidea, p. 187

8. Vein Cu_2 present in the hind wing: mainly small
moths – the 'micros'* – but including some large
species   9
Vein Cu_2 absent from hind wing: mostly large or
medium-sized moths without conspicuous fringes   14

M

9. Stem of vein M more or   10
less fully developed in
front wing so that there
is no large cell

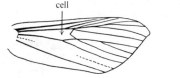

cell

Stem of vein M very reduced   12
or absent in front wing

10. Insects generally over 35mm across   Cossoidea, p. 181
Insects generally less than 35mm across   11

11. Antennae strongly feathered   Tineoidea, p. 184
(Family Psychidae)

Antennae not strongly feathered, if slightly so
the wings are metallic   Zygaenoidea, p. 181

* The early entomologists tended to divide moths into 'macros' and 'micros' mainly
according to their size. Such a division is quite artificial and frequently cuts across true
relationships. The separation of most of the smaller moths in this way has undoubtedly
contributed to their neglect, but the division is still used as a matter of convenience.
The 'macros' include the last four superfamilies in the above key, together with the
Hepialoidea, Cossoidea, and Zygaenoidea, although these last three groups are more
closely related to the 'micros' than to the other 'macros'.

LEPIDOPTERA

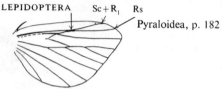

12. Vein Sc+R₁ fused with
Rs for some distance
beyond cell of hind wing:
hearing organs on abdomen
    $Sc+R_1$ Rs

Pyraloidea, p. 182

No fuch fusion of veins: no hearing organs   13

13. Front wings 'squared
off' at the outer edge:
wings always broad with
relatively short fringes:
veins Rs and M₁ of hind
wing usually close to-
gether or even stalked

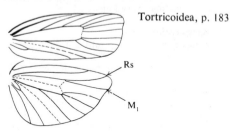

Tortricoidea, p. 183

Rs

M₁

Wings generally narrow,
with long fringes: veins
Rs and M₁ of hind wing
usually quite separate

Tineoidea, p. 184

Rs

M₁

14. Hearing organs present   15
    Hearing organs absent   16

'ear'

15. Hearing organs in
metathorax

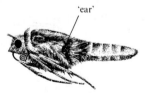

Noctuoidea, p. 187

'ear'

Hearing organs in abdomen

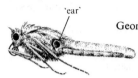

Geometroidea, p. 189

16. Frenulum present although not always obvious:
proboscis well developed: front wings very
narrow with acute angle at apex   Sphingoidea, p. 190
Frenulum and proboscis absent: wings usually
broad: antennae feathery, especially in males   Bombycoidea, p. 190

Superfamily Papilionoidea – The Butterflies

The main features of these insects are the clubbed antennae, lack of a frenulum, and the enlargement of the humeral lobe of the hind wing. Although these features may be found separately in other Lepidoptera, in combination they are found only among the butterflies. As with most of the larger moths, vein Cu_2 is absent from both front and hind wings.

Only eight families, with less than 60 resident species, are found in Britain and one further family occurs on the Continent. All of the families and most of the species can be recognised on sight, using simply the size and colour of the specimen as a guide. In the following paragraphs, the families are arranged in sequence from the most specialised to the least specialised, although it must not be thought that the steps are equal. The Danaidae and Satyridae are far more closely related to the Nymphalidae (some authors include them all in the Nymphalidae) than the Lycaenidae are to the Pieridae.

The **Danaidae** is represented in the British fauna only by a very occasional immigrant from North America. This is the Monarch or Milkweed butterfly, *Danaus plexippus* (Pl. 16). A large and striking insect, it is quite unmistakable – by man and its other enemies. Birds seldom attack it for they know that the bold pattern warns of a tough body and acrid taste. The front pair of legs is degenerate and useless for walking – a feature shared with the next two families. The pupa is suspended.

The **Satyridae** (Pl. 16) contains predominantly brown insects, known to lepidopterists simply as 'the browns'. Most of them are decorated to a greater or lesser extent with pale-centred eye-spots but the most diagnostic feature is the swelling of the bases of certain veins in the front wings. These swellings are hollow and among the suggestions for their function is the idea that they are concerned with sound detection. The antennae are not strongly clubbed. Relationship with the Nymphalidae is indicated by the reduction of the front pair of legs to hairy 'brushes'.

The front wing of a satyrid butterfly, showing the swollen veins, and the front leg of one of these butterflies. The brush-like front legs are alike in both sexes

Most satyrid larvae are grass eaters and are mainly green or brown in colour, with smooth skins. Most pupae are suspended, although the Grayling pupates in the soil.

The browns inhabit places ranging from open grassland (Meadow Brown and Small Heath), through hedgerows and woodland borders (Ringlet and Hedge Brown), to the shadier parts of woods (Speckled Wood). Our only non-brown member of the family is the Marbled White which, as the name suggests, is white with dark markings. This species, common in rough pasture, can be distinguished from the true whites by its four walking legs and the swollen wing veins.

Largest of all the butterfly families is the **Nymphalidae** (Pl. 17), which contains

Plate 23   **MOTHS – Order Lepidoptera** (Contd.)

Family **Noctuidae**   p. 188
A very large family, whose members generally have rather
sombre or cryptically coloured front wings. Veins M_2 and M_3
in the front wing are very close together at base : vein $Sc + R_1$
of hind wing joined to cell only at base

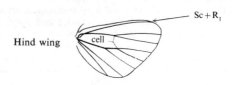

1. Alder moth – *Apatele alni* (L.)

2. Common rustic – *Apamea secalis* (L.)

3. Heart and dart – *Agrotis exclamationis* (L.)

4. Grey dagger – *Apatele psi* (L.)

5. Antler – *Cerapteryx graminis* (L.)

6. Smoky wainscot – *Leucania impura* (Hübner)

7. Green silver lines – *Bena prasinana* (L.)

8. Cream-bordered green pea – *Earias clorana* (L.)

9. Centre-barred sallow – *Atethmia xerampelina* (Esper)

10. Shark – *Cucullia umbratica* (L.)

11. Merveille du jour – *Griposia aprilina* (L.)

12. Red sword-grass – *Xylena vetusta* (Hübner)

13. Herald – *Scoliopteryx libatrix* (L.)

14. Large yellow underwing – *Noctua pronuba* (L.)

15. Silver Y – *Plusia gamma* (L.)

16. Red underwing – *Catocala nupta* (L.)

17. Slender burnished brass – *Plusia orichalcea* (Fabr.)

18. Golden plusia – *Polychrisia moneta* (Fabr.)

Family **Lymantriidae**   p. 189
  Rather hairy moths with feathery antennae in males: proboscis vestigial or absent

1. Pale tussock – *Dasychira pudibunda* (L.)

2. Gold tail – *Euproctis similis* (Fuessly)

3a. Vapourer – *Orgyia antiqua* (L.) – male
3b. female

4. Reed tussock – *Laelia caenosa* (Hübner)

5. Black arches – *Lymantria monacha* (L.)

▲ 6. Gipsy – *Lymantria dispar* (L.)

Family **Lasiocampidae**   p. 190
  Stout moths without a frenulum and with an enlarged humeral region of hind wing

7. Oak eggar – *Lasiocampa quercus* (L.)

8a. Drinker – *Philudoria potatoria* (L.) – male
8b. female

9. Lappet – *Gastropacha quercifolia* (L.)

10. Lackey – *Malacosoma neustria* (L.)

Family **Endromididae**   p. 190

11. Kentish glory – *Endromis versicolora* (L.) – the only member of this family

Family **Saturniidae**   p. 190
  Large moths with no frenulum: nearly all have eye-spots on wings
12. Emperor – *Saturnia pavonia* (L.)

our fritillaries, tortoiseshells, Peacock, Comma, Red and White Admirals, Painted Lady, and Purple Emperor. All are strikingly marked and many of the fritillaries bear silvery patches on the undersides of the wings. As in the previous two families, the front legs are reduced, although brush-like only in the male. The structure of the front legs is almost the only way of distinguishing the sexes in some species. The antennae are clearly knobbed.

The front legs of male (*top*) and female nymphalid butterflies

Both the larvae and the suspended pupae are rather spiny and the pupae are often adorned with metallic spots. The family includes some well-known migrants, such as the Red Admiral and the Painted Lady. The latter is probably the greatest migrant of them all and certainly one of the most widely distributed butterflies. It arrives with us in June, having grown up in North Africa. A British bred generation is on the wing in August but these insects cannot survive our winter. Many of them die but some travel south and reach Africa where another generation is reared ready for the spring migration to the north. A similar situation exists in America where the Painted Lady migrates between Mexico and Canada. Several nymphalids, including the tortoiseshells and the Peacock, hibernate as adults and it is notable that these insects all have very sombre undersides (Pl. 17) consistent with their habit of hiding in dark corners for the winter.

The family **Libytheidae** has only one European member – the Nettle-tree butterfly, *Libythea celtis* (Pl. 16). The family is related to the Nymphalidae, but can be distinguished by the prominent tooth on the outer edge of the front wing and also by the long palps. *L. celtis* is found all over southern Europe. It flies from June to September and then hibernates, waking to lay eggs in March and April.

The family **Nemeobiidae** also has only one European member – the Duke of Burgundy Fritillary, *Hamearis lucina* (Pl. 18). This little butterfly, found locally in woodland glades and on scrub-covered pasture, differs from the Nymphalidae in that, although the male has only four walking legs, the female has all six in walking order. The young stages, too, are very different from those of the Nymphalidae. The caterpillar is flattened and can be likened to a hairy woodlouse, while the pupa is succinctly attached to the food plant (cowslip). In these respects, the Duke of Burgundy resembles the members of the Lycaenidae, and the Nemeobiidae, whose headquarters are in South America, is something of a half-way house between the Nymphalidae and the Lycaenidae.

The **Lycaenidae** (Pl. 18) contains the blues, coppers, and hairstreaks – medium-sized butterflies often brilliantly coloured. All six legs are functional, although the male tarsi are not fully developed. The larvae of all the lycaenids are woodlouse-shaped. The pupae are stout and are attached to the food plant or to the surrounding leaf litter by means of their tail-hooks and a silken girdle. There may be a few other threads of silk as well.

The blues are easily recognised, or at least the males are, by their colour alone. Some of the females are dark brown but there are often a few blue scales, especially near the body. Otherwise, the attractive spotted underside (Pl. 18) will identify them. The Brown Argus is brown in both sexes, although the underside still gives it away as a 'blue'. The rare Large Blue is of particular interest because its larvae enter into a symbiotic association with ants. The first three instars feed on wild thyme but then the larva loses interest in this food and begins to wander. By this time, a honey gland has become active on the larva's abdomen and the larva is attractive to ants which drink the 'honey'. After a while, the larva allows itself to be carried off by an ant – usually a small red ant of the genus *Myrmica* – and deposited in the ant nest. Here it feeds on tiny ant larvae and it continues to give its 'honey' in return for the food and shelter. The large blue pupates in the ant's nest and the adult butterfly emerges through the pathways of the nest. Most of our other 'blue' caterpillars possess these honey glands and are attended by ants, although they are not taken into the nest.

The Small Copper (Pl. 18) – easily identified by its brilliant metallic orange colour – is one of our most attractive butterflies and also one of the last to disappear in autumn. It is on the wing well into November in some years. It is a very common species of rough ground but its relative the Large Copper has very different tastes. The original English Large Copper, *Lycaena dispar dispar*, was once common in the fens of East Anglia where it fed on the great water dock (*Rumex hydrolapathum*), but drainage of the fens and overcollecting contributed to its extinction about 100 years ago. The Large Copper now living in some of the fens is a continental sub-species, *L.d. batavus*, introduced from Holland.

Our hairstreaks, five species in all, get their common names from the narrow streak or row of dots on the underside of the hind wings. The upper surface of all five species is basically brown, although the Purple Hairstreak (*Quercusia quercus*) (Pl. 18) is tinged with iridescent purple. Prominent on the front wings of the male, near the outer edge of the cell, there is a dark patch of scent scales.

Britain's sole representative of the **Papilionidae** is the Swallowtail (Pl. 16), which maintains a rather precarious hold on life in the Norfolk Broads. It is remarkable that our sub-species, *Papilio machaon britannicus*, is confined to the fens and broads, whereas the continental form, *P.m. gorganus*, which occasionally turns up in the south-east of England, is found in meadows, woods, and mountain sides. The front legs are fully developed in both sexes of this insect and the tips of the antennae are curved outwards. The pupa is of the succinct type, supported on the food plant by both cremaster and girdle. Several more members of the family are found on the Continent, including the apollo butterflies of the mountain slopes.

Our only really economically important butterflies – the 'cabbage whites' – belong to the **Pieridae** (Pl. 18), a family whose dominant colours are white and yellow. All six legs are well developed and functional in both sexes and the tips of the antennae are not curved outwards. The pupae are succinct and attached to the food plant or other suitable support.

The Small White (*Pieris rapae*) is perhaps the most destructive of all butterflies, its pale green caterpillar destroying cabbages and other cruciferous crops

Plate 25   **MOTHS** – **Order Lepidoptera** (Contd.)

Family **Sphingidae** – hawk moths p. 190
Stout-bodied moths with long narrow front wings

1. Lime Hawk – *Mimas tiliae* (L.)

2. Death's Head Hawk – *Acherontia atropos* (L.)

3. Pine Hawk – *Hyloicus pinastri* (L.)

4. Humming-bird Hawk – *Macroglossum stellatarum* L.

5. Eyed Hawk – *Smerinthus ocellata* (L.)

6. Poplar Hawk – *Laothoe populi* (L.)

▲ **7.** *Proserpinus proserpina* Pallas

8. Privet Hawk – *Sphinx ligustri* L.

*9. Convolvulus Hawk – *Agrius convolvuli* (L.)

*Only casual migrants reach Britain from the Continent

Family **Sphingidae** (Contd.)

*1. Spurge Hawk – *Hyles euphorbiae* (L.)

*2. Oleander Hawk – *Daphnis nerii* (L.)

*3. Bedstraw Hawk – *Hyles galii* (Rottenburg)

*4. Mediterranean Hawk – *Hyles nicaea* (de Prunner)

*5. Striped Hawk – *Hyles livornica* (Esper)

6. Broad-bordered Bee Hawk – *Hemaris fuciformis* (L.)

7. Elephant Hawk – *Deilephila elpenor* (L.)

*8. Silver-striped Hawk – *Hippotion celerio* (L.)

9. Narrow-bordered Bee Hawk – *Hemaris tityus* (L.)

10. Small Elephant Hawk – *Deilephila porcellus* (L.)

*Only casual migrants reach Britain from the Continent

on both sides of the Atlantic. The Large White (*P. brassicae*) with its yellow and black caterpillar is nearly as bad, although it does not seem to have established itself in the United States yet. The third 'cabbage white' is the Green-veined White (*P. napi*) but this is less of a pest, preferring cruciferous weeds to the cultivated cabbages. Other whites worth mentioning are the Black-veined White, no longer resident here although common enough in France and occasionally crossing the Channel, the attractive Orange Tip (Pl. 18), and the more distantly related Wood White.

Among the yellows, we have only one resident – the Brimstone (Pl. 18). The male is a bright yellow butterfly but the female is a very pale greenish white and looks white when in flight. This species hibernates as an adult and is one of the earliest species to appear in spring. Our other yellows are the Clouded Yellows of the genus *Colias*, which come over from the Continent in early summer and produce a new generation in August. Few, if any, of these butterflies survive our winter, however, and we are dependent on migration to keep these species on the British list. Clouded Yellows are erratic in their visits. A few specimens reach us every year but every now and then we get a huge influx – perhaps the result of climatic conditions in their Mediterranean home. It is 25 years since we had a really good 'clouded yellow year' but the 1890s produced five such years.

The family **Hesperiidae**, containing the skippers, stands apart from the rest of the butterflies and is sometimes placed in a separate superfamily – the Hesperoidea. The main features by which the skippers (Pl. 18) differ from other butterflies include the wide head and wide separation of the bases of the antennae, the gradual thickening of the antennal club, and the way in which all the wing veins come direct from the cell and do not branch. Other differences include the formation of a cocoon by the skippers and their characteristic resting attitude, although they can close their wings above the body like other butterflies.

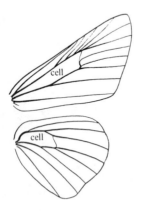

The venation of a skipper butterfly (family Hesperiidae), showing how all the veins come from the cell and do not branch

The skippers are regarded as a rather primitive group of butterflies, showing certain similarities with the more primitive groups of moths. One Australian skipper, in fact, has a frenulum in the male. The British skippers are all medium-sized brownish insects and they get their common name from their short, darting flight from flower to flower. Our representatives include the Small Skipper, Grizzled Skipper, and Dingy Skipper.

Superfamily Micropterigoidea

This group, represented by the single family **Micropterigidae,** stands very much on its own among the Lepidoptera because of the functional mandibles of its members. It is often put into a sub-order of its own (**Zeugloptera**) and some entomologists even suggest that these insects should have an order to themselves. They are certainly the most primitive of the Lepidoptera and show a number of similarities with the caddis flies. There is no proboscis, the maxillae remaining short and separate, and the insects use their mandibles and maxillae to feed on pollen. They are all day-flying moths, rarely exceeding 15mm in wing span. The narrow, pointed wings have a metallic sheen – bronze or golden in the British species – and are coupled with a small fibula. *Micropterix calthella* (Pl. 21) is the commonest of our five species and is a frequent visitor to flowers in May and June. The larvae feed on mosses.

Superfamily Eriocranioidea

This superfamily contains only one major family – the **Eriocraniidae** – represented in Britain by nine small species with a distinctive and somewhat metallic coloration (Pl. 21). The wings are coupled with a small fibula. There is a short proboscis and mandibles are present, although greatly reduced and non-functional. The larvae are legless leaf-miners, living on birch, oak, and hazel mainly, but they pupate in the soil inside a tough silken cocoon. The pupae are exarate, that is with free appendages, and they have relatively huge curved mandibles. These are used to bite through the cocoon and to get to the surface but they are left behind with the pupal skin when the adult emerges.

Superfamily Hepialoidea

This primitive group of moths is concentrated mainly in the Australian region and, to a lesser extent, South Africa. The only family to extend beyond these areas is the **Hepialidae**, represented in Britain by our five Swift moths (Pl. 19). These are medium and large-sized moths but they can be distinguished from our other large moths by their jugum and very short antennae and by the fact that all four wings are of the same shape. As to be expected from their common name, these moths are strong and fast fliers. The Common Swift (*Hepialus lupulina*) frequently comes to lighted windows at dusk but the other species appear to be less attracted to light. The Ghost Swift (*H. humuli*) exhibits an interesting sexual dimorphism, with the male typically a pure white and the female pale brown. The ghost-like appearance of the male as it flits to and fro apparently attracts the female – an unusual reversal of roles.

Swift moth larvae are generally subterranean and feed on the roots of various plants including dandelions, grass, and bracken fern. The pupa, although obtect (with appendages soldered down), is remarkably active and works its way to the surface of the soil before the adult moth emerges.

Superfamily Nepticuloidea (= Stigmelloidea)

To this group belong the smallest of all Lepidoptera. The major family is the
Nepticulidae (= **Stigmellidae**) whose members rarely exceed 7mm in wing span
and are commonly called pigmy moths. The venation is very reduced, especially in
the hind wing, and the wings are fringed with long hairs. The colouring is often
bright and metallic. A fibula is present but it is weak in the male, in which sex
there is a well-developed frenulum. The most characteristic feature is the 'eye-
cap' formed by the swelling of the basal segment of the antenna. The larvae are
legless and most of them are leaf miners. Almost the only way to collect

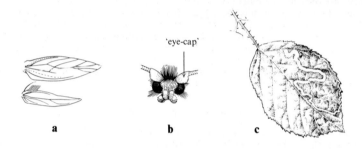

Nepticula (family Nepticulidae): **a,** the very reduced venation; **b,** the characteristic 'eye-cap', formed by the first antennal segment; **c,** the serpentine mine
formed by the larva of *N. aurella* in a bramble leaf

these insects is by sleeving the mined leaves or by collecting them when it
is considered that the larvae are mature. Our commonest species is almost
certainly *Nepticula aurella*, the Golden Pigmy (Pl. 21), whose serpentine mines
decorate bramble leaves all over the country.

Superfamily Incurvarioidea

The members of this group resemble the pigmy moths of the last superfamily in
having reduced venation, a fibula in the female and a frenulum in the male, but
they are generally larger insects and they lack the 'eye-cap'. The dominant family
– often split into several smaller ones – is the **Incurvariidae**, whose members are
generally of a metallic hue and are sometimes known as bright moths. Most of
them fly by day and the males of *Adela viridella* can often be seen 'dancing' in
large swarms around the food plant. Presumably the swarm attracts the females as
it does among mayflies.

The members of the sub-family **Adelinae** are noted for the extremely long male
antennae. They may be as much as six times the length of the body (Pl. 21) and
are responsible for the name 'longhorns' commonly applied to this group of
moths. There is a strong superficial resemblance between some of these longhorn
moths and the 'silver horn' caddis flies (Pl. 29). The larvae are mainly leaf miners
when young but later they leave their mines and make themselves portable cases
with fragments of leaves.

Superfamily Cossoidea

This is a fairly primitive group of generally large moths, retaining a relatively full wing venation. In particular, the stem of the media is retained so that there is no large cell such as is found in most of the Lepidoptera. There is no proboscis but the frenulum is well developed. There are only three British species, all in the family **Cossidae**. They are the Goat Moth (*Cossus cossus*), the Leopard Moth (*Zeuzera pyrina*), and the rather rare Reed Leopard (*Phragmataecia castaneae*). All are of medium or large size and easily identified without delving into the venation (Pl. 19). The Reed Leopard lives in reed stems but the other two species bore into trees and both can be considered pests, although only the Goat Moth – so named because of the strong smell emitted by the larva – can be said to be common. All three species take at least two years to mature and the Goat Moth may take three or more.

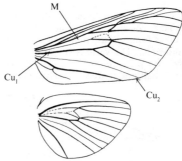

The venation of the goat moth, showing the lack of a large cell

Superfamily Zygaenoidea

These insects resemble the Cossoidea in retaining the basal part of the media, although it is often very faint. Size and appearance easily separate the two groups, however. The major family is the **Zygaenidae**. It contains the burnets and foresters, day-flying moths easy to recognise because of their bright, metallic colours. The front wings of the burnets are black with a deep green or blue sheen and are conspicuously marked with red; the hind wings are red with black edges (Pl. 19). The antennae of the burnets are clubbed but there is a well-developed frenulum on the hind wing and this easily distinguishes the burnets from butterflies. The forester moths (Pl. 19) have shiny green front wings and smoky, but translucent, hind wings. Both burnets and foresters are sluggish fliers and, although they beat their wings rapidly, they seem to drift through the air. The larvae are short and plump, mainly pale with darker spots. They spin tough, yellowish cocoons which are often placed quite high up on grass stems. The pupae are active and break through the cocoons before the adult moths emerge. Vacated cocoons are recognised at once by the empty pupal skins hanging from them.

The other family in the Zygaenoidea is the **Limacodidae** (= **Cochlidiidae**). This contains only two British species – the Festoon (*Apoda avellana*) and the Triangle (*Heterogenea asella*). There is little resemblance between the adults (Pl. 19) but their fleshy, slug-like larvae are clearly related.

Superfamily Pyraloidea

This superfamily contains upwards of 20,000 kinds of rather delicate moths. The British species, numbering in the region of 200, range from about 15mm to about 30mm in wing span. The front wings are generally narrow and the hind wings somewhat broader. Both pairs bear relatively short fringes.

The easiest members of the group to identify are the plume moths of the family **Pterophoridae** (Pl. 20). The wings are slender and each is usually divided up into two or three (occasionally four) feathery plumes. Our commonest species is *Pterophorus pentadactylus* which frequently comes to light; its larvae feed on bindweed. A few members of this family have undivided wings – *Agdistis bennetii*, for example – but the wing shape and the characteristic long legs identify them.

The rest of the members of this superfamily are very much alike and may be conveniently treated as one large family – the **Pyralidae** (Pl. 20). The possession of abdominal tympanal organs distinguishes the pyralids from similar members of the Tortricoidea and Tineoidea but the most characteristic feature of the Pyralidae is found in the hind wing: $Sc + R_1$ is fused with Rs for some distance beyond the cell. The various sub-families – treated as separate families by some authors – are distinguished by relatively minor features of the venation with which we shall not concern ourselves here.

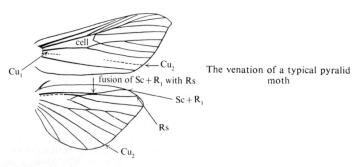

The venation of a typical pyralid moth

Pyralid larvae feed on a wide variety of materials, including dried stored products such as grain, and many of them are serious pests. They have few distinguishing features but one can often recognise a pyralid larva as such simply by its vigorous wriggling when disturbed. Many of them spin silken tubes and tunnels in which they live.

Among the economically important species in the family are the Meal Moth (*Pyralis farinalis*), the Indian Meal Moth (*Plodia interpunctella*), and the Mediterranean Flour Moth (*Ephestia kuehniella*). The larvae of all these feed on cereals and cereal products and they sometimes destroy or damage large quantities of food in granaries and flour mills. They will also attack other stored products such as nuts and dried fruit. The Wax Moth (*Galleria mellonella*) is a pest in bee hives, the larva feeding on the combs and covering them with silken tunnels. Another important species, although not common in Britain, is the European Corn Borer (*Ostrinia nubilalis*). A native of Continental Europe, this species was introduced into America where its stem-boring larva has done untold damage to maize. It will also tunnel into a variety of other plants.

The china-mark moths, such as *Nymphula stagnata*, are interesting because they are aquatic in their early stages. Young larvae mine the stems of various water plants but older ones feed externally on the leaves, often spinning two leaves together to form a shelter. The most familiar pyralids are probably the grass moths, or grass veneers as they are sometimes called. These small moths, typified by *Crambus pratellus*, are very common in grassy places and spend the daytime sitting vertically on the stems. The front wings are generally straw-coloured and they are wrapped tightly around the abdomen when at rest. The moths do not fly far when disturbed but they are not easy to find when they drop down into the grass again. They generally fly at night and often come to light. The stout, forward-pointing palps, projecting horn-like from the head, and the characteristic folding of the wings distinguish the grass moths from most other pyralids.

Superfamily Tortricoidea

These are generally small moths, although some may reach 25mm or more in wing span, and their most noticeable feature is the almost rectangular shape of the front wings: the apical angle is very nearly 90° (Pl. 20). The moths rest with the wings held roof-wise over the body. The wings are all relatively broad and bear short fringes, much shorter than the breadth of the wings. The frenulum and proboscis are well developed.

There are more than 350 British species in the superfamily and more than three-quarters of these are placed in the family **Tortricidae**. Our others belong to the

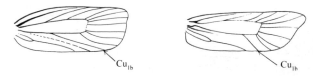

The front wing venation of the Tortricidae (*left*) compared with that of the Cochylidae to show the different origin of vein Cu_{1b}

Cochylidae (= **Phaloniidae**), which may be distinguished by vein Cu_{1b} in the front wing arising in the distal part of the cell instead of near the centre. Otherwise, however, the families are much alike and are often treated together. Most of the species are brownish or mottled grey but some are more brightly coloured: several of the Cochylidae are orange (Pl. 20). A large proportion of the larvae of these moths are leaf-rollers, living within rolled-up leaves or between leaves or flowers spun together with silk. Others bore into stems, flowers, or fruits and many are serious pests. A common example is the Codlin Moth (*Cydia pomonella*) (Pl. 20), whose larvae burrow into apples. One of the best known British tortricids, however, is *Tortrix viridana* (Pl. 20), a small pale green moth that in some years can be beaten from oak trees in very large numbers. The larvae live in rolled leaves, from which they fall on silk threads when disturbed, and frequently defoliate the trees.

Superfamily Tineoidea

This is a very large and varied superfamily, with members ranging from large, hornet-like clearwings, through typical clothes moths, to tiny leaf miners. About one-third of all Lepidoptera belong here, including nearly 800 British species. There is now a tendency to split this group into several smaller superfamilies but we shall not follow it here.

The family **Sesiidae**, with 15 British species, is easy to pick out because its members' wings are nearly devoid of scales (Pl. 20). These moths are called clearwings and they have extremely narrow front wings which distinguish them at once from the bee hawk moths (Pl. 26). They are day-flying moths and many of them resemble wasps and other Hymenoptera, providing excellent examples of mimicry (p. 258). Some larvae feed on the roots of herbaceous plants but most of our species are wood feeders, tunnelling into the wood of various broad-leaved trees. Some species cause considerable damage in fruit-growing areas, the Currant Clearwing (*Synanthedon tipuliformis*) being a common pest of black and red currants.

The rest of the superfamily Tineoidea are mainly small moths and are less easily placed in their families but they can generally be identified as a group by their narrow wings and broad fringes (Pl. 21). Some have broader wings and short fringes but the front wings are never squared off as they are in the tortricids

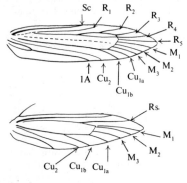

The venation of a typical member of the Tineoidea

The lack of tympanal organs distinguishes the Tineoidea from the pyralids Larval foods and habits are extremely varied but most of them conceal themselves by boring or mining, or by constructing shelters of silk and/or leaves. Only the larger families, or those with important British genera are mentioned here.

The **Gelechiidae**, whose members are sometimes known as the nebs and groundlings, can usually be distinguished because of the wavy outline of the hind wing (Pl. 21). There are some 150 British species, of which the Angoumois Grain Moth (*Sitotroga cerealella*) is one of the most important. Its larva causes severe damage to wheat and maize grain, both in the field and in store. Another serious pest, although not found in Britain, is the Pink Bollworm (*Pectinophora gossypiella*) which is very destructive to cotton crops. The majority of the larvae of this family feed within spun-up leaves or shoots, and some species cause galls.

The members of the closely related **Oecophoridae** are rather dull-coloured, flattened moths whose wings are rounded at the tips (Pl. 21). There is usually a small tuft of hairs on the base of the antennae, although such a feature is found in certain other moths and is not diagnostic. There are about 80 British species. The larvae of these moths feed on leaves and flower heads mainly, draping them with silk to form a shelter. *Depressaria pastinacella*, sometimes known as the Parsnip Flat-body Moth, spins up the flower-heads of several umbelliferous plants and feeds on the developing seeds. A number of species, however, have rather different feeding habits. The Brown House Moth (*Hofmannophila pseudospretella*), for example, normally lives in birds' nests where it feeds on plant and animal debris. It often finds its way into houses and attacks clothing and stored food materials.

The **Elachistidae** contains about 40 British species, all small and with very narrow, pointed wings (Pl. 21). The larvae live as miners in grasses and other narrow-leaved plants. The **Cosmopterygidae** is another family with very narrow wings, often heavily fringed. There are about 30 British species, many of them brilliantly marked. The larvae are mostly leaf miners. The family **Glyphipterygidae** has its headquarters in the southern hemisphere but there are about a dozen British species. All are small moths and some resemble the tortricids in general appearance. Many of them are metallic in colour. The larvae feed mainly on grasses, binding the leaves together with silk to form shelters.

The **Yponomeutidae** (sometimes spelled Hyponomeutidae) contains about 50 small and medium-sized British species without obvious familial characteristics. Vein R_5 in the front wing arises directly from the cell and does not share a common stalk with R_4. The hind wings are perhaps a little broader than they are in other families of this group. The most familiar of these moths are the small ermines, or ermels, of the genus *Yponomeuta* (Pl. 21). The front wings are white, spotted with black, and the hind wings are dark grey. The larvae of the small ermines live in communal 'tents' which they spin among the shoots of the trees and shrubs on which they live. Hedges and trees are sometimes completely covered with these webs and may be completely defoliated.

Members of the family **Coleophoridae** are small moths with very narrow, pointed wings. They can usually be distinguished from the Elachistidae because their antennae are held forwards when at rest. There are about 80 species on the British list and all but three belong to the genus *Coleophora* (Pl. 21). The larvae usually start life as leaf miners but soon emerge and spin a portable case of silk, sometimes strengthened by pieces of leaf. The moths of this family are therefore generally known as case moths. The cases are attached to leaves, stems, or seed pods and the larvae are thus protected while they feed. Neat little holes are left when the larvae move away to another feeding site. A very common case moth is *C. alticolella*, whose cases are attached to the fruiting heads of rushes.

The family **Gracillariidae** (also called **Lithocolletidae**) contains small and minute moths with very narrow, long-fringed wings (Pl. 21). Most of them can be recognised by their habit of resting with the body at an angle to the surface, propped up by the front legs. The majority of our 80-odd species belong to the genus *Phyllonorycter* (=*Lithocolletis*) and are sometimes known as midget moths. The larvae of this genus make blotch mines in the leaves of various trees and shrubs, although some other genera in the family make serpentine mines similar to those of the pigmy moths (p. 180).

Members of the family **Plutellidae** (Pl. 21) look very much like the Yponomeutidae in size and shape but can be distinguished at rest by the fact that they hold their antennae forwards. Veins M_1 and M_2 are also stalked in the hind wing of the Plutellidae. These moths are generally dull grey or brown with darker markings and are often called smudge moths. The larvae feed under flimsy webs and pupate attached to the leaves. The family has about 25 British members, including *Ypsolophus mucronellus* (Pl. 21), with a wing span of nearly 30mm.

Most of our household 'clothes moths' belong to the family **Tineidae**. The members of this family are generally small insects, often with a golden or silvery sheen. The head is rather roughly haired and the proboscis is reduced or absent altogether. The adult insects therefore do not feed and it is the larvae that do the damage. Clothes moths in general are dark-loving insects and, although males and spent females sometimes come to light, they are more likely to scuttle for shelter than to fly out into the open when disturbed. The larvae feed mainly on dried plant and animal material and the clothes moths are among the few insects able to digest the keratin of hair and feathers. The natural haunts of these insects include the nests of birds and small mammals, from where it is but a short step to human households in which carpets, clothing, and general debris provide abundant food. Pipe-lagging, because it is left undisturbed and is often warm, is a particularly favourable site for these moths, although the modern fibre-glass and polystyrene materials are safe from attack.

The most important species, from the point of view of damage done, is the Common Clothes Moth, *Tineola bisselliella* (Pl. 21). Its larvae feed on all keratin-containing materials – hair, wool, silk, feathers, and so on – and will also consume vegetable material such as cotton and stored cereal products. The Case-bearing Clothes Moth (*Tinea pellionella*) (Pl. 21) plays a smaller role in fabric damage but is still a serious pest. Its common name stems from the larval habit of constructing a tubular case from fragments of material. Other moth species contributing to the destruction of fabrics include the black and white Tapestry Moth (*Trichophaga tapetzella*) (Pl. 21), which may reach 25mm in wing span, and the Brown House Moth (family Oecophoridae) mentioned on p. 185. Clothes moth damage has fallen off sharply in recent years as a result of more frequent dry-cleaning and the use of residual insecticides, but damage and the cost of controlling it amount to perhaps £3 million annually in Britain alone.

Cases of clothes moth larva (*left*) and bag-worm larva

The **Psychidae** is a very specialised family with only a few species in Britain. They are known as bagworms because the larvae make little cases for themselves. These cases are made from fragments of bark, bud scales, grains of sand, and so on, bound together with silk. Each species makes its own characteristic type of case and it is often possible to recognise the species from its case alone. The cases are carried about by the larvae and are enlarged as the larvae grow. Most species are found on trees.

When the bagworm larvae are ready to pupate, the cases are firmly attached to a leaf or twig and pupation takes place within. The adult female is wingless and often lacks legs and antennae as well. With few exceptions, she remains in her case, mating, laying eggs, and dying there. The male, on the other hand, is a fully winged and active insect, with feathery antennae associated with the need to seek out the concealed female. The wings are sparsely covered with scales and hairs and have a dusky appearance – hence the common names of 'smokes' and 'sweeps' sometimes given to these insects. There is a well developed frenulum and the moths are active daytime-fliers, but their adult life is short. There is no proboscis. The only British species to exceed 15mm in wing span is *Sterrhopteryx fusca* (Pl. 21).

Superfamily Copromorphoidea

This group contains but one British species – the Many-plumed Moth (*Alucita hexadactyla*) – which is placed in the family **Alucitidae**. *A. hexadactyla* is a small greyish moth about 15mm across and distinguishable from other plume moths (p. 182) by having six plumes to each wing (Pl. 20).

Superfamily Noctuoidea

This is a very large superfamily, containing rather stout-bodied moths on the whole, characterised by the possession of tympanal organs on the metathorax. The various families are separated by relatively minor differences and the whole superfamily is quite uniform in appearance as far as the adults are concerned. The majority of species fly at night and, with a few notable exceptions, they are rather dull in colour.

The **Notodontidae** (Pl. 22), containing the prominents, Puss Moth, Buff-tip, and a few others, can be separated from the other families in the group because vein M_2 in the front wing is not close to M_3 at the base as it is in the other families.

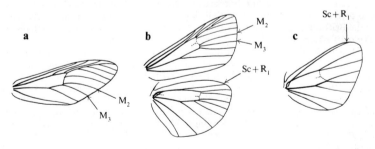

The venation of the Noctuoidea to show the differences between the families: **a,** Notodontidae (front wing only); **b,** Arctiidae; **c,** Noctuidae (hind wing only)

Most of the prominents can be recognised on sight because of the little tuft they carry on the hind margin of the front wings. When the moths are at rest, these tufts come together to make the little hump that gives the moths their name. The Buff-tip (*Phalera bucephala*) and the Puss Moth (*Cerura vinula*) are also easy to recognise but it is the caterpillar of the latter that makes it well known. The full-grown larva is green with a reddish brown 'saddle' and it is very well camouflaged among the sallow leaves on which it feeds, especially when the head is withdrawn into the thorax. The last pair of prolegs – the claspers of other larvae – are specially modified as defence organs. They are in the form of fleshy 'horns', each containing a whip-like filament that is protruded when the caterpillar is disturbed. These waving filaments, together with the grotesque appearance of the withdrawn head and the ability to eject irritating fluid from a gland on the thorax, protect the caterpillar from most of its enemies.

Thaumetopoeia processionea (Pl. 22) is the European Processionary moth, whose caterpillars 'march' in long columns over the vegetation. This species, which does not occur in Britain, is often placed in the Notodontidae, but some entomologists recognise a separate family – the **Thaumetopoeidae** – for the various processionary moths.

The **Arctiidae** is characterised by the venation of the hind wing: vein $Sc + R_1$ is fused with the cell for about half the length of the cell. Most members of the family, however, can be recognised as such without detailed examination. There are two fairly distinct groups, or sub-families – the tigers and ermines on the one hand and the footmen on the other (Pl. 22). The tigers and ermines are stout, hairy moths with broad wings, the tigers being brightly coloured with reds and orange while the ermines are usually white or cream with black spots (the male Muslin Ermine, however, is brown). The larvae are large and hairy and feed on a variety of low-growing plants. The Cinnabar Moth (*Callimorpha jacobaeae*) is generally included with the tigers, although it is not typical of the group. The footmen moths are much more slender and their front wings are relatively narrow. Most of them are drab in colour and their larvae feed almost entirely on lichens. The larvae are hairy and, like the tigers, they pupate in flimsy cocoons incorporating the larval hairs.

Closely related to the Arctiidae is the family **Amatidae** (= **Syntomidae**), although its members look more like burnets on first sight. Many are brightly coloured and several species mimic wasps. Only a few species live in Europe and none lives in the British Isles, although two species have occasionally crossed the Channel. *Syntomis phegea* (Pl. 22), is the commonest of the European species.

The largest of all families of the Lepidoptera is the **Noctuidae** (= **Agrotidae**), although this group is sometimes split into several smaller families. The venation, (Fig. p. 187), is characterised by the fact that the vein $Sc + R_1$ in the hind wing fuses with the cell only at the base (see also Lymantriidae below). A proboscis is almost always well developed. Browns and greys are the dominant colours of the front wings, although the hind wings are sometimes brilliantly coloured, as in the Red and Yellow Underwings. These insects provide good examples of flash coloration. When disturbed, they fly off and the coloured hind wings 'flash' periodically. This confuses the attacker and makes the insect very hard to follow in flight. The yellow underwing is, in fact, one of the most difficult moths to capture when in flight. The larvae are generally without many hairs, and they usually pupate below ground. A selection of our noctuids is illustrated on Pl. 23.

The family **Lymantriidae** (Pl. 24), containing the tussock moths, is hard to distinguish from the Noctuidae as far as the venation is concerned, and the most obvious differences are the reduction or loss of the proboscis and the feathery nature of the male antennae in the tussocks. Tussock moths are generally very hairy and the hairs are often barbed and irritating, thus making the moths unpleasant to handle. The larvae, too, are hairy and equally unpleasant to handle although they are some of the most attractive of all caterpillars with their tufts of brightly coloured hairs. The pupae are found in loose cocoons, spun up among the food plants and incorporating the larval hairs. Common species include the Gold Tail (*Euproctis similis*), often a pest of fruit trees, the Pale Tussock (*Dasychira pudibunda*) and the Vapourer (*Orgyia antiqua*). The latter species is of special interest because the female has only vestigial wings. She rarely moves from her cocoon after emerging and lays her eggs all over it. There are seven other British species.

Superfamily Geometroidea (Pl. 27)

This is another very large group, whose members are mainly small or medium-sized. Although the wing span may exceed 50mm in some species, the wings are relatively flimsy and the body is generally narrow. Most species therefore have a very delicate appearance. Few of them are strong fliers. There is quite likely to be some confusion between these moths and some of the larger pyralids (p. 182). Both groups possess abdominal tympanal organs but they can be separated because vein Cu_2 is present in the pyralid hind wing and never present in the Geometroidea.

The family **Thyatiridae** differs somewhat from the other families in this group because its members are quite stout. They resemble the noctuids more than the other geometers except that they possess abdominal hearing organs. Commonest of our nine species is the Buff Arches (*Habrosyne pyritoides*).

Most of the members of the family **Drepanidae** can be separated from the Geometridae by their hooked wing tips – they are called hook-tip moths. The only exception is the Chinese Character moth (*Cilix glaucata*) shown on Pl. 27. Hook-tip larvae are unusual in that they have lost the last pair of prolegs – the claspers – and they rest with the tip of the abdomen turned up (Fig. p. 163). There are only six British species.

The family **Geometridae** contains a large number of species, differing widely in size and shape but nearly all rather flimsy. The name of the family means 'ground measurer' and is derived from the behaviour of the caterpillars. These are generally long and slender and they have only two pairs of prolegs – on segments 6 and 10 of the abdomen. Many of them feed on trees and shrubs and they clasp the twigs with their prolegs and then stretch out, as if measuring length, to find a hold with their thoracic legs. Having found a hold, they draw the prolegs up close to the thoracic ones and in doing so they curve the body up in a loop – hence their name of 'loopers'. Many of the larvae are very twig-like and, when they grip the twigs with their prolegs only, they look just like branches of the twigs. The pupae may be found under the ground or in flimsy cocoons among the herbage.

The females of some species, particularly those that emerge in the winter months, have only vestigial wings (Pl. 27). Examples include the Winter Moth (*Operophtera brumata*) and the Mottled Umber (*Erannis defoliaria*). The Peppered Moth (*Biston betularia*) is of special interest because of the rapid increase of its

melanic form (var. *carbonaria*) during the last 100 years. The dark form is protec-
tively coloured in the smoke-blackened industrial regions, but it is now common
in rural areas too and it must have some other advantage over the typical mottled
form as well.

Superfamily Sphingoidea

The only family included in this group is the **Sphingidae**. Its members are the
hawk moths – large, swift-flying insects with 17 British species, although not all
are resident. They are easily recognised by their large size, stout bodies, and
narrow front wings which have very acute apical angles (Pl. 25). The proboscis is
usually very long – in the Convolvulus Hawk (*Agrius convolvuli*) it is so long
that it has a special sheath to itself in the pupa – and the moths are able to take
nectar from flowers while hovering in front of them. Most hawk moth larvae can
be recognised as such on sight by the abdominal 'horn' (Fig. p. 163). The larvae of
our common species are normally green with oblique stripes which aid conceal-
ment by breaking up the shape and by resembling leaf veins. One notable
exception is the larvae of the Elephant Hawk Moth (*Deilephila elpenor*) (Pl. 26),
brought to the writer on more than one occasion as 'a funny sort of lizard'. This
larva is dark brown and bears three pairs of 'eye spots' on the front part of the
abdomen. When disturbed, the caterpillar withdraws its head and thorax into
the abdomen and puffs out the eye-spot region, giving itself a threatening appearance). The larva of the Small Elephant Hawk Moth (*D. porcellus*) (Pl. 26) is
similar except that it lacks the abdominal horn. Pupation normally takes place
in the soil beneath the food plant.

Hawk moths are generally nocturnal insects but some fly by day. The Humming
Bird Hawk moth (*Macroglossum stellatarum*) (Pl. 26) is a day-flier, as are the
two Bee Hawks (*Hemaris fuciformis* and *H. tityus*) (Pl. 27). The bee hawks are
fully scaled when they first emerge from the pupa but most of the scales fall off
during the first flight and leave the wings largely naked. The moths have some
resemblance to bumble bees when in flight.

Superfamily Bombycoidea

The members of this group, with few exceptions, lack both proboscis and
frenulum. They are generally large, hairy moths with broad wings. The major
family in Britain is the **Lasiocampidae**, whose members are all some shade of
brown (Pl. 24). The humeral region of the hind wing is enlarged and supported
by two or more humeral veins. The moths are good fliers. Both sexes bear
pectinate antennae, although this is much more marked in the males. The larvae
of the Lackey Moth (*Malacosoma neustria*) live gregariously in their early
stages and often cover hawthorn, apples, and other rosaceous fruit trees with
their silken 'tents'. Pupation takes place in a cocoon attached to the food plant.
There are 11 British species in this family.

The Emperor Moth (*Saturnia pavonia*) (Pl. 24) is the only British representative of the **Saturniidae**, a family that contains some of the largest insects in the
world, including the giant silk moths of India. The Giant Peacock moth, not unlike a large Emperor, has a wing span of six inches and it is the largest of the
European moths.

The only other British member of the Bombycoidea is the rare Kentish Glory
Moth (*Endromis versicolora*), belonging to the family **Endromididae** (Pl. 24),

but one introduced species deserves mention and that is *Bombyx mori*, the Cultivated Silk Moth. It is not found in the wild state, even in its native China, but several races exist in silk farms. Centuries of breeding have increased the silk content of the cocoon until well over half a mile of unbroken silk thread is now yielded by one well-formed cocoon. During the process of domestication, however, the moth has completely lost its power of flight. It belongs to the family **Bombycidae** which is found mainly in Africa and the East.

Collecting and Preserving

Most entomologists probably start by collecting butterflies and moths because these are the most obvious insects and because their distinctive patterns make them fairly easy to identify. Adult butterflies and day-flying moths are generally caught by chasing them with a net. Night-flying moths, however, must be brought to the collector, by attracting them with light or with sugar.

The majority of our moths are attracted to light and they spiral round and round a lamp until they crash into it. An ordinary bulb in a porch, or taken out into the garden on a long lead well protected from damp, will attract plenty of moths, especially if it is used in conjunction with a white sheet. The moths can be picked off the sheet and surroundings, or picked up as they fall from the lamp. Street lamps also attract a fair assortment of moths and the greenish mercury-vapour lamps are particularly good. A long-handled net, and a thick skin to ward off the comments of passers-by are the main requirements for collecting at street lamps.

Specially constructed mercury-vapour moth traps are used by many entomologists. The powerful light attracts moths from quite a distance and these traps are very useful for finding out what moths are around in a particular area. The trap normally consists of the lamp set at the centre of a shallow funnel which leads into a closed box. Moths come to the lamp and fall down the funnel into the box from which they cannot escape. This box is usually filled with egg-packing material which provides plenty of nooks and crannies in which the moths can rest. The advantage of this trap is two-fold; it can be left unattended all night, and it does no harm to the moths as far as we know. The catch can be examined during the day and then released. There are, however, indications that traps used every night in one area lead to a decline in the numbers of moths. This is not a direct effect of the light but results from birds getting to know that good pickings may be found around the trap at day-break. In this respect, care must be taken when releasing the night's catch: release them among undergrowth where they are relatively safe.

'Sugaring' for moths involves more work than light-trapping and usually produces fewer specimens but it is certainly more instructive. The idea is to daub tree trunks, fence posts, and so on with sweet aromatic bait. A considerable mystique attaches to the brewing of this mixture and many collectors have their own peculiar and often exotic recipes, but brown ale ($\frac{1}{2}$ pint), black treacle (1 lb), and rum (2 nips) make a highly effective – and palatable – mixture. Pear-drop flavouring (amyl acetate) is added to increase the efficiency of the bait. A clean paint brush is used to put a streak of bait on the tree at about head height. In the absence of suitable trees or posts, pieces of rag may be treated and tied to tall grasses or hedges. The sugaring should be completed before nightfall and the treated sites should not be too far apart. Each can then be visited at intervals during the night to collect the 'drunken' moths. There is something quite exciting about finding a

Plate 27   MOTHS – **Order Lepidoptera** (Contd.)

Family **Thyatiridae**   p.189
Relatively stout moths with abdominal hearing organs

1. Peach blossom – *Thyatira batis* (L.)

2. Buff arches – *Habrosyne pyritoides* (Hufnagel)

3. Frosted green – *Polyploca ridens* (Fabr.)

Family **Drepanidae**   p. 189
Slender moths, usually with hooked wings: hearing organs
on upper side of abdomen

4. Scalloped hooktip – *Drepana lacertinaria* (L.)

5. Pebble hooktip – *Drepana falcataria* (L.)

6. Chinese character – *Cilix glaucata* (Scopoli)

Family **Geometridae**   p. 189
Slender moths with hearing organs on lower side of abdomen

7. Lime-speck pug – *Eupithecia centauriata* (Schiff.)

8. Tawny speckled pug – *Eupithecia icterata* (Vill.)

9. Green carpet – *Colostygia pectinaria* (Knoch)

10. Pretty chalk carpet – *Melanthia procellata* (Schiff.)

11. Speckled yellow – *Pseudopanthera macularia* (L.)

12. Clouded border – *Lomaspilis marginata* (L.)

13. Blood-vein – *Calothysanis amata* (L.)

14a. Mottled umber – *Erannis defoliaria* (Clerck) – male
14b. Mottled umber – female

15. Early thorn – *Selenia bilunaria* (Esper)

16. Magpie – *Abraxas grossulariata* (L.)

17. Large emerald – *Geometra papilionaria* (L.)

18a. Peppered moth – *Biston betularia* (L.) – normal form
18b. Peppered moth – melanic form

19. Swallowtailed moth – *Ourapteryx sambucaria* (L.)

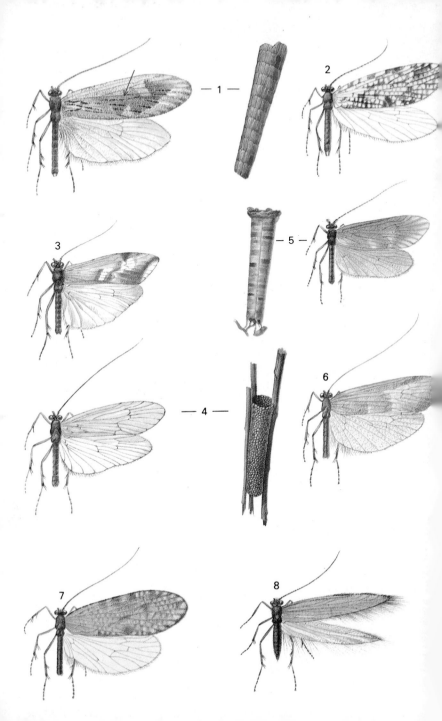

Insects with hairy wings and few cross veins: usually near water   p. 195

Family **Phryganeidae**   p. 202
Spurs 2, 4, 4: very long discoidal cell in front wing
1. *Phryganea grandis* L. ×2

Family **Philopotamidae**   p. 202
Last palpal segment longer than all others together: ocelli
2. *Philopotamus montanus* (Donovan) ×3

Palp

Family **Limnephilidae**   p. 202
One spur or none on front tibia
3. *Limnephilus lunatus* Curtis ×2
4. *Anabolia nervosa* (Curtis) ×2

Family **Sericostomatidae**   p. 202
Basal segment of antenna stout and hairy: hind tibia with 3 or 4 spurs
5. *Brachycentrus subnubilus* Curtis ×3

Family **Hydropsychidae**   p. 202
Last palpal segment longer than all others together: no ocelli: first apical fork present: spurs 2, 4, 4
6. *Hydropsyche ornatula* McLach. ×3

Family **Polycentropidae**   p. 202
Last palpal segment much longer than all others together: no ocelli: spurs 3, 4, 4
7. *Polycentropus flavomaculatus* (Pictet) ×5

Family **Hydroptilidae**   p. 202
Very small insects, with long fringes
8. *Hydroptila sparsa* Curtis ×10

The insects illustrated are all males. There is often a difference in the shape and size of the wings between male and female. The drawings in the central column show a variety of larval cases, belonging to the species indicated by the pointers

group of moths feeding at bait. Contrary to what might be expected, the moths are not sticky – their table manners are good and they keep their hands and feet out of their food. They can be seen sitting all around the edge of the patch with their tongues reaching inwards.

Do not expect to obtain much on your first night's sugaring: knowing where to put the bait comes with experience. Baiting inside a wood is not usually profitable: isolated trees, hedgerows, and fences are best. The weather is also important, as it is with light-trapping. Humid, overcast nights are usually far better mothing nights than clear, moonlight nights.

Flowers are of interest to both butterflies and moths and sweet-scented or nectar-rich flowers will attract many species. The entomologist's garden should always contain plants like the buddleia tree, honeysuckle, stocks, michaelmas daisies, dahlias, and petunias.

The young stages of the Lepidoptera can be obtained by searching, beating, and sweeping in the usual way and most species are easy to rear in captivity. The main exceptions are those that hibernate as larvae and they require constant attention to humidity. Rearing is the only way to get good specimens of some of the smaller Lepidoptera – the leaf miners for example. Mined leaves can normally be kept in good condition by placing them on damp, sterilised peat or sand in a closed container.

Pupa-digging is a rather hit-and-miss business involving careful sifting of soil and litter at the base of the food plant but may be worthwhile when certain species are known to exist in an area.

Specimens intended for the cabinet should be killed as soon as possible after capture otherwise they may well damage their wings by trying to fly in a confined space. Scales come off very easily under such conditions. The larger species are set in the normal way, with the hind edge of the front wings at right angles to the body as a rule. It is a good plan to set butterflies in their resting position in order to show the underside. This looks much more natural than setting them upside down. The smaller species are difficult to set neatly but good results can be obtained with practice.

Order Trichoptera – Caddis Flies

Recognition features Small, medium, and large insects with two pairs of wings covered with tiny hairs. The wings have few cross-veins and are held roof-wise over the body when at rest. Antennae very slender, often as long as and sometimes longer than the wings. Normally found near water. Caddis flies are structurally very similar to certain moths and some of the smaller members of the two groups are easily confused. The hairy (not scaled) wings and the lack of a coiled proboscis, however, distinguish the caddis flies. Caddis can be separated from lacewings by the few cross veins and from stoneflies and mayflies by the few cross veins and the position of the wings at rest.

A typical caddis fly at rest

This is the only order of holometabolic insects in which the young stages are primarily aquatic. Of the 189 British species, only *Enoicyla pusilla* does not have an aquatic larva – it lives in damp moss at the base of trees. Adult caddis flies are rather dull, brownish insects, usually flying at dusk. The smaller ones rarely travel far from their pond or stream, although the larger species, with stronger powers of flight, often turn up in light traps some distance from water. During the daytime, most caddis flies hide among the waterside vegetation and are usually overlooked.

The young stages are far better known than the adult caddis: few boys will not have dredged them up from the local pond or stream. These caddis-worms, or stickworms, are of immense importance in freshwater ecology, being eaten in large numbers by fish and water birds. Consequently, caddis flies are of interest to the fisherman to whom they are also known as sedge flies or rails (Ireland).

The caddis antennae are slender and bristle-like. They are composed of many segments and are often as long as the wings, sometimes longer. At rest, they are held straight forward in front of the head. The compound eyes are normally small and the ocelli, if present, are three in number, although the central one is often right between the antennae, and difficult to detect. Caddis flies have simple biting mouths but these are poorly developed, often vestigial, and the adults rarely feed. The maxillary palps are long and often clearly visible at the sides of the head or covering the face. These palps clearly distinguish their owners from apparently similar micro-lepidopterans. All our female caddis flies have five-segmented palps but the number varies in the males and is used in classification.

The maxillary palps of three families of caddis flies: **a,** Phryganeidae; **b,** Rhyacophilidae; **c,** Philopotamidae

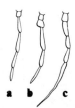

Plate **29**   **CADDIS FLIES** – **Order Trichoptera** (Contd.)

Family **Rhyacophilidae**   p. 203
  First two palpal segments short and thick, third segment
  long and thin: no discoidal cell
1. *Rhyacophila obliterata* McLach.   ×3   Palp

Family **Psychomyidae**   p. 203
  Last segment of palps much longer than all others together:
  no ocelli: first apical fork usually absent: very small discoidal
  cell
2. *Tinodes waeneri* (L.)   ×4
3. *Ecnomus tenellus* (Rambur):   ×6 a rare species in which
1st apical fork is present and spurs are 3, 4, 4 instead of 2, 4, 4

Family **Odontoceridae**   p. 203
Antennae toothed on inner side
4. *Odontocerus albicorne* (Scopoli)   ×3

                    Section of antenna

Family **Leptoceridae**   p. 203
  Antennae very long: only two spurs on hind tibia
5. *Leptocerus nigronervosus* (Retz.)   ×3

Family **Glossosomatidae**   p. 203
  First two palpal segments short and thick, third segment
  long and thin: discoidal cell present
6. *Agapetus fuscipes* Curtis   ×6

Family **Molannidae**   p. 203
  No ocelli: no discoidal cell: spurs 2, 4, 4
7. *Molanna angustata* Curtis   ×3

Family **Beraeidae**   p. 206
  No ocelli: no discoidal cell: spurs 2, 2, 4
8. *Ernodes articularis* (Pictet)   ×6

The insects illustrated are all males. There is often a difference
in the shape and size of the wings between male and female.
The drawings in the central column show a variety of larval
cases, belonging to the species indicated by the pointers

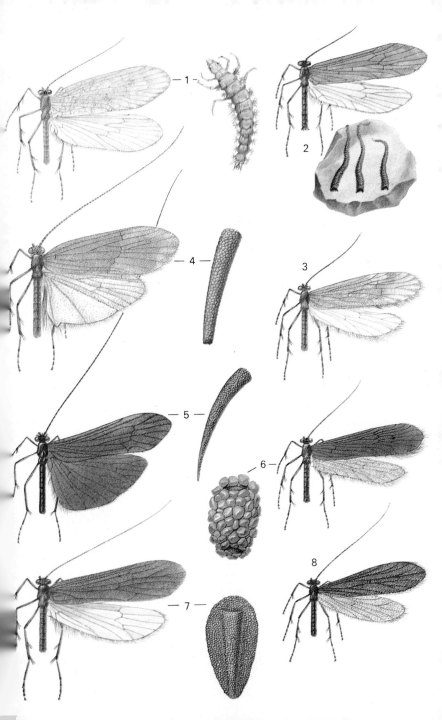

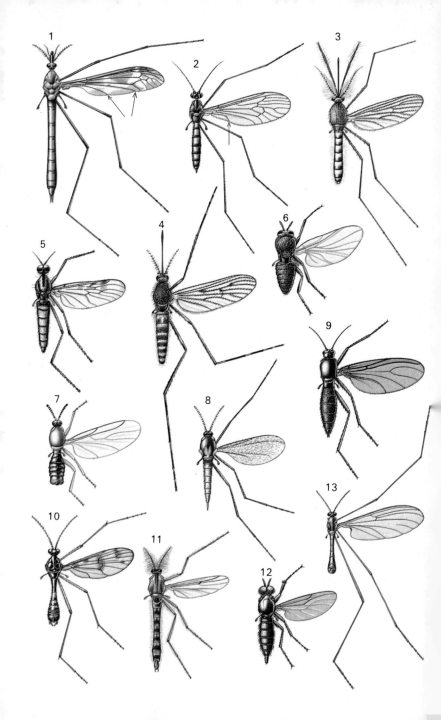

FLIES – Order Diptera Plate 30

Insects with only two wings, the hind wings being repre- p. 207
sented by club-shaped halteres

Tipulidae – crane-flies. Long-legged flies with two long anal veins p. 125
and a V-shaped suture on thorax
1. *Tipula maxima* Poda

Trichoceridae. V-shaped suture on thorax: vein 2A short: ocelli p. 216
present
2. *Trichocera annulata* Meigen ×4

Culicidae – mosquitoes. Slender flies with 10 veins reaching wing p. 217
margin: veins and hind margin of wings bearing scales
3. *Culex pipiens* L. – male ×4
4. *Theobaldia annulata* (Schrank) – female ×4

Anisopodidae. No V-shaped suture on thorax: wings normally p. 216
with discal cell: only one anal vein reaches wing margin
5. *Anisopus fenestralis* (Scopoli) ×4

Simuliidae. Small dark flies with very broad wings and short p. 219
antennae
6. *Simulium equinum* (L.) ×5

Scatopsidae. Small dark flies with posterior veins more or less in- p. 220
visible
7. *Scatopse inermis* (Ruthe) ×5

Cecidomyiidae. Tiny flies with no more than 4 veins reaching wing p. 220
margin: beaded antennae: body often orange
8. *Taxomyia taxi* (Inchbald) ×6

Mycetophilidae. Delicate flies with humped thorax and long p. 220
antennae
9. *Sciara thomae* (L.) ×4   Thorax of Mycetophilidae

Ptychopteridae. Long-legged flies with tibial p. 216
spurs: deep U-shaped suture on thorax
10. *Ptychoptera contaminata* (L) ×2½

Chironomidae. Humped thorax and very weak posterior veins: p. 218
male antennae feathery
11. *Chironomus annularius* (DeGeer) ×2½

Bibionidae. Dark hairy flies with stout antennae inserted well be- p. 220
low eyes: prominent spines on front tibia
12. *Dilophus febrilis* (L.) ×3

Head of bibionid fly from front

antennae

△ **Blepharoceridae.** Slender flies with very long legs: network of very p. 220
faint folds on wings: near swift streams
▲ **13.** *Liponeura cinerascens* Loew ×3

The prothorax is small and the mesothorax is the larger of the other two thoracic segments. Wings are fully developed in most caddis flies, the only exception among the British species being the female *Enoicyla pusilla*, a species which we have already seen to be an oddity on account of its terrestrial larvae. The name Trichoptera means 'hairy wings' (Greek *trichos* = of hair) and refers to the tiny hairs that clothe the veins and membranes of the wings. Unlike the scales of butterflies and moths, these hairs do not rub off easily. The front wings are relatively narrow and are rather more hairy and opaque than the broader hind wings. In most species there is an amplexiform type of wing coupling, the hind edge of the front wing being folded and engaging with the costa of the hind wing.

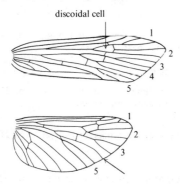

The wings of *Hydropsyche*, showing the apical forks formed by the division of the veins. There are five on the front wing of *Hydropsyche*, but the fourth fork is absent from the hind wing

The basic caddis fly wings have few cross veins but the main veins divide noticeably in the outer third of the wing to form the apical forks. Differences in venation lead to the disappearance of some of the forks, which are therefore useful identification guides. M_{3+4} does not divide in the hind wing and so apical fork 4 is never present. Another useful identification aid is the discoidal cell. Its shape varies considerably and in many species it is absent, in other words there is no cross vein between R_3 and R_4. One fairly constant feature is the thyridium, a small, pale, hairless spot near the centre of each wing. Its significance is not clear but it is possibly connected with some sort of sense organ.

Caddis fly leg, showing three spurs on the tibia

The legs are long and the tibiae are provided with spurs. These spurs are quite large structures and not to be confused with the smaller, darker spines that clothe much of the leg. The number of spurs on each tibia is used in classification and identification. When referring to the spurs, it is usual to give just the numbers for the three legs: spurs 2, 4, 4 means simply that the front leg has two spurs and the others have four each.

Caddis flies pair while resting on the vegetation and egg-laying follows in due course. Some species lay their eggs on vegetation around the water or overhanging it: others lay on the water surface or below it. The laying and spent flies are attractive to fish and the angler uses a number of caddis species as models for his artificial lures.

Caddis larva removed from its case

The eggs are laid in strings or masses which are covered with mucilage. This swells up when wetted, rather like frogspawn jelly, and protects the eggs. The eggs hatch in two or three weeks and tiny soft-bodied larvae appear. Those whose eggs were laid out of water make their way into it, simply by falling if they are on overhanging branches.

The caddis larva has a well sclerotised head and biting jaws. They are largely omnivorous in their feeding habits but some species tend to be carnivorous. The thorax is partly sclerotised and bears well developed legs, but the abdomen is soft and fleshy. Most of our caddis species use materials from the surroundings to build the familiar caddis cases which protect the soft abdomen. A gland near the mouth produces a sticky silk thread which the larva spins around itself and to which it fixes the case-building materials. Each species uses its own particularly favoured building materials: grains of sand, fragments of plant material, or even empty mollusc shells. Many species build to their own specific pattern so that it is possible to identify the species simply from its 'house'. A variety of these cases is shown in Pl. 29 from which you can see the wonderful way in which the sand grains and other fragments are cemented together to form a mosaic. As the larva grows, it adds more material to the front end of the case and often removes pieces from the hind end.

Caddis cases are always open at both ends, although the rear opening may be very narrow, and movements of the larva's body draw water through the case. In this way, the caddis gets a constant supply of oxygen which it extracts from the water through feathery gills along the sides of the body.

The head and legs protrude from the case, enabling the larva to move about in search of food. Two strong hooks at the tip of the abdomen grip the silken lining of the case and ensure that the caddis and its home do not part company. Caddis living in fast-flowing water often add larger stones to their cases, presumably an instinctive action that serves to prevent their being swept away by the current. Another 'survival trick' is shown by the caddis *Anabolia nervosa* (Pl. 28). Trout and other fishes, as well as water birds, feed readily on caddis larvae which they usually swallow case-and-all. *Anabolia*, however, attaches one or more twigs to its case and therefore cannot be swallowed. This species lives quite openly in trout streams where other species would soon be snapped up if they ventured into open water.

Not all caddis species make cases: a number make non-movable silken nets among the vegetation. The net affords a certain amount of protection but it also traps food. Clearly, these net-spinners must live in running water if food is to be carried to them in this way. Members of the genus *Rhyacophila* (Pl. 29) make neither cases nor nets but simply live among the gravels on the stream bed. The non-case-bearers have tougher bodies than those that do make cases.

Pupation takes place in the case which is previously cemented to some submerged object. Non-case-bearing larvae construct a special pupal chamber of sand in which they spin a silken cocoon for pupation.

The caddis pupa is quite active and continues the ventilation movements of the larva. It also retains the larval gills by means of which it obtains its oxygen. The pupa has free legs, antennae, and wings, and it also has a pair of large jaws. When the time arrives for the adult to emerge, the pupa becomes very active and bites its way out of the case with its jaws. It then either crawls to the surface or swims up using a pair of heavily fringed legs as oars. The adult emerges and flies away almost immediately: the wings expand very rapidly upon emergence, although they still need a period of hardening before the insects can fly well.

The newly emerged caddis flies can be seen flying in large numbers over the water, often dancing vertically in little swarms. At such times, bats and birds take a heavy toll of them. The whole life cycle takes a year, of which the greater part is usually taken up by the larval life. A few species overwinter as pupae but most pupate in spring and emerge as adults in early summer.

Caddis flies are not easy to identify because the diagnostic features are small and often covered by the hairs. However, the 14 families of European caddis may be separated with the aid of the following key and a good lens. Whenever possible, use fresh or spirit-preserved material as the legs and palps can be manipulated more easily then.

Key to the Families of European Trichoptera

1. Insects minute and hairy   Hydroptilidae, p. 202
   Insects larger and with relatively short fringes   2

2. Maxillary palps with five segments   3
   Maxillary palps with less than five segments (males)   15

3. Last segment of palp much longer than all others together   4

   Last segment of palp not or only just longer than all others together   7

4. Ocelli present   Philopotamidae, p. 202
   Ocelli absent   5

5. Anterior tibiae with three spurs   Polycentropidae*, p. 202
   Anterior tibiae with less than three spurs   6

* But see *Ecnomus tenellus*, p. 203.

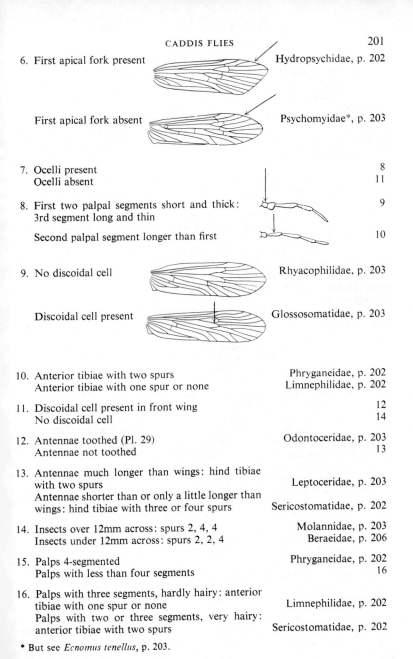

6. First apical fork present   Hydropsychidae, p. 202

   First apical fork absent   Psychomyidae*, p. 203

7. Ocelli present   8
   Ocelli absent   11

8. First two palpal segments short and thick: 9
   3rd segment long and thin

   Second palpal segment longer than first   10

9. No discoidal cell   Rhyacophilidae, p. 203

   Discoidal cell present   Glossosomatidae, p. 203

10. Anterior tibiae with two spurs   Phryganeidae, p. 202
    Anterior tibiae with one spur or none   Limnephilidae, p. 202

11. Discoidal cell present in front wing   12
    No discoidal cell   14

12. Antennae toothed (Pl. 29)   Odontoceridae, p. 203
    Antennae not toothed   13

13. Antennae much longer than wings: hind tibiae
    with two spurs   Leptoceridae, p. 203
    Antennae shorter than or only a little longer than
    wings: hind tibiae with three or four spurs   Sericostomatidae, p. 202

14. Insects over 12mm across: spurs 2, 4, 4   Molannidae, p. 203
    Insects under 12mm across: spurs 2, 2, 4   Beraeidae, p. 206

15. Palps 4-segmented   Phryganeidae, p. 202
    Palps with less than four segments   16

16. Palps with three segments, hardly hairy: anterior
    tibiae with one spur or none   Limnephilidae, p. 202
    Palps with two or three segments, very hairy:
    anterior tibiae with two spurs   Sericostomatidae, p. 202

* But see *Ecnomus tenellus*, p. 203.

The families Phryganeidae, Limnephilidae, and Sericostomatidae are included in the sub-order **Inaequipalpa** because the males have fewer segments to their maxillary palps than the females. All the other British European have the same number of palpal segments in both sexes and are included in the sub-order **Aequipalpa**.

The **Phryganeidae** contains the largest of our caddis species, *Phryganea grandis*, which has a wing span of about 50mm (Pl. 28). In this family, the antennae are stout and about as long as the front wings. The discoidal cell is closed in both wings, being particularly long and narrow in the front wing, and the tibial spurs are 2, 4, 4. The larvae all live in still or very slow-moving water and build their cases with plant material which is arranged in spiral fashion.

The family **Limnephilidae** is a large one, containing 55 British species of widely varying size. Most are pale brown with darker markings. The antennae are usually about as long as the front wings, and their basal joints are bulbous. The discoidal cell is always closed in the front wing and apical fork 4 is absent from both wings. The wings are never very hairy and the front wings show a number of clear patches. The hind wings are particularly clear. The anterior tibia never has more than one spur. *Limnephilus* (Pl. 28) is the typical genus and *Enoicyla* is very atypical as we have already seen (p. 198). The larval cases are made from various materials and are often quite large. Members of this family live mainly in slow moving water.

In the **Sericostomatidae** the antennae are moderately stout and the large basal joint is very hairy. The maxillary palps of the male are turned up in front of the face. None of the British species has any ocelli. The wings are usually very hairy and the anterior tibia always has two spurs. The larvae live in running water and build cases of various materials. The Grannom (*Brachycentrus subnubilus*) (Pl. 28) is a common species and is unusual in that it fixes its vegetable case to the vegetation and uses its comb-like middle legs to filter food from the water.

Members of the **Hydroptilidae** are very active insects and are quite unmistakable on account of their small size together with the relatively long fringes of hairs on the hind wings (Pl. 28). The fringes effectively double the width of the narrow wings. The antennae are relatively short and stout and there are no spurs on the front legs. The larvae feed on the juices of algae and make no case until the last instar, when they construct a little silken chamber, sometimes re-inforced with sand grains or plant fragments.

In the **Philopotamidae** the antennae are stout and short-jointed, but the form of the palps and the possession of ocelli should distinguish the family. The wings are either smoky brown or patterned with brown and yellow (Pl. 28). A discoidal cell is always present in both wings. The larvae are net-spinners and the family is found mainly in upland streams.

Members of the **Polycentropidae** have densely haired wings and the front wings are more rounded distally than in most other caddis flies (Pl. 28). All our species are brown or grey, marked with yellow. A discoidal cell is always present in the anterior wing but sometimes missing from the hind wing. The antennae are stout and the spurs are 3, 4, 4. The larvae are net-spinners and primarily carnivorous: *Polycentropus* species make pouch-shaped nets in which they lie waiting for anything the current carries in.

In the **Hydropsychidae** the discoidal cell of the front wing is always broad and short (Pl. 28) and the spurs are 2, 4, 4. The basal joint of the antenna is swollen. *Hydropsyche* species are somewhat unusual in flying in bright sunlight. Like the two previous families, the Hydropsychidae is found mainly in streams and rivers, for the larvae spin net-traps among the stones on the stream bed.

In the **Psychomyidae** the wings are densely haired and usually of a fairly uniform dark colour. The discoidal cell is very small in the front wing and usually absent in the hind wing. The hind wing is much shorter and narrower than the front wing and the front edge is generally cut away to some extent in the distal part (Pl. 29). The spurs are usually 2, 4, 4, except in the rare *Ecnomus tenellus* in which they are 3, 4, 4. This species also differs from the rest of the family in retaining the first apical fork. All our species are small, being less than 12mm across the wings. The larvae usually make cases but they are in the form of long galleries attached to stones and submerged logs.

The **Rhyacophilidae** contains some of the more primitive caddis flies, in the genus *Rhyacophila*. The antennae are shorter than the front wings and rather slender. The front wings are quite pointed at the distal end and contain no discoidal cell (Pl. 29). The spurs are 3, 4, 4. Adults of this genus are quite easily identified by their bright green and brown bodies. The larvae are free-living and build neither case nor net. They hunt among the stones on the beds of fast-flowing streams.

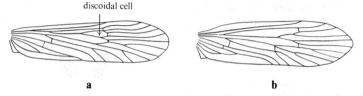

discoidal cell

a   b

Front wings of caddis flies: **a**, Glossosomatidae, showing discoidal cell; **b**, Rhyacophilidae, without discoidal cell

The **Glossosomatidae**, often regarded as a sub-family of the Rhyacophilidae, is distinguished by the discoidal cell in the front wing and by the tibial spur count of 2, 4, 4. The larvae are somewhat less carnivorous than those of the previous family. The genus *Agapetus*, which lives in fast-moving water, builds cases which are flattened on one side and domed on the other.

Odontocerum albicorne, the only British member of the **Odontoceridae**, is easily recognised by virtue of its greyish colour (fishermen call it the Grey Sedge) and toothed antennae (Pl. 29). It has a wing span of over 25mm and is found near running water where the larva makes a curved case of sand grains.

The family **Leptoceridae** is easily recognised by the antennae, which may be twice, sometimes three times as long as the front wings. The antennae are often very pale and several species are known as silverhorns. The insects are very hairy and generally dark in colour. The discoidal cell is present in the front wing but not the hind wing. The latter is much shorter than the front wing (Pl. 29) and is joined to it by a row of tiny hooks. The larvae build slender, often curved, cases of sand or plant material.

The **Molannidae** contains only two British species of which *Molanna angustata* (Pl. 29) is the commoner. The palps are very hairy and the antennae are stout and somewhat longer than the wings. The larvae live in still water and use sand grains to make very characteristic cases consisting of a central tube and a broad 'shield'.

Plate 31   **FLIES** – **Order Diptera** (Contd.)

Stratiomyidae. Feet with 3 pads: veins crowded near front of wing often metallic   p. 229
1. *Oxycera pulchella* Meigen ×3

Tabanidae – horse-flies. Feet with 3 pads: veins forming broad fork across wing tip   p. 229
Foot
2. *Haematopota pluvialis* (L.) ×3
3. *Tabanus bromius* L. ×2
4. *Chrysops relictus* Meigen ×2

Cyrtidae. Flies with bulbous bodies and very small heads: venation reduced   p. 229
5. *Ogcodes pallipes* (Latreille) ×3

Bombyliidae. Furry, bee-like flies with long thin legs and often with a long proboscis: wings often coloured   p. 229
6. *Bombylius major* L. ×2
7. *Thyridanthrax fenestratus* (Fallen) ×2

Empididae. Bristly flies, usually with a rigid proboscis, and with a little nick on the inner margin of the eye   p. 230
8. *Empis tessellata* Fabr. ×2
9. *Hilara maura* (Fabr.) ×3   eye nick

△ **Mydaidae.** Large flies with clubbed antennae   p. 231
▲ 10. *Leptomydas corsicanus* Bequaert ×1½

Scenopinidae. Small naked flies with pendulous antennae   p. 230
11. *Scenopinus fenestralis* (L.) ×3

Rhagionidae. Feet with 3 pads: body slender: legs long   p. 229
12. *Rhagio scolopacea* (L.) ×2

Therevidae. Feet with 2 pads: stout antennae: no groove between eyes   p. 230
13. *Thereva nobilitata* (Fabr.) ×2

Lonchopteridae. Small flies with pointed wings and no obvious cross veins   p. 232
14. *Lonchoptera lutea* Panzer ×4 – female (male venation differs slightly)

Asilidae. Medium or large hairy flies with strong legs: feet with 2 pads: a groove between the eyes   p. 230
15. *Asilus crabroniformis* L. ×1½   *Asilus* head

△ **Nemestrinidae.** Large-headed: several veins running parallel to hind margin of wing: often many cells near apex   p. 231
▲ 16. *Fallenia fasciata* Meigen ×2

Phoridae. Small: obvious veins only in basal part of wing   p. 232
17. *Phora aterrima* (Fabr.) ×4

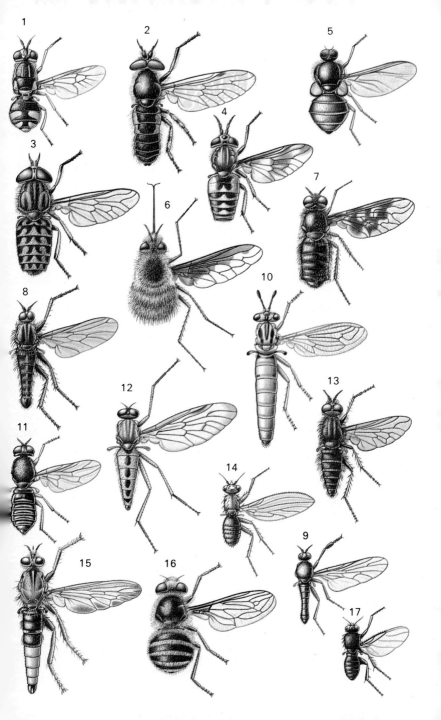

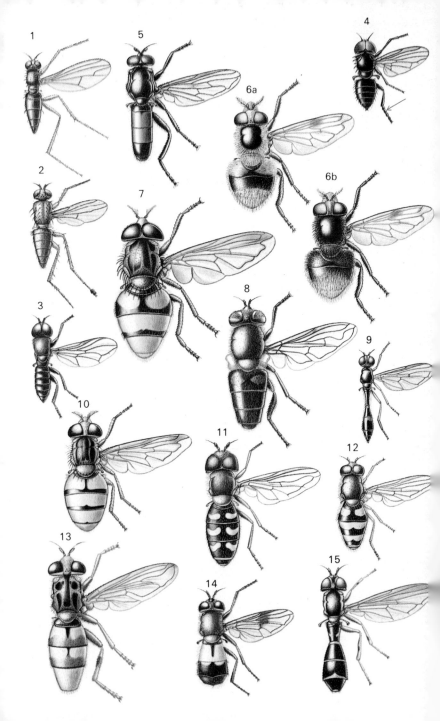

Family **Dolichopodidae**   p. 231
  Bristly metallic coloured flies with head long in profile:
  only one obvious cross vein
1. *Sciopus platypterus* Fabr. ×4
2. *Dolichopus popularis* Wiedemann ×3

Dolichopus head from the side

Family **Pipunculidae**   p. 232
  Small dark flies with an extremely large head, almost all eyes
3. *Dorilas thomsoni* (Becker) ×3

Family **Platypezidae**   p. 232
  Hind tarsal segments usually dilated
4. *Clythia atra* (Meigen) ×4

Family **Syrphidae** – hover-flies   p. 232
  Some veins running parallel to edge of wing and forming a
  false margin: often brightly coloured: eyes large

5. *Xylota lenta* Meigen ×2

6a. *Volucella bombylans* (L.) ×1½
6b. *Volucella bombylans* (L.) ×1½

7. *Volucella zonaria* (Poda) ×1½

8. *Eristalis tenax* L. ×2

9. *Baccha elongata* (Fabr.) ×2

10. *Volucella inanis* (L.) ×1½

11. *Scaeva pyrastri* (L.) ×2

12. *Syrphus ribesii* (L.) ×2

▲ 13. *Milesia crabroniformis* Fabr. ×1½

14. *Leucozona lucorum* L. ×2

15. *Doros conopseus* (Fabr.) ×2

The British members of the **Beraeidae** are all black insects no more than 12mm across. The maxillary palps are very hairy and held upright in front of the head. The antennae are about as long as the wings and quite stout. The tibial spurs are 2, 2, 4. Shallow streams and marshes are the places for this family.

Collecting and Preserving

You will find caddis flies in most places where you find stretches of water but, because most of them are nocturnal or crepuscular insects, you will have to look for them. Beating waterside vegetation and following up with a net is the best method of obtaining specimens but smaller numbers can also be found by searching tree trunks and rough walls near the water. If you live near water, a porch light left on during the evening will attract a number of caddis.

Several killing agents are useful for caddis but it is necessary to ensure that the insects do not get wet, for this spoils their hairy coats. Freshly crushed laurel is probably the best killing agent for it has the added advantage that it keeps the insects in a relaxed condition. Caddis flies dry out rather rapidly and are not easy to relax when once dry. The larger species can be pinned and set on boards but the smaller ones, and any intended for detailed study, should be preserved in spirit, for pinning damages the thoracic structures so important in critical study.

Caddis-worms are easily collected from water and most species can be kept in small aquaria, as long as they are not overcrowded. Their case-building activities can be watched in this way and information can be obtained on feeding habits. This is also a convenient way of getting cabinet specimens should one so desire. The cases can be dried when empty and kept with the adult specimens.

Order Diptera – Two-winged Flies or True Flies*

Recognition features Minute to large insects in which the hind wings are reduced to club-shaped halteres or balancers, leaving only one pair of membranous wings. A few species are completely wingless, sometimes in association with parasitic habits. Mouth-parts are always suctorial and frequently adapted for piercing.

Many flies resemble bees and wasps as a result of mimicry but such resemblances are only superficial – involving colour for example – and closer examination will reveal only two wings, clearly indicating a true fly. Some of the smaller mayflies have only two wings but they never have halteres and their 'tails' should leave you in no doubt as to their identity.

A typical two-winged fly of the sub-order Cyclorrhapha

The true flies make up a very large order with somewhere around 70,000 known species, of which about 5,200 occur in Britain. Apart from the major feature of having only two wings – hence the name of the order (Greek *di* = two) – there is little to suggest that all these insects belong to a single order. There are the stout-bodied house-flies and blow-flies or bluebottles, the hover-flies and horse-flies, the slender crane-flies and mosquitoes, and a host of smaller species commonly referred to as gnats and midges.

These insects have exploited a very wide range of food materials, from decaying matter on the one hand, to nectar or blood on the other, and the order as a whole is of great economic importance. Dung-flies and others whose larvae and adults feed on decaying matter perform a useful scavenging role in the economy of nature. Flower-feeders also act as pollinators. A number of species, such as the Carrot-fly and the ubiquitous crane-flies, are agricultural pests. But it is as enemies of man and his livestock that flies are most important. Blood-sucking flies are found in many families of the order but blood-feeding is often confined to the female of the species. The male mosquito, for example, feeds on nectar and other plant juices. The blood-sucking flies, such as the mosquitoes and tsetse-flies, are important not for the amount of blood that they take but on account of the dangerous diseases they carry; diseases including malaria, yellow fever, and sleeping sickness. The Common House-fly is not a blood-feeder and it does not attack man directly but, because of its liking for both filth and sweet things, it often contaminates human food and it has been shown to spread a number of human diseases.

* A great many insects have the word 'fly' in their common names and, to distinguish between the true flies and these other insects, we are following Oldroyd's suggestion of hyphenating the names of true flies – house-fly, dung-fly, and so on. Other insects' names are spelled without hyphens – dragonfly, lacewing fly, and so on.

Veterinary pests include the green blow-flies (*Lucilia* spp) whose maggots eat away the flesh of sheep; the wingless, blood-sucking Sheep Ked (*Melophagus ovinus*); and the warble-flies (*Hypoderma* spp) whose larvae burrow through the bodies of cattle (Pl. 34).

The head of a true fly is usually relatively large and a fair proportion of it is occupied by the compound eyes. These are generally larger in the male than in the female and sometimes meet in the mid-line – the holoptic condition. There are usually three ocelli on the top of the head – the vertex – although they are absent in some families. The region of the front of the head between the eyes and reaching down as far as the antennae is called the frons, although this does not correspond with the frons in other insects. The rest of the head, below the antennae, is called the face. The more advanced families all possess a conspicuous suture forming an inverted 'V' around the antennae. This is the ptilinal suture (sometimes called the frontal suture) and it marks the position of the ptilinum, an eversible sac used by these insects to break open their puparia (p. 213). The presence or absence of this suture is an important guide when you are trying to identify members of this order.

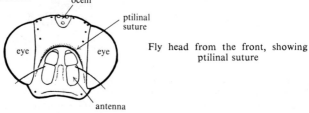

Fly head from the front, showing ptilinal suture

Among the more primitive flies – the crane-flies and gnats – the antennae are relatively long and are composed of numerous distinct and more or less similar segments. These flies are placed in the sub-order **Nematocera** which means 'thread-horns' and which refers to the long, slender antennae. In the more advanced flies, however – belonging to the sub-orders **Brachycera** and **Cyclorrhapha** – there are only two or three distinct segments, the rest being more or less fused to form a spur or a bristle. The antennal structure is very important in the classification of the Diptera.

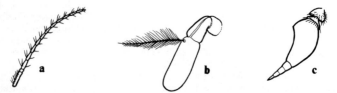

Antennae of: **a**, crane-fly; **b**, house-fly; **c**, horse-fly

The flies are all liquid feeders but even so there is great variation in their feeding habits and in the form of their mouth-parts. Even the simplest dipteran mouth-parts are a far cry from the primitive biting mouth of the cockroach (Fig. p. 17). The constant features of the dipteran feeding apparatus are the labrum, which forms the front wall or roof of the feeding channel; the hypopharynx, which

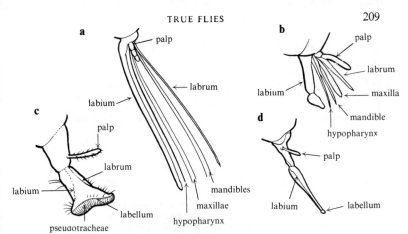

Four kinds of sucking mouths found among the Diptera: **a**, mosquito; **b**, horse-fly; **c**, house-fly; **d**, stable-fly. In the mosquito the labium acts merely as a sheath for the needle-like mandibles and maxillae which all fit together to form a sharp piercing organ. The mandibles and maxillae of the horse-fly are more blade-like, and the labium also has a 'mop' at the tip for soaking up blood that oozes from the wound. The house-fly has a fleshy proboscis, formed mainly from the labium, and it can only mop up surface liquids through the little tubes called pseudotracheae. The proboscis of the stable-fly has been modified for blood-sucking, and it has numerous small teeth on the labellum. These make a wound in the victim and the horny proboscis is then pushed in to suck up the blood

carries the salivary duct and which forms the back wall or floor of the feeding channel; and the labium. Mandibles and maxillae are present only in some of the blood-sucking flies – the mosquitoes, horse-flies, and a few others – and they are sharp, piercing organs. Maxillary palps, however, are almost always present. The labium exhibits much variation, from being little more than a sheath for the stylets of the mosquito to being the main feeding organ of the non-blood-suckers. The tip of the labium carries two lobes or labellae, small in most blood-suckers but large and spongy in the other flies and it is these that mop up their liquid food. In a number of blood-sucking species the labium, or proboscis as it is often called, is sharp and replaces the mandibles as the penetrating organ. Four of the main types of feeding apparatus are shown here and are more fully described under the relevant family. There are, however, a few groups of flies with poorly developed mouths or even with no mouth-parts at all in the adult state.

Fly head from the front to show the positions of the main bristles

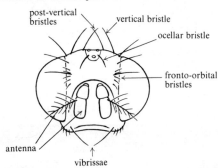

Among the higher members of the order, the head and thorax bear a number of distinct bristles, the arrangement of which is of great value in classifying and identifying the flies. Although relatively stout, these bristles break off very easily -- hence the advice to kill and pin flies as soon as they are caught. The arrangement of the main bristles of the head is shown below, although not all of them necessarily appear together. As far as the identification of families is concerned, the main bristles of the head are the post-verticals just behind the ocelli, the fronto-orbitals just in front of the eye, and the vibrissae which are large crossed bristles just above the mouth.

As would be expected, the thorax is composed mainly of the mesothorax, the prothorax and metathorax being reduced to little more than leg-bearing collars fore and aft. The upper surface of the mesothorax is clearly divided into pre-scutum, scutum, and scutellum, although the transverse suture separating prescutum and scutum is not always fully developed. There is also a post-scutellum but this, together with the metathorax, is generally hidden beneath the scutellum. On each side of the prescutum, near the front outer edge, there is usually a swelling called the humeral callus. Similar swellings often occur on the hind outer margins of the scutum and these are known as the posterior calli. The notopleura are two somewhat triangular regions of the thorax, generally evident at the ends of the transverse suture.

The figure shows the positions of the main groups of thoracic bristles. As far as identification of the insects is concerned, the main ones to look for are the dorso-centrals and the hypopleural bristles. The latter, well seen in the blow-flies

Fly thorax from the side (*top*) and from above to show the positions of the main bristles

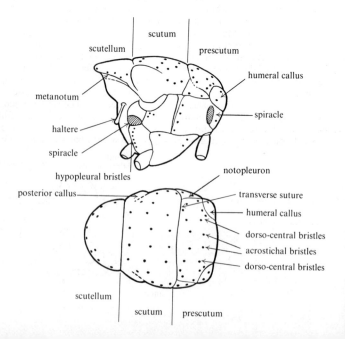

of the family Calliphoridae, stand on the hypopleuron – which is just above the coxae of the second and third legs – and form an arc bulging backwards.

Wings are present in almost all flies, the main exceptions being some of the parasites – the Sheep Ked for example. The venation is fairly complete in the crane-flies and mosquitoes and also in the horse-flies and snipe-flies (Rhagionidae) but it is reduced in most other families, many of which can be recognised by venation alone. The gall-midges of the family Cecidomyiidae, for example, have a distinctive venation – almost a non-venation (Pl. 30). Among the higher flies, however, the venation is relatively uniform and, as you will see from the keys provided later in this chapter, we must rely on other characteristics to separate these families.

Along the hind edge of the wing, close to the body, the membrane usually forms three lobes. The outer one is fairly conspicuous and is known as the alula, the middle one, known as the alar squama, is generally smaller, while the inner lobe is smaller still and quite inconspicuous in most flies. This inner lobe is attached to the side of the thorax and is known as the thoracic squama. Although small in most flies, the thoracic squamae are very well developed in house-flies and blow-flies in which they completely cover the halteres.

The halteres develop on the metathorax and are actually the highly modified hind wings. Striking proof of this relationship has been obtained with the famous *Drosophila*, well known to all who study genetics. Certain mutations are known in which the halteres develop as stunted wings. Normally, the haltere is a pin-like

The wings of: **a**, *Tipula*; **b**, *Conops*; **c**, *Musca*, showing the major features of fly venation

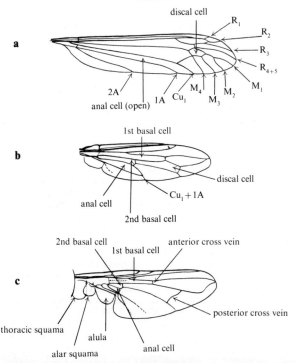

structure protruding from the thorax. It is very well seen in crane-flies (Pl. 30) but needs to be looked for in some flies, particularly those with well developed squamae. In flight, the halteres vibrate with the wings but, because of their relatively heavy heads, they continue to vibrate in the same plane even when the fly changes direction. This state of affairs produces a strain on the cuticle at the base of the halteres and the strain is detected by tiny sensory cells. Impulses sent to the brain inform the fly that it is deviating from straight and level flight and it can then make the necessary correction. The halteres therefore act just like gyroscopic balancers or stabilisers.

The various spurs and bristles on the legs play some part in the classification of the Diptera but the most important feature concerns the feet. There are normally two claws and most flies possess two pad-like pulvilli surrounding a central bristle or empodium. The major variations are the absence of the pulvilli

Feet of a horse-fly (*left*) and a house-fly, showing how the empodium may be pad-like or bristle-like

pulvillus

empodium   empodium

in many Nematocera, and the pad-like nature of the empodium in horse-flies and some other Brachycera.

The abdomen varies a great deal in size and shape among the Diptera – compare the crane-fly and the bee-fly for the two extremes – and may often give a clue to the identity of a specimen. Its anatomical details, however, are of little practical concern until one comes to identify individual species and we will say no more about it.

Most species of Diptera lay small, cigar-shaped eggs that hatch rapidly under favourable conditions to produce pale, legless larvae. There are some exceptions to the egg-laying habit, however, especially among the parasitic species of the group Pupipara (p. 242).

There is an immense range of form and habit among dipteran larvae; in fact no other insect order can approach it in this respect. There are a few straightforward phytophagous or plant-feeding families, some of which are of great concern to the farmer. Some families have parasitic larvae, affecting both vertebrate and invertebrate hosts. The great majority of dipteran larvae, however, feed on decaying matter of one sort or another. A large number of them are aquatic. Even among the terrestrial species, the larvae usually live on quite different food from the adults and it is normally only one stage in the life history that is a nuisance to us. The mosquito larva, for example, lives harmlessly in stagnant water. Adult gall-midges are tiny, insignificant insects that do no harm but some of their larvae do extensive damage to crops by inducing galls and other deformities.

Fly larvae are always legless, although there may be some fleshy stumps not unlike the prolegs of caterpillars. The larvae move about by wriggling movements, aided by the false legs and various spines if they are present. Among the lower families – the Nematocera – the head capsule is generally well developed and bears biting mouth-parts. Mosquito larvae possess a particularly well developed

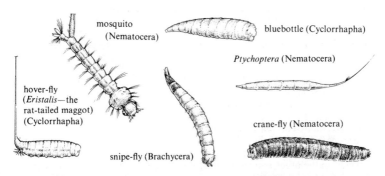

mosquito
(Nematocera)

bluebottle (Cyclorrhapha)

Ptychoptera (Nematocera)

hover-fly
(*Eristalis*—the
rat-tailed maggot)
(Cyclorrhapha)

crane-fly (Nematocera)

snipe-fly (Brachycera)

A selection of fly larvae

head capsule. In the Brachycera, the head capsule and mouth-parts are still present but there is a tendency towards the reduction of the head. The head capsule has been further reduced in the Cyclorrhapha which have mouth-parts in the form of a pair of hooks. The larvae of this group, typified by that of the House-fly are carrot-shaped maggots with few obvious external features. The front end is the narrow end.

There are generally four larval instars in the Nematocera, five to eight in the Brachycera, and only three in the Cyclorrhapha. Among the Nematocera and Brachycera, the last larval skin is cast off to reveal the obtect, but quite mobile pupa. The mosquito pupa, for example, is very mobile although the appendages are all firmly bonded to the body. Some sort of cocoon or other pupal shelter is formed by some of these insects. The mobility of the pupa enables it to position itself suitably for the emergence of the adult insect. The pupae of the cyclorrhaphous flies, however, are not free to move for they are imprisoned in the last larval skin which forms a hard, barrel-shaped puparium.

A few families of cyclorrhaphous flies, including the hover-flies, have no special apparatus for escaping from the puparium. Most of them, however, have a special balloon-like sac which they blow up and which forces the end off of the puparium. This sac is called the ptilinum and it lies within the head, its position marked by the ptilinal suture (Fig. p. 208). When the time for emergence arrives, the ptilinum expands and pushes the front part of the face forwards and downwards, thus opening up the suture for further expansion of the balloon. This further expansion breaks open the puparium and the fly escapes. The ptilinum then deflates, its function fulfilled, and the suture closes over it.

The life cycle may be extremely short, less than a week under favourable conditions, but it depends upon the species. House-flies, bluebottles, and others may have several generations in a year, even in the British climate, but many others have only a single generation and their life cycles take a whole year.

The true flies are divided into three sub-orders: Nematocera, Brachycera, and Cyclorrhapha. The Nematocera contains the most primitive of the flies and these are easily recognised by their relatively long antennae which are composed of distinct and similar segments. Nematocera means 'thread horns'. The Brachycera and the Cyclorrhapha all have short antennae and they differ mainly in the method by which the skin splits at each moult. Among the Brachycera, the split is straight or T-shaped and on the dorsal surface, but it extends all the way round the body in the Cyclorrhapha and cuts off a cap or lid. This feature does not help us to place the adult insects in their correct group and so the Brachycera and Cyclorrhapha are keyed out together. A separate key is provided for the Nematocera.

SUB-ORDER NEMATOCERA

Apart from their characteristically slender antennae, these insects are generally recognisable by their slender bodies. There are a few families in which both body and antennae are stouter than usual but these can be recognised as Nematocera by the venation. The space between veins Cu and 1A is open and always widens towards the wing margin. This space should strictly be called the cubital cell but many authors retain the older system of naming the cells and call it the anal cell. In the other two sub-orders, veins Cu and 1A converge or even meet. The cell is therefore narrowed towards the wing margin or completely closed.

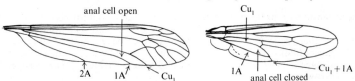

Wings of Nematocera (*left*) and Cyclorrhapha, showing the nature of the anal cell

Many Nematocera have the habit of swarming. Clouds of these insects can be seen, usually towards evening, 'dancing' up and down a few feet from the ground. These are mating swarms in which female insects are relatively scarce. As in several other groups of insects, females that approach the swarm are appropriated by males and the pairs then leave the swarm.

Key to the Major Families of British Nematocera

1. Small, very hairy moth-like flies   Psychodidae, p. 217
   Not like this   2

2. Two anal veins reaching wing margin: V-shaped
   suture on thorax   3
   One anal vein at most reaching margin: no V-
   shaped suture   4

3. Ocelli present: vein 2A
   very short   Trichoceridae, p. 216

   Ocelli absent: vein
   2A longer   Tipulidae, p. 215

4. Ocelli present   5
   Ocelli absent   9

5. Tibiae spurred at tip   6
   Tibiae without spurs   8

6. Discal cell usually present: vein Rs forks at or
   near r–m cross vein (Pl. 30)   Anisopodidae, p. 216
   No discal cell: vein Rs forks, if at all, well beyond
   r–m cross vein   7

7. Antennae short and inserted   Bibionidae, p. 220
   below the eyes

   Antennae longer, with well separated segments,
   and inserted near middle of eyes   Mycetophilidae, p. 220

8. Antennae short: wings naked and with anterior
   veins strong   Scatopsidae, p. 220
   Antennae longer, with distinct segments: wings
   fringed: venation very reduced: anterior veins not
   strong   Cecidomyiidae, p. 220

9. Ten or more veins reaching wing margin   10
   No more than eight veins reaching margin   11

10. Tibiae spurred: U-shaped suture on thorax   Ptychopteridae, p. 216
    Tibiae without distinct spurs: no such suture   Culicidae, p. 217

11. Four veins at most reaching wing margin   Cecidomyiidae, p. 220
    At least six veins reaching wing margin   12

12. Wings very broad: antennae naked   Simuliidae, p. 219
    Wings not particularly broad: antennae hairy   13

13. Front legs often longer than   Chironomidae, p. 218
    others: vein M_{1+2}
    not forked

    Front legs not longer than   Ceratopogonidae, p. 218
    others: vein M_{1+2}
    forked

The **Tipulidae** contains slender, long-legged flies popularly called crane-flies or daddy-long-legs. They can be recognised quite easily by the V-shaped suture on the thorax, together with the two long anal veins which both reach the wing margin. Other features include the ease with which the legs break off in the living insect and the possession of a discal cell. The only other Nematocera with a

head

DIPTERA

Thorax of *Tipula*, showing the V-shaped suture

discal cell are the Trichoceridae and the Anispodidae. We have close on 300 species of crane-flies in Britain, ranging in size from *Tipula maxima* (Pl. 30) which, at about 65mm wing span, outstrips all other British flies, to small gnat-like flies with wing spans of only 15mm. Swarming is not common among the larger species but is very frequent among the smaller ones. Many of the latter are known as bobbing gnats because of the way they raise and lower the body when at rest. These insects often come to light.

Larval crane-flies normally live in the soil, in decaying wood or leaf litter, or else they lead an aquatic existence among the debris on the bottom. Some of the soil-living ones – known as leather-jackets – damage crops by eating the roots. *Tipula paludosa* is one of the commonest of these pests. This is the common, grey daddy-long-legs. The adults themselves do no harm. They can only lap up liquids with their fleshy labella at the end of a beak-like extension of the head.

Closely related to the Tipulidae is the **Trichoceridae** with 10 British species. They can be distinguished from the smaller crane-flies by the short second anal vein (Pl. 30) and also because the legs are not deciduous. These insects swarm throughout much of the year, but especially in the winter months and they are therefore called winter gnats. The larvae live in decaying matter.

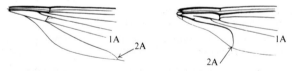

Wing bases of *Tipula* (*left*) and *Trichocera*, showing the very short vein 2A in *Trichocera* and other members of the Trichoceridae

The window-midges of the **Anisopodidae** resemble both the winter gnats and the smaller crane-flies but there is no thoracic suture in the window-midges and the second anal vein does not reach the wing margin (Pl. 30). Four of our five species possess a discal cell which, together with the lack of a suture, immediately identifies them. The common name of these insects refers especially to *Anisopus fenestralis* (Pl. 30) which very often comes into houses. The larvae generally live in decaying matter and those of *A. fenestralis* are quite common in sewage beds.

The **Ptychopteridae** is another family resembling the crane-flies but the thoracic suture here is U-shaped and there is only one anal vein. The insects are generally black with yellow markings and they have spotted wings. *Ptychoptera contaminata* (Pl. 30) is the commonest of our seven species, being abundant in damp places

head

Thorax of *Ptychoptera*, showing the U-shaped suture

throughout the summer. The larvae are aquatic and breathe through a thin whip-like extension of the body which carries tracheae (Fig. p. 213).

One of the easiest families to recognise is the **Psychodidae** which contains the moth-flies or owl-midges. We have about 70 species, all minute insects with very hairy wings which are folded roof-wise over the body when at rest. The larvae live in decaying matter, or else are aquatic and may be abundant in sewage filter beds. The family is of little importance in Britain but species of the genus *Phlebotomus*, known as sand-flies, are blood-suckers and carry a number of human and animal diseases in other countries.

Psychoda – one of the owl midges (family Psychodidae), easily recognised by the hairy wing and numerous veins. At rest, the wings are folded roof-like over the body

Most important of all nematocerous families is the **Culicidae**, containing the mosquitoes. They are slender, long-legged flies in which the veins and the hind margins of the wings are usually covered with scales (Pl. 30). The male antennae are normally feathery and the females usually possess a piercing, blood-sucking proboscis that sticks out noticeably from the front of the head.

The mosquitoes are nearly all blood-sucking insects and they are responsible for the spread of several important diseases, including malaria, yellow fever, and elephantiasis. We have about 30 species in Britain, of which *Culex pipiens* (Pl. 30) is one of the commonest, especially in buildings. Fortunately, this species rarely bites man. Our largest species, in fact one of the largest of all mosquitoes, is *Theobaldia annulata* (Pl. 30), easily recognised by the black and white banding on its legs. Its bite is quite painful and often results in blisters and severe inflammation in the victim, but it does not seem to carry any diseases. Only the female mosquitoes are blood-suckers and their mouth-parts are admirably suited for this. The mandibles and maxillae are needle-like and these are the main piercing organs. The pointed labrum and hypopharynx also enter the wound. The labrum is grooved and, together with the hypopharynx, it forms the food canal through which the blood is taken (Fig. p. 209). The hypopharynx, as usual, carries the salivary duct. All six structures are carried in a groove in the labium. The labium itself does not play any part in puncturing the skin, although its sensitive labellae may select a suitable site. Most female mosquitoes require a meal of blood before they can lay fertile eggs but some species can make do with nectar and other plant juices. These are the main foods of the male mosquitoes who lack the piercing mandibles and do not take blood.

There are two distinct groups of mosquitoes – the culicines and the anophelines. Only the anophelines, of which we have four species in Britain, are capable of transmitting malaria. This is because the malaria parasite has to undergo a period of development in the mosquito and then reach the salivary glands before it can get into another human host. The parasite is geared to do this only in anopheline mosquitoes. Although *Anopheles maculipennis* is quite common in Britain, malaria is rare here. Anopheline mosquitoes can be distinguished from culicines by their longer palps and by their position at rest.

The young stages of mosquitoes are spent in water, although many species are very particular about the type of water in which they live. The eggs are usually laid on the water surface and the females of some species, such as *Culex*, stick their eggs together to form tiny 'rafts'. The larvae have a well developed head, in which one can see the developing compound eyes of the adult, and a very broad

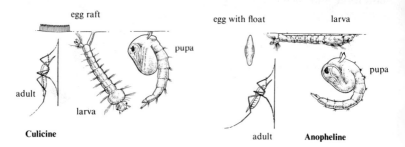

The life cycles of culicine and anopheline mosquitoes

thoracic region. They are well supplied with hairs and move with a jerking motion. They feed by wafting particles into the mouth with tufts of hair. Culicine larvae 'hang' from the water surface while anophelines rest horizontally just below the surface. This difference is associated with the positions of the spiracles – on a 're-spiratory horn' in culicines and on the dorsal body surface in anophelines. The mosquito pupa is a very active comma-shaped creature, breathing by means of a pair of respiratory horns at the back of the head.

The members of the **Chironomidae**, with about 400 species in Britain, are generally small flies in which the thorax is conspicuously humped and often conceals the head from above (Pl. 30). The male antennae are very feathery. The mouth-parts are poorly developed and the insects are not blood-feeders. Many of them do not feed at all as adults. They are known as non-biting-midges to distinguish them from the blood-sucking Ceratopogonidae but it is not easy to

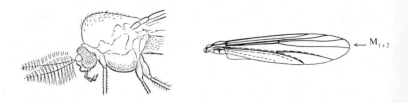

The venation of a chironomid midge and (*left*) the thorax from the side to show the marked hump overhanging the head

separate the smaller chironomids from the biting-midges. Helpful differences include the elongated front legs of the chironomids, the less marked hump of the biting-midges, and the wing venation, although the latter is not easily made out because the posterior veins are so weak. Chironomid larvae live in water or in decaying matter and one of the best known types is the blood worm (*Chironomus* spp.) which lives in the detritus at the bottom of stagnant water and which contains haemoglobin to help it obtain sufficient oxygen.

The biting-midges of the **Ceratopogonidae** are generally minute insects, rarely exceeding 5mm in length. Although so small, their bite* is intensely irritating. The insects approach and bite almost unnoticed but the irritation soon starts. In America, these insects have the amusing and very appropriate name of 'No-see-ums'. Luckily, only a few of our 130 species bite man, the commonest one being *Culicoides obsoletus*. All *Culicoides* species feed on birds or mammals but the other British genera attack other insects. Male biting-midges are unusual in that they retain the mandibles, although they are not blood-feeders. The biting-midges rest with their wings folded flat over their backs – another difference between them and the chironomids, for the latter rest with the wings held roof-wise over the body. Larval ceratopogonids live mainly in water, particularly in swamps and ditches.

forked vein M_{1+2}

A biting midge (*Culicoides*) of the family Ceratopogonidae, showing the humped thorax. Most of these insects are very small. They can be distinguished from the small chironomids by the forked vein M_{1+2}

We have 19 species in the family **Simuliidae**, all of them in the genus *Simulium*. Known as black-flies, they are rather squat flies in all their features and can be recognised by their broad wings. The females are blood-suckers and similar in effect to the biting-midges. *S. equinum* (Pl. 30) sometimes plagues horses in this country but our species are not particularly important. Elsewhere in the world, the black-flies transmit a number of human and animal diseases. The larvae live in running water, attaching themselves to stones by means of hooks and sometimes silken webs.

* We commonly talk about flies that bite but we should strictly talk of piercing flies, for none of them bites in the sense of closing two jaws together.

Members of the **Bibionidae** are rather stouter than other nematocerous flies. They are black, hairy flies and their short, stout antennae are inserted below the eyes. The tibiae bear characteristic clusters of spines (Pl. 30). The adults are often abundant on grassland, especially in the spring – they are commonly called March-flies, and they are thought to play a part in pollinating flowers. The

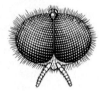

The head of *Bibio* from the front, showing the position of the antennae below the eyes

larvae live in the soil and among decaying matter, often causing some damage to plant roots. There are 18 British species, of which *Bibio marci* and *Dilophus febrilis* (Pl. 30) are particularly common.

The **Scatopsidae**, with 29 small or minute British species, is closely related to the Bibionidae but the tibiae have no spines and the body is not hairy (Pl. 30).

The **Mycetophilidae**, whose members are known as fungus-gnats because of the dominance of fungi in the larval diet, contains about 500 British species. They are very delicate flies with long, slender antennae and long legs, especially the back ones. The thorax is generally humped to some extent. The larvae are pale with dark heads and can be found in abundance in fungi. They are easy to rear if the fungus is placed on bran or sawdust into which the larvae can crawl to pupate. Species of *Sciara* (Pl. 30) often cause damage to mushroom beds.

The largest of all our nematocerous families is the **Cecidomyiidae**, with over 600 British species. These insects are the gall-midges, although not all of them actually induce gall formation. They are very delicate insects with long legs and the wings are generally hairy. The most characteristic features, however, are the bead-like segments of the antennae and the very reduced venation (Pl. 30). The gall-midges rarely exceed 5mm in length. One of our commonest gall-causing species is *Cecidomyia veronicae* which causes fluffy white galls on the shoot tips of speedwell. These galls are really clusters of swollen and deformed leaves among which the tiny orange larvae live. *Taxomyia taxi* (Pl. 30) induces galls on the tips of yew shoots. Among the non-gall-causing species, the Hessian-fly (*Mayetiola destructor*) causes much damage to wheat in Europe and America, although not to any great extent in Britain. A few species are predaceous in the larval state, feeding on other insects and mites.

Several other families of Nematocera occur on the Continent, but few of them are likely to attract attention. One exception perhaps is the **Blepharoceridae**, whose members inhabit mountainous areas. The larvae live in fast-moving streams and the emergence of the adults from the pupae is most unusual. .The pupa comes to the surface and 'explodes' – catapulting the adult fly into the air. The wings are already expanded in the pupa, although they are folded. When the insect emerges they merely unfold and the insect flies away, although its wings never lose their creases. The adults have long, slender legs. They fly rather weakly along the borders of streams. *Liponeura cinerascens* (Pl. 30) is a typical example.

Key to the major families of British Brachycera and Cyclorrhapha, based upon that given by Oldroyd in the RES Handbook but excluding certain small and/or rare families

1. Foot with three pads*   2

   Foot with two pads   5

2. Third antennal segment clearly made up of several fused parts   3

   Third antennal segment without such traces   4

3. Stoutly built flies with large squamae: veins fork to form a large 'Y' across the wing tip   Tabanidae, p. 229
   Flattened, often elongated flies with small squamae: no such 'Y' across wing tip   Stratiomyidae, p. 229

4. Stout, rounded flies with small head much narrower than thorax   Cyrtidae, p. 229
   Slender flies   Rhagionidae, p. 229

5. Frons without ptilinal suture   ptilinal suture   6
   Frons with ptilinal suture   16

basal cells

6. Anal cell long and pointed, sometimes open   7

   Anal cell short and blunt or absent   anal cell   11

7. Veins R_4 and R_5 separate   8

   Veins R_4 and R_5 fused so that the radius has only three branches   14

* A few Empididae and Dolichopodidae may have three pads.

8. Generally furry, bee-like flies with long, thin legs Bombyliidae, p. 229
 Not like this 9

9. Small, black, naked flies Scenopinidae, p. 230
 Larger, bristly flies 10

10. Flies with a distinct groove between the eyes Asilidae, p. 230

 No such groove: male eyes touching Therevidae, p. 230

11. Anterior veins very prominent and joining costa
 well before wing tip: other veins faint and parallel Phoridae, p. 232
 Venation not like this 12

12. Wings pointed Lonchopteridae, p. 232
 Wings rounded 13

        1st basal cell

13. First basal cell long Empididae, p. 230

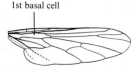

        1st basal cell

 First basal cell very short Dolichopodidae, p. 231

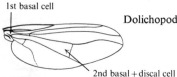

       2nd basal + discal cell

14. Wing with a 'false Syrphidae, p. 232
 margin' formed by
 veins running
 parallel to edge of wing

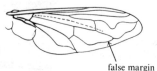

       false margin

 Veins not running parallel to edge of wing 15

15. Head very large and spherical: hind tarsi normal Pipunculidae, p. 232
 Head not particularly large: hind tarsi flattened
 and dilated Platypezidae, p. 232

16. Normal-looking flies, not flattened   17
    Abnormal, parasitic flies, flattened and often wing-
    less   46

17. Anal cell almost reaching   Conopidae, p. 233
    wing margin

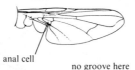

anal cell

    Anal cell short   18

anal cell

18. Thoracic squamae usually vestigial,   no groove here   19
    if developed (Fig. p. 211)
    then posterior calli are not:
    eyes always well separated:
    2nd antennal segment usually   transverse
    without a groove: suture weak
    transverse suture weak

   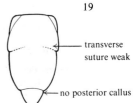

                                                               no posterior callus

    Squamae usually well   43
    developed and concealing
    halteres from above: transverse suture
    posterior calli well   groove
    marked: male eyes
    often close together:
    2nd antennal segment
    usually with a groove:
    transverse suture strong   posterior callus

                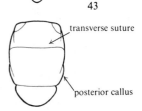

19. Mouth-parts vestigial: flies up to 20mm long   Gasterophilidae, p. 233
    Mouth-parts well developed: flies generally much
    smaller   20

†20. Costa not interrupted before tip of   break
     R₁, or if interrupted the break
     is near humeral veinlet   21
     Costa interrupted at least partially,
     usually near vein Sc   28

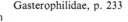
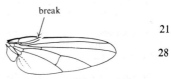

21. Legs very long and thin   Micropezidae, p. 234
    Legs normal   22

22. Small, naked, ant-like flies with rounded heads and
    constricted abdomens: often with black spot near
    wing tip   Sepsidae, p. 234
    Not fitting this description   23

† The costal breaks are not easy to see in some species and great care is needed here.

Plate 33   **FLIES – Order Diptera** (Contd.)

Gasterophilidae. Large flies with vestigial mouthparts   p. 233
1. *Gasterophilus intestinalis* (DeGeer) × 3

Conopidae. Anal cell long and pointed: proboscis long   p. 233
2. *Conops quadrifasciata* DeGeer × 3

Otitidae. Distinct grooves on face: p. 233
wings often 'pictured'   Face of *Melieria*
3. *Melieria omissa* (Meigen) × 3

Sc

Trypetidae. Wings normally 'pictured':   grooves   p. 233
vein Sc sharply angled
4. *Urophora cardui* (L.) × 4

Wing base of
Urophora

Lauxaniidae. Anal cell closed by curved   p. 234
vein (See Fig. below): post-vertical bristles converge
5. *Calliopum aeneum* (Fallen) × 4

Sciomyzidae. 2nd basal and anal cells short: tibia with pre-apical   p. 234
bristle. (See Fig. below.)
6. *Tetanocera elata* (Fabr.) × 4

Platystomidae. 'Pictured' wings: costa broken near humeral vein   p. 234
7. *Platystoma seminationis* (L.) × 4

Dryomyzidae. Large wings: 2nd basal and anal cells large   p. 234
8. *Dryomyza flaveola* (Fabr.) × 3   (See Fig. below.)

Coelopidae. Small bristly flies of the sea shore: legs stout   p. 235
9. *Coelopa frigida* (Fabr.) × 4

Psilidae. Ocellar triangle distinct: costal margin clearly broken   p. 234
10. *Psila rosae* (Fabr.) × 5

Micropezidae. Legs extremely long and slender   p. 234
11. *Trepidaria petronella* (L.) × 4

Chamaemyiidae. No costal breaks or pre-apical bristle on tibia   p. 235
12. *Chamaemyia aridella* (Fallen) × 5

Lonchaeidae. Shiny metallic flies; costa broken at tip of vein Sc: p. 234
eyes semi-circular in profile
13. *Lonchaea chorea* (Fabr.) × 4

Sepsidae. Constricted abdomen: *Piophila*   p. 234
wings often spotted near tip   head from side
14. *Sepsis punctum* (Fabr.) × 4

Piophilidae. Dark, shining: strong vibrissae: eyes   p. 234
rounded in profile: costa broken near tip of vein Sc
15. *Piophila casei* (L.) × 4 2nd basal cell

2nd basal cell

2nd basal cell

Calliopum   *Tetanocera*   *Dryomyza*
anal cell   curved vein   anal cell   anal cell

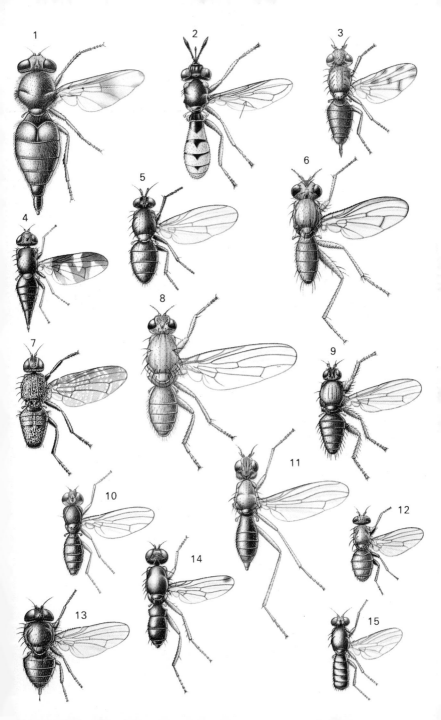

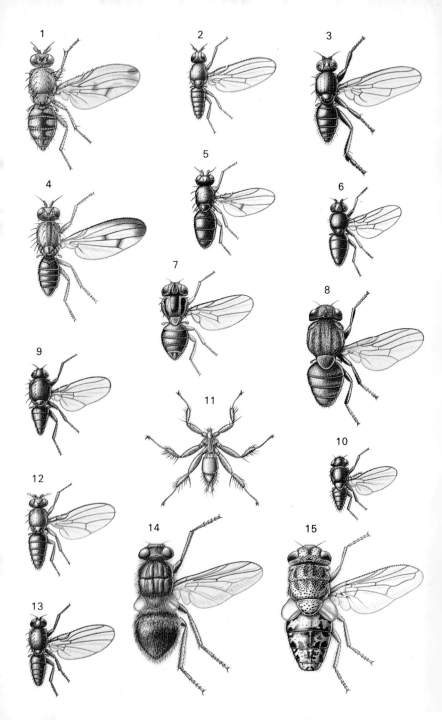

Family **Helomyzidae**   p. 235
   Costal margin strongly spined
1. *Helomyza* sp. ×4

Family **Anthomyzidae**   p. 235
   Long cilia on costal margin of wing: posterior cross vein near
   middle of wing
2. *Anthomyza gracilis* Fallen ×6

Family **Borboridae**   p. 236
   1st segment of hind tarsus short and fat
3. *Trichiaspis similis* Collin ×5

Family **Opomyzidae**   p. 236
   1st two long veins converge at tip
4. *Opomyza germinationis* L. ×6

Family **Ephydridae**   p. 236
   Small flies with two costal breaks: no anal cell
5. *Psilopa nigritella* Stenhammar ×7

Family **Chloropidae**   p. 237
   Plate-like ocellar triangle
6. *Oscinella frit* (L.) ×7
7. *Thaumatomyia notata* (Meigen) ×8
8. *Lipara lucens* Meigen ×4

Family **Milichidae**   p. 236
   Minute, dark: large wings: two costal breaks
9. *Meonura obscurella* (Fallen) ×8
10. *Carnus hemapterus* Nitzsch ×8

Family **Nycteribiidae**   p. 242
   Wingless parasites of bats: head folded back on thorax
11. *Nycteribia biarticulata* (Hermann) ×6

Family **Drosophilidae**   p. 236
   2 costal breaks: anal cell present: tibiae with pre-apical
   bristle: antennae apparently forked at tip
12. *Drosophila funebris* Fabr. ×6

Antenna of *Drosophila*

lower fronto-orbital bristles

Family **Agromyzidae**   p. 236
   Post-vertical bristles divergent: 1 costal break:
   lower fronto-orbital bristles pointing inwards
13. *Phytomyza ilicis* Curtis ×7
                            Face of agromyzid fly

Family **Oestridae**   p. 237
   Well developed post-scutellum: hypopleural bristles present
   on sides: insects softly hairy
14. *Hypoderma bovis* (L.)
15. *Oestrus ovis* L.

23. Tibiae with dorsal pre-apical bristle   24

    No such bristle   27

24. Post-verticals (p. 209) converging or crossed   25
     Post-verticals parallel or diverging   26

25. Anal cell closed by a straight vein: sea-shore flies   Coelopidae, p. 235
     Anal cell closed by a curved vein   Lauxaniidae, p. 234

curved vein

26. 2nd basal and anal cells short   Sciomyzidae, p. 234

anal cell
2nd basal cell

     2nd basal and anal cells longer   Dryomyzidae, p. 234

anal cell
2nd basal cell

27. Anal vein reaching almost or quite to wing margin   Otitidae, p. 233
     Anal vein more or less absent   Chamaemyiidae, p. 235

28. Costal break well before tip of R_1 break   29

R_1

     Costal break near tip of R_1 break   38

29. Vein Sc distinct   30
     Vein Sc vestigial or very weak   34

30. Post-verticals divergent, parallel, or absent   31
    Post-verticals convergent or crossed   33

31. Vein Sc bent sharply   Trypetidae, p. 233
    forward, almost into
    a right angle: wings
    often patterned

    Vein Sc not sharply bent, although it may be curved   32

32. Eyes semi-circular in profile   Lonchaeidae, p. 234
    Eyes circular in profile   Piophilidae, p. 234

33. Costal margin spined   Helomyzidae, p. 235
    Costal margin not spined   Chiromyiidae, p. 235

34. Anal cell present   35

    Anal cell absent   Chloropidae, p. 237

35. Vibrissae distinct   36
    Vibrissae absent: small bristles may be present
    around the mouth but then there is only one fronto-
    orbital bristle   37

36. Post-verticals divergent   Agromyzidae, p. 236
    Post-verticals convergent or absent   Anthomyzidae, p. 235

37. First two long veins of wing converge   Opomyzidae, p. 236
    Veins not converging   Psilidae, p. 234

38. One or more lower fronto-orbital bristles   39
    directed inwards

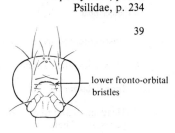

    None of these bristles pointing inwards   40

39. Costa interrupted once   Agromyzidae, p. 236
  Costa interrupted twice   Milichidae, p. 236

40. Posterior metatarsus short and thick Borboridae, p. 236
  Posterior metatarsus not like this   41

41. Anal cell present   Drosophilidae, p. 236
  Anal cell absent   42

42. Costa with only one break   Chloropidae, p. 237
  Costa with two distinct breaks   Ephydridae, p. 236

43. Mouth-parts small, usually functionless: flies more
  or less covered with soft hair   Oestridae, p. 237
  Mouth-parts usually well developed: flies with
  bristles   44

44. Hypopleural bristles present   45

  No hypopleural bristles   Muscidae, p. 239

45. Post-scutellum strongly developed Tachinidae, p. 238

Calliphoridae   Tachinidae

  Post-scutellum weak or absent Calliphoridae, p. 238

46. Insects less than 1.5mm long: wingless parasites of
  bees   Braulidae, p. 235
  Insects larger   47

47. Head small and folded back on to thorax: wingless
  parasites of bats   Nycteribiidae, p. 242
  Head larger and not folded back on to thorax:
  sometimes winged   Hippoboscidae, p. 242

SUB-ORDER BRACHYCERA

The members of this sub-order are generally well built flies with short, stout antennae. The third antennal segment is often ringed and may or may not carry a bristle or spur. The brachycerous flies are in this respect intermediate between the Nematocera and the Cyclorrhapha. The larvae, too, are something of a half-way house: their incompletely developed heads link the fully developed heads of the Nematocera with the headless maggots of the Cyclorrhapha.

The structure of the feet is important in the classification of these flies and, unless otherwise stated, there are two pads (p. 212).

The family **Stratiomyidae** contains over 50 British species known as soldier-flies. They are small and medium-sized insects, rather flattened, and with bright, often metallic colouring (Pl. 31). The discal cell is small and the veins running outwards from it are rather faint. The scutellum often bears spines, although these are not present in all species. The feet have three pads. Soldier-flies are rather lazy insects and are most often found sunning themselves on the herbage. The larvae live among leaf litter and so on, or else in water. They feed on debris and probably on other small insects.

The **Rhagionidae** contains 18 British species of slender, long-legged flies known as snipe-flies. Browns and yellows are the dominant colours, as shown by the common *Rhagio scolopacea* (Pl. 31). The feet have three pads. These flies are believed to prey upon other insects, but the extent of predation is not fully established. The larvae are predatory, however, feeding upon other insects living in leaf litter and fallen trees.

The only brachycerous flies that harm man are the horse-flies and their relatives in the **Tabanidae**. We have about 30 species of these flies, all of which are heavily built with a large head and bulging eyes. The latter are well known for their iridescent colours in life. The feet have three pads and the thoracic squamae are large. The flies are readily identified, however, by the broad fork which is formed by veins R_4 and R_5 and which encloses the wing tip (Pl. 31). The male insects feed on nectar and other juices but the females are blood-suckers and inflict painful bites on man as well as on horses and cattle. The mouth-parts are basically similar to those of the mosquito (p. 217), although the stylets are broader and more blade-like in the horse-flies. The labium, however, has well developed labellae (Fig. p. 209) which are used to mop up surface fluids in addition to the blood feeds. Larval tabanids live mainly in damp soil and mud where they consume other insects and assorted small creatures.

Our three genera are represented on Pl. 31. Many people will agree that the dull grey Cleg (*Haematopota pluvialis*) is one of the most obnoxious of flies. It flies with absolute silence, selects a suitable exposed area of skin, and sinks its mouth-parts into our flesh – the first indication we have of its presence. Most flies do at least make some sort of noise as they approach and we can take evasive action, but not so with the Cleg.

The **Cyrtidae** has only three British representatives, easily recognised by their bulbous bodies and small heads (Pl. 31). Like the three previous families, they have three pads on the feet. Our species are not common but deserve mention because the larvae are internal parasites of spiders.

The members of the **Bombyliidae** well deserve their common name of bee-flies for they are nearly all stout, furry insects with a strong superficial resemblance to bumble bees. The legs, however, are long and slender. We have 12 species in

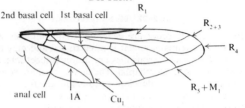

Venation of the bee-fly *Bombylius*

Britain, of which *Bombylius major* (Pl. 31) is the best known. It is commonly seen in spring, plunging its long proboscis into flowers. Although appearing to hover, the insect usually clings to the flower with one pair of legs. Not all bee-flies have long probosci. Bee-fly larvae are all parasitic on other insects, especially on solitary bees and wasps. Eggs are laid near the nests and the young larvae make their way into the nests where they attack both the food stores and the young bees or wasps.

The **Scenopinidae** is a small family represented in Britain by three species of the genus *Scenopinus*. These are small, black, bristleless flies often abundant in old buildings. The situation is especially characteristic of *S. fenestralis* (Pl. 31) which, as the name suggests, congregates around the windows. The larvae are thought to feed on the larvae of clothes moths and other similar scavenging insects, including flea larvae.

Members of the **Therevidae** are rather elongated and very hairy flies with relatively slender legs. The latter readily distinguish them from the Asilidae. The proboscis is short and bears fleshy labellae. Some species are thought to be predatory. The larvae live in soil and leaf litter and are at least partly predatory. There are 10 British species of which *Thereva nobilitata* (Pl. 31) is very common.

The **Asilidae** contains medium and large-sized flies, rather slender, yet strongly built and with very powerful legs (Pl. 31). The feet normally have two pads, although some species have none. The vertex of the head is sunk between the eyes to form a groove (Pl. 31). These insects are called robber-flies and they live on other insects of one sort or another. Some robber-flies fly in search of food but others lie in wait and pounce on their prey. The proboscis is very horny and is used to pierce the prey and suck its juices. In spite of their large size – *Asilus crabroniformis* is one of our largest flies – the robber-flies are quite harmless to man. Their larvae feed on humus and other decaying material.

The **Empididae** contains small and medium-sized bristly flies with over 300 British species. The head is more or less spherical and supported on a slender neck. There is a horny proboscis, often quite long, that is used for sucking the

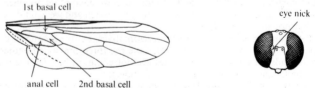

Left, the venation of an empidid fly, showing the long first basal cell. *Right*, its face, showing the characteristic eye-nick

juices of other insects – usually other flies. The feet usually have only two pads but *Clinocera* spp. have three. The most constant feature of the family, although not readily observed without a microscope, is the presence of an 'eye-nick' – a small indentation in the inner edge of each eye (Pl. 31). The larvae live in decaying vegetation or in water and are partially predatory. The adults often congregate in dancing swarms, like gnats, and are often called 'dance flies'.

In the family **Dolichopodidae** (Pl. 32) we have over 250 species of small, bristly, metallic flies with long legs. They are often called long-legged-flies. The feet usually have only two pads but some species have three. These flies can be recognised by the venation, however, only one cross vein being at all prominent. The flies prey upon other small insects which are enveloped by the fleshy labellae. The latter bear small 'teeth' in some species and the teeth help to crush the food and release the juices. The larvae live in humus or else are aquatic and they are mainly carnivorous.

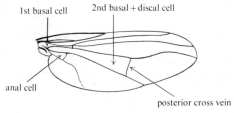

Wing of Dolichopodidae, showing the very short first basal cell and the long cell formed by fusion of the second basal and discal cells

The **Nemestrinidae** contains a number of large-headed flies, many of which have numerous cells at the apices of the wings. These flies sit on flowers and do not fly a great deal. The bee-like *Fallenia fasciata* (Pl. 31) lives in Southern Europe.

The **Mydeidae** contains a number of large and more or less hairless flies with clubbed antennae. The family is centred in the tropics and contains the largest of all flies. Four species reach Europe, *Leptomydas corsicanus* (Pl. 31) being common in Corsica. Two species live in Spain and the fourth lives in Sardinia.

There are a few other families of Brachycera on the Continent, but they are rarely met with.

SUB-ORDER CYCLORRHAPHA

These are the flies that pupate in a barrel-shaped puparium and escape through a more or less circular opening. The antennae have three segments, the third one being large and bearing a bristle. Wing venation is fairly uniform in the sub-order, and somewhat reduced. There is great variation in the size of the insects but most of them are well-proportioned if not actually stout (Fig. p. 207). The larvae of many Cyclorrhapha are known as maggots; they have no head and taper markedly towards the front (Fig. p. 213).

There are two distinct groups or series within the Cyclorrhapha: the **Aschiza**, in which there is no ptilinum; and the **Schizophora**, in which a ptilinum is used to escape from the puparium. The Aschiza is a sort of transition group between the

Brachycera and the rest of the Cyclorrhapha and its members show affinities with both groups. The Schizophora is itself divided into three groups: the **Acalypterae**, in which the thoracic squamae (or calypters) are not usually well developed: the **Calypterae**, in which the squamae are generally large and cover the halteres; and the **Pupipara**, parasitic flies whose larvae develop inside the female parent.

SERIES ASCHIZA

The family **Lonchopteridae** (Pl. 31) can be recognised at once by the pointed wings. We have only seven species, all brownish. The larvae live in leaf litter and the possession of a vestigial head indicates their relationship with the Brachycera.

The **Phoridae** contains (Pl. 31) small hump-backed flies, generally black or brownish and with a very characteristic wing venation. The front edge of the wing is usually very spiny near the base and these features together easily identify the family. The larvae generally feed in decaying material but some appear to parasitise other insects. There are more than 250 British species.

Members of the **Platypezidae** are small or medium-sized flies with relatively large wings. They are commonly known as flat-footed-flies because the hind tarsi are flattened and enlarged. This feature makes the flies easily recognisable (Pl. 32). The larvae are fungus feeders. There are 23 British species.

The **Pipunculidae** contains small dark flies with long wings that narrow abruptly towards the base (Pl. 32). The most characteristic feature, however, is the large head, composed almost entirely of the eyes. These insects, of which there are about 40 British species, rival the syrphids in hovering ability. The larvae are internal parasites of other insects, especially plant hoppers.

The hover-flies of the family **Syrphidae** are among the most striking of the Diptera because of their generally bright colours and their hovering ability. They vary a great deal in size and shape – a selection of hover-flies is illustrated on Pl. 32 – but they are easily identified by the venation. There is a 'false margin' to the wing, formed by cross vein m and M_{1+2} which bends and runs parallel with the wing margin, closing cell R_5 in the process. The true wing margin is often difficult to see. There is also a 'false vein' running between veins R and M. It is really only a thickening of the wing membrane and is not connected to any true vein. Mimicry (p. 258) is well illustrated by the hover-flies, the models being various species of wasps and bees. The large *Volucella bombylans* exists in several forms

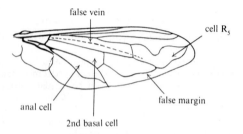

The venation of a hover-fly, showing the false margin and the false vein

and actually mimics several species of bumble bee. Hover-fly larvae are very varied in their habits: some live on growing plants, including fungi; others feed on decaying wood; many are predatory and are economically important on account of the numbers of aphids they consume; some live as scavengers in the nests of bees and other social insects, feeding on debris and on dead and dying insects; some live in water, feeding on the organic sediments. Among the last group is the Drone-fly, *Eristalis tenax* (Pl. 32), whose larva has a long telescopic breathing tube and is known as a 'rat-tailed maggot' (Fig. p. 213). There are about 250 British species of hover-fly.

SERIES SCHIZOPHORA – ACALYPTERAE

These are the flies in which the thoracic squamae or calypters are usually poorly developed and in which the thoracic suture is generally weak or absent. The posterior calli are poorly developed and there is no distinct groove on the antenna. With the notable exception of the bot-flies, most of these insects are very small.

transverse suture weak

no groove here

Thorax and antenna of typical acalypterate fly

no posterior callus

Members of the **Gasterophilidae**, known as bot-flies, are among our largest flies. The mouth-parts are vestigial and the squamae are very small. The larvae are parasites of horses and other equines and the adults, although they do not bite, seem to upset their hosts far more than the biting horse-flies. Eggs are laid on the host's body, usually on the front legs, and the larvae are licked off when they hatch. They find their way into the horse's stomach and attach themselves to the lining by their mouth-hooks. They feed there for about nine months and then pass out with the faeces to pupate in the ground. Heavy infestations of bot-fly larvae produce serious loss of condition in the host and may open the way for secondary infection of the stomach. *Gasterophilus intestinalis* (Pl. 33) is the commonest of our four species.

The **Conopidae** may be distinguished from other Schizophora because the anal cell reaches almost or quite to the wing margin (Pl. 32). They are small or medium-sized insects, often with marked resemblances to solitary bees and wasps. The head is as wide as or wider than the thorax and there is usually a slender, jointed proboscis. The antennae in some species are long, forward-pointing, and clubbed. The adult flies feed on nectar but the larvae are internal parasites of bees and wasps.

There are several small families with 'pictured' wings – spotted or marked with dark areas. Two main ones are the **Otitidae** and **Trypetidae**. Vein Sc in the Trypetidae is sharply elbowed and fades away towards the wing margin (Pl. 33). The families can also be distinguished by the pronounced grooves on the face of the otitids. The Otitidae has about 20 British species, most of which slowly move their wings up and down when at rest. This 'wing waving' occurs in several other families. The larvae of the Otitidae live in decaying matter. The **Platystomidae** (Pl. 33) is often regarded as part of the Otitidae and it has not been separated from them in the key, but differs in having a break in the costa near the humeral veinlet.

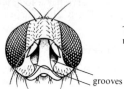

The face of *Melieria omissa*, showing the pronounced grooves characteristic of the Otitidae

The Trypetidae contains more than 70 British species whose larvae are plant feeders and often cause gall formation. *Urophora cardui* (Pl. 33) causes woody galls in thistle stems. The Mediterranean Fruit-fly, *Ceratitis capitata*, attacks fruit of various kinds and is a serious pest in European orchards. *Philophylla heraclei* is the Celery-fly whose larvae mine celery leaves and other umbellifers.

Members of the **Piophilidae** are small shiny flies in which vein Sc is very close to R_1 (Pl. 33). The head bears very prominent vibrissae. The larvae are scavengers and are particularly attracted by protein-rich foods such as carrion. *Piophila casei* is the Cheese-skipper whose larvae often infest stored cheese and bacon. There are eight other British species.

The **Lonchaeidae** contains 11 British species of small metallic flies with clear, rather broad wings (Pl. 33). There is a marked break in the costa near vein Sc. The larvae feed on a variety of living and dead vegetable matter.

The families **Lauxaniidae**, **Dryomyzidae**, and **Sciomyzidae** contain between them about 100 British species of small or medium-sized flies, all fond of damp places. Many of them have pictured wings (Pl. 33). The converging post-vertical bristles will separate the Lauxaniidae but the other two families, both with rather large wings, are not so easy to distinguish. Useful pointers include the conspicuous, forward-pointing antennae of many Sciomyzidae and the generally longer anal cell in the Dryomyzidae. Most of the larvae live in decaying matter on land or in the water, but those of the Sciomyzidae are parasitic in slugs and snails.

The **Micropezidae** contains small or medium-sized slender flies with long legs and wings (Pl. 33). They are commonly called stilt-legged-flies and they prey on other insects. The larvae live in humus. There are nine British species, none of them common.

The **Psilidae** contains small and medium-sized flies that are not unlike those of the Sepsidae. They differ, however, in possessing a costal break and a cross-fold – a pale streak running backwards across the wing from the costal break (Pl. 33). The larvae feed on plants and the most important of our 28 species is the Carrot-fly, *Psila rosae*. The maggots feed in the roots of carrots and other umbelliferous crops. The presence of the insects can often be detected by the rusty appearance of the leaves.

The **Sepsidae** contains small, dark, ant-like flies, the resemblance being due to the constriction of the abdomen at the base. The head is more or less spherical and the legs of the males are frequently deformed and spiny. There is often a dark spot towards the tip of the wing (Pl. 33) and wing-waving is common in this family. The adults often occur in vast swarms, running about over the vegetation – the writer has counted more than 50 on a single bramble leaf and this sort of density was maintained over several square yards. The larvae live in decaying matter and the swarm mentioned above was near a farmyard manure heap. There are 23 British species.

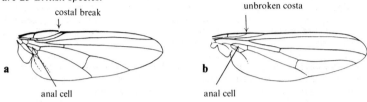

Wings of **a**, Lonchaeidae; **b**, Sepsidae, showing differences in venation

Members of the **Chamaemyiidae** are small greyish flies, easily recognised by the very characteristic venation – the great thickening of the anterior veins and the lack of the anal vein (Pl. 33). The larvae are largely predatory, feeding on aphids and scale insects. Most of our 13 species are to be found among damp grass.

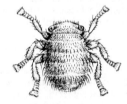

Braula coeca, the bee-louse

The **Braulidae** are very abnormal flies, minute in size – less than 1.5mm long – and living as ectoparasites of bees. The adults are like the Pupipara but they lay eggs. The larvae consume wax and stored pollen in the bee's nest. The only species is the Bee-louse, *Braula coeca*.

The **Coelopidae**, known as kelp-flies because the larvae feed on stranded sea-weed, are small or medium-sized flies. They are rather hairy and flattened and may be distinguished from similar families by the straight, not bowed vein closing the anal cell (Pl. 33). There are seven British species, often found swarming on the sea shore.

Members of the **Helomyzidae** are minute, small, or medium-sized flies, brownish yellow in colour. They are easily identified by the small spines scattered at intervals all along the costal margin (Pl. 34). The larvae are carrion feeders mainly but dung and rotting vegetable material are also used. The **Chiromyiidae** is a rather similar family but lacks the costal spines.

The **Anthomyzidae** are small, slender flies with relatively narrow wings (Pl. 34). Most of them are less than 3mm long. The long costal cilia and the rather central position of the posterior cross vein should identify the family. The larvae develop in the leaf sheaths of reeds and rushes and the insects are therefore found mainly in marshy places. There are 16 British species.

The **Opomyzidae** are all small flies with spotted wings (Pl. 34). They resemble the Psilidae and Anthomyzidae in many respects but are easily separated by the apical convergence of the first two long veins. The larvae live in the shoots of grasses, including cereals. There are 13 British species.

Members of the **Ephydridae** are all minute or small insects. Their common name is shore-flies because they are frequently found on the sea shore and around the edges of lakes and ponds. The wing venation is characteristic: two costal breaks, and the second basal and discal cells joining to form one long cell (Pl. 34). Adults are predatory in some species, otherwise feeding mainly on decaying matter. The larvae include leaf miners and predators as well as detritus feeders both in water and on land. There are more than 120 species in Britain.

The **Borboridae** contains minute or small dark flies with short, fat hind metatarsi. There are about 100 British species and they can often be recognised because some of the posterior veins frequently stop short at the posterior cross vein, or continue to the wing margin only as faint traces (Pl. 34). The adults often visit animal droppings in large swarms and they lay their eggs there.

The **Drosophilidae** contains minute and small yellowish flies whose main claim to fame lies in the Vinegar-fly *Drosophila melanogaster*. This species, usually abbreviated simply to *Drosophila*, is the geneticist's main tool. The large salivary gland chromosomes and the short life cycle make this fly ideal for genetical work. The whole family is attracted by fermenting materials and they are commonly called fruit-flies on account of their liking for rotting fruit. They sometimes plague jam factories and similar places. Members of this family can be recognised by the apparent forking of the antennal bristle (Pl. 34) and by the venation; the second basal and discal cells are usually joined but, unlike the Ephydridae and Chloropidae, there is an anal cell. There are two costal breaks. Most larvae feed upon rotting vegetable matter but a few species are predatory or parasitic. There are 31 British species.

Members of the **Agromyzidae** are minute or small flies, looking like miniature house-flies at first sight (Pl. 34). The venation is rather varied and it is not easy to recognise the family. The larvae, however, are all leaf miners and it is usually possible to breed out the flies from their mines. Each species has a more or less characteristic mine and tends to keep to one particular group of plants such as grasses. One of the commonest mines is that of *Phytomyza ilicis*, an irregular yellowish blotch on holly leaves. There are about 90 British members of the family.

inward pointing bristles

Head of agromyzid fly, showing inward-pointing lower fronto-orbital bristles

The family **Milichidae** contains minute or small blackish flies with quite large wings (Pl. 34). There is a marked costal break near the tip of vein R_1. There is usually a long, jointed proboscis, although *Carnus hemapterus* has a short proboscis which is used for sucking the blood of various host birds. The larvae of this species live among the debris in the host's nest and the emerging adults attach themselves to young birds in the nest. The flies then break off their wings. Other larvae in the family live in decaying matter and a few live in ants' nests. There are 26 British species.

Members of the **Chloropidae** are readily recognised by the greatly enlarged ocellar triangle that occupies most of the frons area (Pl. 34). The venation is reduced, there being no anal cell. All the species are minute or small, dark in

Wing of chloropid fly, showing lack of anal cell

no anal cell

colour, and with brilliantly coloured eyes. Some larvae are predatory but the majority are plant feeders and the family includes some important agricultural pests. The Frit-fly, *Oscinella frit*, is only about 1.5mm long but causes heavy losses among cereal crops. The fly larvae burrow into the stems and the developing ears. Probably the most noticeable member of the family is the Small Cluster-fly, *Thaumatomyia notata*. This species enters houses in the autumn, often in vast numbers, for hibernation. There are more than 80 British species in the family.

SERIES SCHIZOPHORA – CALYPTERAE

These are the flies in which the thoracic squamae are normally well developed and conceal the halteres. Some members of the family Muscidae have vestigial squamae but are distinguished from the Acalypterae by the complete dorsal suture and the well developed posterior calli.

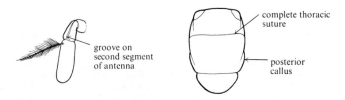

groove on second segment of antenna

complete thoracic suture

posterior callus

Antenna and thorax of typical calypterate fly

The **Oestridae** (Pl. 34) is closely related to the Tachinidae and contains a number of stout, rather fluffy flies whose larvae are internal parasites of mammals. Among the species are the notorious warble-flies, *Hypoderma bovis* and *H. lineatum*, and the Sheep Nostril-fly, *Oestrus ovis*. The Warble-fly lays its eggs on the legs of cattle and the larvae bore in through the skin. They then work their way through the body and end up just under the skin on the host's back.

The larvae are then fat and spiny and they make a small breathing pore in the host's skin. The tissues around the larvae become swollen and inflamed and produce the 'warbles'. The irritation causes the cattle to lose condition and the damage to the skin also means that the hides are of little value. When fully grown, the larvae drop out of their warbles and pupate in the soil. The adults do not feed and have a relatively short life.

The Sheep Nostril-fly undergoes a similar life history but it passes its larval life in the nasal cavities and sinuses of sheep, causing a good deal of distress to the host animal. Symptoms include nasal discharge and giddiness.

The **Tachinidae** is a large family containing over 250 British species. Most of them are medium-sized insects with sombre colouring and a strongly developed post-scutellum (Pl. 35). The larvae are all internal parasites, mainly of other insects, and their behaviour is very much like that of the ichneumon flies (p. 263) in that they attack the non-essential organs of the host first and kill it only when they themselves are fully grown and ready to pupate. The main hosts among insects are butterflies and moths, but nearly all the orders with large insects are liable to attack. Tachinid larvae get into the hosts in one of several ways: the female parasite may pierce the host and lay inside it; eggs may be laid on or near the host and the larvae then bore their way in; or eggs may be laid on the host food plant and not hatch until eaten by the host.

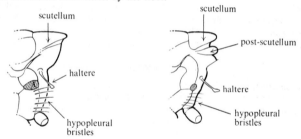

Thorax of Calliphoridae (*left*) and Tachinidae, from the side to show the hypopleural bristles. The tachinid flies also exhibit a well-developed post-scutellum

The **Calliphoridae** (Pl. 35) is another large family and one whose members are often very common and well known. They are the blow-flies – also called bluebottles and greenbottles according to their colour – and the flesh-flies, together with some lesser-known groups. They are generally medium-sized flies, recognised by the hypopleural bristles and the poorly developed or non-existent post-scutellum. The adults are surface-feeders and their mouth-parts are much the same as those of the house-fly (p. 239). Carrion and other decaying matter are the main larval food materials but some species are parasites or blood-suckers.

The commonest bluebottle is *Calliphora vomitoria*, the large buzzing insect that so often comes into houses in the summer in search of a juicy joint in which to lay its eggs. Although its buzzing makes it more irksome than the house-fly, it is less dangerous because it is less attracted to our foodstuffs. It is usually only the female flies that come indoors: the males prefer flowers. The true greenbottles are species of *Lucilia* but there are several other metallic green flies that may be mistaken for them. Most of these other flies are in the Muscidae and can be distinguished by their lack of hypopleural bristles. *Lucilia* does not often come indoors, although it may show interest in the dustbin if scraps of meat are thrown there. Dead animals are the main egg-laying sites but *Lucilia* is a serious problem in sheep-raising areas. The female lays her eggs in sores or cuts in the sheep's skin and the larvae develop there, eating the sheep's flesh away with alarming rapidity. Other common members of this family include the Flesh-fly, *Sarcophaga carnaria*, in which the eggs hatch before they are laid, and the Cluster-fly, *Pollenia rudis*. The latter species comes into houses in large numbers in the autumn and hibernates in attics and roof-spaces. It is recognisable by the furry golden hair on the thorax. The larva of this species is a parasite of earthworms. The family has nearly 100 British species.

The **Muscidae** may be distinguished from the similar, but generally larger Calliphoridae by the absence of hypopleural bristles. Among our 500 or more species there is a very wide range of appearance and habit and the family is often broken down into smaller ones. This is particularly so with the dung-flies and others of the sub-family **Cordilurinae** which, with their reduced thoracic squamae, form a link between the Acalypterae and the Calypterae. One of the commonest members of this sub-family is *Scatophaga stercoraria*, the predatory Yellow Dung-fly (Pl. 35) that is a frequent visitor to cow dung for both egg-laying and catching its prey. Not all the species are predatory, however. The larvae include dung-feeders and plant-eating species.

The rest of the Muscidae are more closely related to each other. There are surface-feeders, blood suckers, and predatory species among the adults, while the larvae exist in decaying matter or on living plants. Many species are agricultural pests. A selection is shown in Pl. 35.

The Common House-fly, *Musca domestica*, is the commoner of the two flies occurring regularly indoors. It belongs to the sub-family **Muscinae**, characterised by the converging of the second and third long veins – R_{4+5} and M_1. The other household fly is the Lesser House-fly, *Fannia canicularis*, in which the veins do not converge. *Musca domestica* is one of the most widely spread of all animals, having followed man to all parts of the world. It does not bite us but, as a result of its liking for almost any organic material, it carries a good many germs around and many of them land on our food and reach our digestive and respiratory systems. Its world-wide distribution and huge numbers make it one of the world's worst pests. The feeding apparatus consists largely of the labium which forms a retractable proboscis. The labellae are large and fleshy and traversed by numerous fine canals known as pseudotracheae. When the fly feeds, it pushes out the proboscis and places the labellae on the food surface. Saliva then runs out through the canals and its enzymes begin to break up the food. The partially digested, liquid food is then sucked up. The fly often regurgitates some of its previous meal when feeding and this is one of the main ways in which germs are carried to our food. Some are also carried on the legs of the insects. House-fly eggs are laid in decaying material – rubbish dumps and manure heaps are particularly favoured – and they develop in the normal way. Under warm conditions, the whole life cycle may be complete in two weeks. Covering breeding sites with soil is one of the best ways of reducing the house-fly population.

Another common fly in the Muscidae is the Stable-fly, *Stomoxys calcitrans*. It looks reasonably like a house-fly but it bites. Its usual victims are cattle and horses but it will bite man. The labium is a rigid, non-retractile proboscis which is

Plate 35   **FLIES – Order Diptera** (Contd.)

Family **Tachinidae**   p. 238
Fan of hypopleural bristles on side: well developed post-scutellum

1. *Larvaevora fera* (L.) × 2

2. *Gymnochaeta viridis* (Fallen) × 2

3. *Salmacia divisa* (Meigen) × 2

4a. *Alophora hemiptera* Fabr. male × 2
4b. female × 2

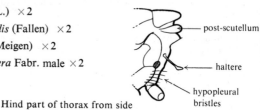

Hind part of thorax from side

— post-scutellum

— haltere

hypopleural bristles

Family **Calliphoridae**   p. 238
Fan of hypopleural bristles on side: post-scutellum very small or absent

5. *Lucilia caesar* (L.) × 2

6. *Calliphora vomitoria* (L.) × 2

7. Cluster-fly – *Pollenia rudis* (Fabr.) × 3

8. *Sarcophaga carnaria* (L.) × 2

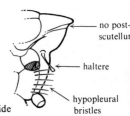

Hind part of thorax from side

— no post-scutellum

— haltere

hypopleural bristles

Family **Muscidae**   p. 239
No fan of hypopleural bristles on side: halteres usually concealed by thoracic squamae (not in dung flies): posterior calli well developed (Fig. p. 237)

9. *Scatophaga stercoraria* (L.) × 2 – one of the dung flies

10. *Mesembrina meridiana* (L.) × 2

11. Stable-fly – *Stomoxys calcitrans* (L.) × 2

12. *Dasyphora cyanella* (Meigen) × 2

13. House-fly – *Musca domestica* L. × 2

Family **Hippoboscidae**   p. 242
Head sunk back into thorax: wings often reduced or absent: large claws   p. 242

14. *Hippobosca equina* L. × 2

15. Sheep ked – *Melophagus ovinus* (L.) × 3

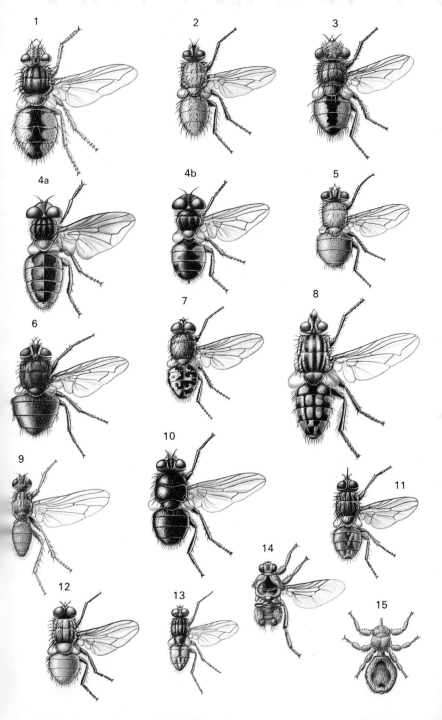

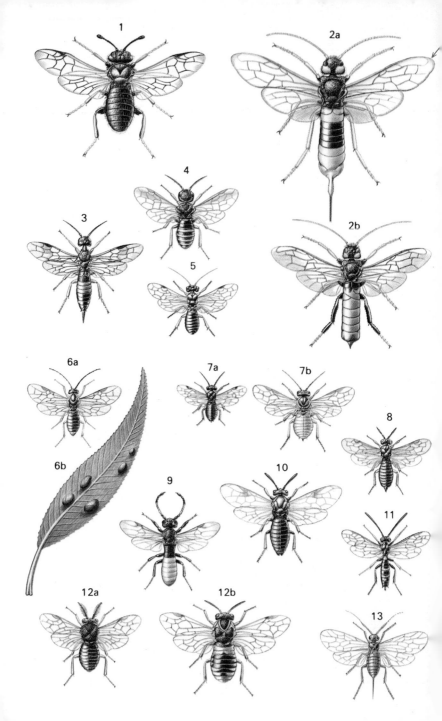

ORDER HYMENOPTERA

Plate 36

Insects in which the wings, when present, have large cells

SUB-ORDER SYMPHYTA – SAWFLIES

Body without a marked 'waist'   p. 251

Cimbicidae. Strongly clubbed antennae   p. 254
1. *Trichiosoma tibiale* Stephens

Siricidae. Large, cylindrical: with vein Rs recurved at tip   p. 253
2a. *Urocerus gigas* (L.) – female
2b. male

Xiphidriidae. Cylindrical: vein Rs not recurved at tip   p. 254
3. *Xiphydria prolongata* (Geoffroy) ×1¼

cross vein 2r

△ **Megalodontidae.** Flattened: flabellate   p. 253
   antennae: cross vein 2r present
▲ **4.** *Megalodontes klogi* Leach ×1¼

   Front wing and antenna (with
   enlargement) of *Megalodontes*

Pamphilidae. Flattened: thread-like antennae of 11+ segments   p. 253
5. *Pamphilus sylvaticus* (L.) ×1¼

Tenthredinidae. Antennae normally with 9 segments   p. 254
6a. *Pontania proxima* (Lepeletier) ×1½
6b. Bean galls caused by this species on willow
7a. Gooseberry sawfly – *Nematus ribesii* (Scopoli) – male ×2
7b. female ×2

△ **Blasticotomidae.** Antennae with 4 segments (4th minute): pear-   p. 253
   shaped cell in wing
▲ **8.** *Blasticotoma filiceti* Klug. ×1½   Head of *Orussus*

△ **Orussidae.** Antennae inserted below eyes: no   p. 253
   closed submarginal cells in hind wing
▲ **9.** *Orussus abietinus* Scopoli ×2   antenna

Argidae. Antennae with only 3 segments, the last very long   p. 254
10. *Arge ustulata* (L.) ×1½

Cephidae. No cenchri: body very slender   p. 254
11. *Cephus pygmaeus* (L.) ×1½

Diprionidae. ♂ antennae feathered, ♀ lightly toothed: cross vein 2r   p. 254
   absent: large open cell below stigma
12a. *Diprion pini* (L.) – male ×1½   open cell
12b. female ×1½   Front wing of *Diprion*

Xyelidae. Tiny: thread-like flagellum beyond 3rd antennal seg-   p. 253
ment
13. *Xyela julii* (Brébisson) ×4

able to pierce the skin of the victim and withdraw blood (Fig. p. 209). Both sexes are blood feeders in this and related species.

The flies in this group are all parasites of birds and mammals and they show many modifications associated with this way of life. The wings are often reduced or absent altogether and the insects possess well developed claws with which they cling to hair and feathers. The body is flattened and leathery. The mouth-parts are not unlike those of *Stomoxys* but they are more slender and the bite of these insects – although they rarely bite man – is less painful. Both sexes take blood. The group name derives from the life history. The female periodically brings forth a single larva which is almost fully grown before it is born and which pupates almost immediately.

The **Hippoboscidae** (Pl. 35) is represented in Britain by nine species, parasitic on birds and large mammals. *Hippobosca equina* is the Forest-fly, a winged species particularly common on ponies and cattle in the New Forest region. *Lipoptena cervi* is the Deer-fly, affecting our various species of deer. The species is winged when it first emerges but sheds its wings on finding a suitable host. The Sheep Ked, *Melophagus ovinus*, is completely wingless and often wrongly called the Sheep Tick. It does not do much direct harm to the sheep on which it lives but the sheep often scratch the irritation and open up the way for *Lucilia* and other infections.

The **Nycteribiidae**, of which we have only two species, are minute wingless parasites of bats. They can be distinguished from the previous family by their relatively longer legs and by the way in which the head folds back into a groove in the thorax.

A few other families of Diptera – mainly acalypterate insects – occur in Southern Europe, but they are all rather small and are unlikely to be collected by the non-specialist.

Collecting and Preserving

The larger flies, such as horse-flies and hover-flies, can be stalked individually and taken with a normal 'butterfly net' but sweeping is the best way to obtain the smaller species that do not fly much. Bear in mind the delicate bristles on which identification depends and make only one or two sweeps before examining the net. Flies in the net while it is being swept through the herbage will soon be damaged. Specimens intended for the collection should be killed right away and pinned or packed in cellulose wadding – not cotton wool. This treatment minimises the risk of broken bristles. Ethyl acetate is the recommended killing agent because it induces the dying flies to extrude their mouth-parts and genitalia and so makes identification easier. Laurel leaves are also useful, but most other killing agents will do if the insects are to be pinned straight away. Do not allow the specimens to get wet.

The method of display depends very much on the size of the flies. Large ones can be pinned, usually through the thorax and to one side of the middle line. The smaller flies can be mounted on points but those with long legs – the crane-flies and other Nematocera – are best carded.

Order Siphonaptera – Fleas

Recognition features Small wingless insects, flattened from side to side and living ectoparasitically on mammals and birds. Generally brownish in colour. Mouthparts adapted for blood-sucking.

Fleas are readily distinguished from other orders of insects on account of their lateral compression.

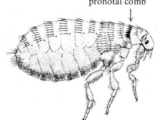

pronotal comb

The common cat flea, *Ctenocephalides felis*

This is a relatively small order, with about 1,400 known species. Of these, about 60 are established in the British Isles, although not all are natives. Adult fleas show no obvious connection with any other insect order but specialisation for a parasitic life can be held responsible for removing any similarities there might have been. The larvae, however, are not parasitic and show a number of similarities with certain fly larvae. Fleas are clearly related to winged insects and current ideas indicate a relationship with the scorpion flies (Mecoptera).

The whole life cycle is spent in the vicinity of the host but only the adult fleas are actually parasitic and even these leave their hosts from time to time. There is thus less of a bond between the flea and its host than there is between the louse and its host, and host-specificity is much less marked among the fleas. Flea larvae live on detritus, including the droppings of their parents, in the nest or home of the host and they require rather precise conditions. What host-specificity there is among fleas is therefore controlled more by the homes and nesting habits of the hosts than by the nature of their blood. Many flea species will feed on a variety of host animals but they can breed only when they meet one with suitable nesting habits. Fleas are therefore not regularly associated with nomadic animals. Apes and monkeys are basically nomadic and, although often acquiring fleas of one sort or another, have none they can call their own. It seems that man, too, was flealess until he abandoned his nomadic ways and began to settle down. The so-called 'Human Flea', *Pulex irritans*, is primarily a parasite of foxes, badgers, and other hole-dwelling animals and was not introduced to man until he began to live in caves. About 95 per cent of known fleas are parasites of mammals and the remaining 5 per cent are associated with birds.

Fleas are small insects, ranging from about 1mm to 8mm in length. The largest British representative is the Mole Flea, *Hystrichopsylla talpae*, which reaches about 6mm. The characteristic lateral compression of the flea facilitates its movement through fur or feathers and enables it to escape the attention of the host (and the fingers of the would-be flea-catcher). Compare this action with that of the louse which sits tight and resists detachment by being closely pressed against the skin. Fleas are well known for their jumping powers – long-jumps of more than 30cm have been recorded for *P. irritans* – but while actually on the host they usually walk (scuttle is perhaps a better word), aided by strong claws that grip the hairs or feathers, and numerous strong, backward-pointing bristles that prevent them from slipping backwards on a vertical surface. On the sides of the head and on the pronotum the spines are often very stout and form the genal and pronotal combs which are useful in identifying certain species. The whole body is strongly sclerotised, hence the difficulty of squashing these insects.

The head, which is not distinctly separated from the thorax, is strongly hypognathous and carries two short, stout antennae partially concealed in grooves. Eyes may or may not be present and are often vestigial. The mouth-parts are adapted for blood-sucking and the piercing stylets are the modified maxillae and epipharynx. The maxillae have serrated edges and their inner surfaces are grooved. They fit tightly together to form a narrow canal through which saliva is ejected. The epipharynx is grooved on its lower surface and the two maxillae fit closely against it to form a second canal through which blood is drawn from the host. The labial and maxillary palps cover the stylets when they are not in use but play no part in the actual penetration of the host's tissues. This is done by the saw-edged maxillae which carry the epipharynx in with them.

The three thoracic segments are quite distinct and the pronotum is often decorated by the pronotal comb – a row of stout spines on the hind margin. There are no wings in the adult flea but the pupae of certain species possess wing-like rudiments on the mesothorax – further evidence of a relationship with winged insects. The legs all have unusually large coxae and long, 5-segmented tarsi. The hind legs are particularly long in association with the insect's jumping abilities.

The abdomen is composed of 10 segments with the terga generally overlapping the sterna at the sides. Segments 8 and 9 are modified for reproductive functions, segment 9 of the male carrying a pair of claspers. The shape of these is very important in the specific determination of fleas and may be the only way of separating some species. The dorsal surface of segment 9 in both sexes also bears a sensory area called the sensilium. The last segment is very small and inconspicuous.

Adult fleas may lay their pearly white eggs while still on the host or they may leave and lay directly in the nest or other immediate surroundings. The result is the same because the eggs are not attached to the host and many of them will sooner or later fall off into the nest. Several hundred eggs are produced by each female flea and they normally hatch within a week or two to produce white,

A flea larva

worm-like larvae. These have neither legs nor eyes but they are equipped with biting jaws. They live by eating detrital material in the nest or home of the host and do not directly affect the host. Blood does, however, seem to be necessary for the proper development of some species and the adult fleas periodically pass undigested host blood out through the anus. The adults' droppings also contain partly digested blood and the needs of the larvae are thus well supplied. Investigation of the resting places of cats and dogs will usually reveal numerous specks of dried blood released by the fleas in this way.

The length of the larval period varies with the species and season but probably averages two to three weeks, during which time the larvae moult twice. When fully grown, the larva spins a silken cocoon among the debris. For two or three days it remains motionless in the cocoon – the so-called prepupal stage – and then moults to reveal the exarate pupa. The length of the pupal stage is also dependent upon temperature and species and it is likely that many fleas pass the winter as pupae. Mammal fleas often breed throughout the year, although the rate falls during the winter. Bird fleas, however, must restrict their breeding to the breeding season of the host – the only time that the host regularly uses a nest – and this extra problem is reflected in the relatively few flea species that parasitise birds.

Adult fleas need a mechanical stimulus to initiate their emergence from the cocoon and this is generally in the form of vibration caused by the movements of the host. This is a very neat arrangement which ensures that the fleas do not emerge to find no hosts about. If no such stimulus is forthcoming, the fleas can remain unharmed in their cocoons for many months – hence the frequent reports of houses, empty for some time, 'coming alive' with fleas as soon as they are occupied. Old birds' nests also often yield fleas when disturbed, fleas which were too late maturing to catch the departing birds.

Newly emerged fleas, or fleas that have left their hosts for any reason find new hosts primarily by detecting the warmth of their bodies. The majority of flea species will jump on to and feed from almost any host but they show a marked preference for their regular host(s) which they detect by chemical means. Fleas can go without food for quite long periods but the females require a blood meal before they can produce eggs and generally need a meal before laying each batch of eggs.

The occasional flea-bite resulting from nursing the family cat or other pet can be very irritating – more so for some people than for others – but the real problem with fleas is their ability to transmit disease. The most important of the infections spread by these insects is plague, caused by the bacillus *Pasteurella pestis*. This disease is primarily one of rats and other rodents but wherever rats live in close proximity to man there is the chance of an outbreak through rodent fleas which transfer their attention to man.

Transmission of plague may be mechanical, involving simply the contamination of the mouth-parts of the insects, or it may involve regurgitation of infected blood into the puncture. Most infected fleas develop blockages in their digestive tracts as a result of the multiplication of the bacteria and, when they try to feed, the blood simply flows back down into the host, taking with it some of the germs from the gut. Because no food can get past the blockage, the fleas become 'hungry' and try to feed more frequently than they otherwise would. The result is that plague spreads more rapidly. Murine typhus – a less severe form of ordinary typhus fever – is also carried by rodent fleas.

The identification of fleas is not easy, especially in view of their small size, but the following key will serve to separate the families occurring naturally in Britain:

1. Hind coxa with a group of short stout spines   Pulicidae
   on inner side

   No such spines   2

   spines on inside
   of hind coxa

2. Metanotum without small spines on margin   Hystrichopsyllidae

   Metanotum with very small marginal spines   pronotal comb   3

   inter-antennal
   suture

   marginal
   spines

   antenna

3. Interantennal suture strong   genal comb   4
   Interantennal suture absent   Ceratophyllidae

4. Head with vertical comb of spines below or behind
   eye (genal comb)   Leptopsyllidae
   No such comb: on bats   Ischnopsyllidae

The majority of the fleas that come to general notice belong to the **Pulicidae**. *Ctenocephalides felis* is the Cat Flea and this is probably the most numerous of all domestic fleas, although the Dog Flea, *C. canis*, is often quite common. It is quite usual to find cat fleas on dogs and vice versa and both species are ready to bite man whenever the opportunity arises. They breed very rapidly in warm weather and control methods involve treatment of animals with a suitable insecticide and regular cleaning of their sleeping quarters to destroy the larvae. *C. canis* is a vector of the Dog Tapeworm *Dipylidium caninum* which can also affect man. The larval fleas are infested with tapeworm eggs from the host's nest and the early stages of tapeworm development take place in the flea. The worms re-enter the dog when it swallows fleas during cleaning. The prominent pronotal and genal combs of *Ctenocephalides* species distinguish them at once from the Human Flea, *Pulex irritans*. The latter species is much less common now than it was 100 years ago.

Our bird fleas belong primarily to the **Ceratophyllidae**. *Ceratophyllus gallinae* is very widespread and attacks a wide variety of bird species. This family, together with the **Hystrichopsyllidae**, contains a number of rodent fleas too, among them some of the species known to carry murine typhus.

The Rabbit Flea, *Spilopsyllus cuniculi*, which is the main vector of the myxomatosis virus in Europe, differs from our other fleas in that the females, when once adult, remain more or less permanently attached to the host. They select a suitable feeding site – usually the ear – and attach themselves by the mouth-parts. This sedentary habit is taken even further by the so-called stick-tight fleas and jiggers of the family **Pulicidae**. The stick-tight fleas are common in most warmer parts of the world and cause serious damage to poultry and other birds by attaching themselves in large masses to the head and neck – regions not easily accessible for the birds. Jiggers or sand-fleas, are thought to have originated in South America but they have now spread to most of Africa as well. The larvae live on the ground in the host's home area and freshly emerged adults actively roam the ground. When a suitable host is found – man, pigs, and many other animals are attacked – the females bury themselves almost entirely under the skin and here they remain for the rest of their lives, sucking blood and ejecting large numbers of eggs. The males of these sedentary fleas are mobile and live just like the other fleas described.

Collecting and Preserving
Fleas can be collected in much the same way as lice by examining the host animals, although fleas are considerably more difficult to catch. Combing, or even just blowing through the fur will cause many fleas to jump off the host. Freshly killed hosts can be put into containers with chloroform and this will kill the fleas which are then easy to pick up. However, the flea's life cycle and the readiness with which it leaves its host means that fleas can be obtained simply by examining the nests or homes of the hosts. Old bird nests (make sure they are old and the birds have flown) and sweepings from the sleeping quarters of other animals will usually yield all stages in the life cycle of the fleas. Pupae can usually be relied on to produce adults and, although larvae are more difficult, they too can be bred if kept under the right conditions of temperature and humidity and fed with debris from the appropriate source.

The hard nature of the body means that fleas may be preserved dry if required and pointing is suitable for this purpose. Microscope slides are, however, more suitable for detailed work.

Order Hymenoptera – Bees, Wasps, Ants and others

Recognition features Minute to large insects, usually with two pairs of membranous wings of which the front pair is the larger. The wings are coupled with a row of tiny hooks on the front edge of the hind wings.

Venation often greatly reduced, with large cells. At first sight, many flies may be confused with Hymenoptera but the flies have only two wings and are easily distinguished on closer examination. No other insect group has the large wing cells typical of many Hymenoptera.

A common wasp

The Hymenoptera is an immense order, containing well over 100,000 known species. Its members are extremely varied in size, appearance, and habits but the order can be split into two fairly well defined sub-orders. These are the **Symphyta**, in which there is no 'waist', and the **Apocrita**, in which there is a very narrow 'waist' between thorax and abdomen. The first sub-order contains the sawflies and these are the most primitive members of the order. The Apocrita contains the bees, wasps, ants, ichneumon flies, and several other groups, many of which are very advanced and specialised insects. Only in this order and among the termites do we find true social behaviour. A great many species are parasites of other

Hymenopteran mouth-parts: **a**, sawfly; **b**, wasp; **c**, bee; drawn from below to show how the labial glossa or tongue has become broad in the wasps and long and slender in the bees

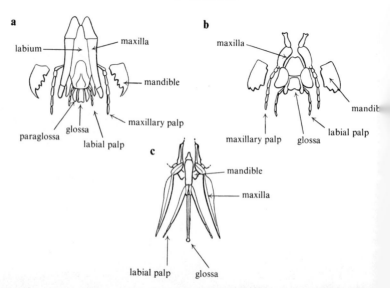

insects and play a vital role in maintaining the balance of nature. Bees all feed on pollen and nectar and, while collecting it from flowers, they perform the all-important function of pollination. Admittedly, many other insects help in pollination but they visit flowers only for their own satisfaction and do not go relentlessly from flower to flower as the bees do.

The head is heavily sclerotised and quite hard. It is attached to the thorax by a slender 'neck' and able to swivel freely. The compound eyes are almost always of large size and three ocelli are generally present. The antennae are often longer in male insects than in females and are rather variable, particularly among the lower families.

Hymenopteran mouth-parts are basically of the biting type and mandibles are always present, although they are not always used for feeding. The sawflies, particularly the carnivorous species, possess the most primitive mouth-parts in the order. There are toothed mandibles, fully developed maxillae, and a labium whose distal part is clearly divided into a glossa and two lateral paraglossae. The glossa may be used for lapping up nectar. The wasps and ants and the parasitic members of the Apocrita retain most of the sawfly features, although there is some reduction in the paraglossae and sometimes in the labial and maxillary palps as well. Particularly among the wasps and ants, there is an increase in importance of the glossa which becomes broad and tongue-like. It is used for lapping up sweet liquids. Some primitive bees retain the wasp-like mouth-parts but in most bees there is a much longer 'tongue' than in the wasps. This is associated with the bees' nectar-feeding habits. All stages of tongue development exist, from the primitive wasp-like *Prosopis* to the highly evolved honey bees and bumble bees in which the glossa is drawn out into a long sucking tube sheathed by the labial palps. These bees can draw nectar up from deep-throated flowers. Although they possess these elaborate suctorial mouths, the bees still retain their mandibles. But they use them more for nest-building and other chores than for feeding.

The thorax is composed of the usual three segments but, among the Apocrita,

Hymenopteran thoraxes from above, showing how the pronotum (black) may or may not reach the tegulae at the bases of the front wings

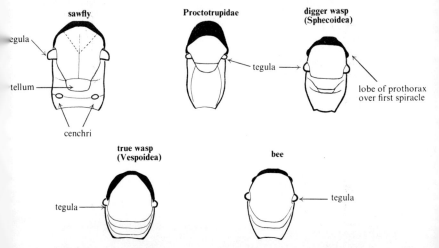

the first abdominal segment becomes fused with the thorax and is known as the propodeum. The characteristic 'wasp-waist' is not therefore strictly between the thorax and abdomen but between the first and second abdominal segments. The pronotum is usually small, although often extending backwards along the sides to reach the tegulae. The latter are always present, in the form of 'shoulder pads' at the bases of the front wings, but they are occasionally very small and difficult to see. There is a distinct division of the mesonotum into scutum and scutellum but the smaller metanotum is tucked away under the scutellum and not usually very visible.

There are usually two pairs of membranous wings which give the order its name (Greek *hymen* = membrane), although several groups – notably the ants – produce wingless individuals. The hind wings are considerably smaller than the front ones and the two pairs are linked by a number of minute hooks on the front edge of the hind wing (Fig. p. 21). A pigmented pterostigma may or may not be present in the front wing.

The main veins are reduced in the Hymenoptera but there is some development of cross veins and branches so that the wings often have a reticulate appearance, with large cells. This is characteristic of all the larger Hymenoptera and these insects are not easily confused with any other order. The venation has deviated so much from the basic pattern that it is difficult to decide which vein is which and there is no widely accepted system of naming them. The sawflies have the most complete venation, in which there are four rather irregular major veins – Rs, M, Cu, and 1A. Both wings have a fairly distinct fold, known as the vannal fold, near vein 1A and this fold is a useful marker. There is a second fold, known as the jugal

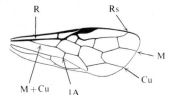

The venation of the front wing of the sawfly *Diprion pini*, showing the large cells characteristic of the Hymenoptera

fold, nearer the hind margin. It is not very obvious in the front wing but it marks off the anal lobe in the hind wing. The area between the two folds is the vannal lobe and both this and the anal lobe may be missing in the hind wings of the more advanced Hymenoptera. Some idea of the variety of wing venation in this order can be gained from the illustrations in this chapter.

As already mentioned, the first abdominal segment becomes fused with the thorax in the Apocrita and is known as the propodeum. The rest of the abdomen, starting with the second segment, is known as the gaster and is greatly constricted at the front to form the 'waist'. The length of the constricted part, which is often called the petiole, varies from group to group and involves two complete segments in some ants. The sawflies are without any such constriction.

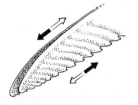

The ovipositor of a sawfly, used for cutting slits in plants

A well developed ovipositor is usually present in the female. The sawflies take their name from the saw-like nature of the ovipositor which they use for cutting plant tissues. Among the other Hymenoptera, the ovipositor is either used for drilling into plant and animal tissues during egg-laying, or it is modified as a sting (p. 255) and no longer used in laying eggs. Because the sting is a modified egg-laying tool, only female insects can sting.

The eggs of Hymenoptera are generally white and sausage-shaped and they are usually laid singly. Parthenogenesis is common in several groups: drone (male) bees, for example, are produced from unfertilised eggs, while many gall wasp species (Cynipidae) exhibit an alternation of sexual and parthenogenetic generations. Males are extremely rare in some species and parthenogenesis is almost the only method of reproducing.

Hymenopterous larvae are of two distinct types. Sawfly larvae are rather like caterpillars, with well developed heads and thoracic legs, and often with fleshy abdominal legs as well. The larvae of the Apocrita, on the other hand, are legless and their heads are generally greatly reduced. This is in connection with the fact that these larvae are always surrounded by food and do not have to search for it. The pupa has free appendages (exarate condition) and is usually enclosed in some sort of cocoon, although this may be so flimsy as to appear absent.

SUB-ORDER SYMPHYTA – THE SAWFLIES (Pl. 36)

These insects are readily separated from the rest of the Hymenoptera by the absence of a 'waist'. The first abdominal segment, although modified to some extent, is not fused with the thorax and there is no constriction behind it. This is the more primitive of the two sub-orders and its members do not exhibit the highly specialised habits, such as parasitism and social behaviour, that we find among the Apocrita.

Most sawflies, other than Cephidae, bear two small knobs called cenchri on the metanotum. These raised areas are often pale in colour and they have rough surfaces. Each one engages with a similar roughened patch on the underside of the front wing when the wings are closed and the wings are thus held firmly in place. Sawflies can fly well but many of them are more likely to scuttle away when disturbed. They spend much of their time just sitting on leaves and flowers. Umbellifers are particularly attractive to them. Pollen is the main food of adult sawflies, although some species are at least partly carnivorous.

The common name for these insects refers to the ovipositor, which is usually like a minute saw (Fig. p. 250). The pattern of the teeth varies from species to species. The females use their saws to cut slits in stems and leaves and then lay their eggs in the slits. Some species, however, have sharp, boring ovipositors that act more like drills. The Wood Wasp or Horntail, *Urocerus gigas* (Pl. 36) has a very long and powerful ovipositor which can bore into wood. Although the eggs are usually laid inside stems and leaves, most sawfly larvae feed freely on the leaves of the food plant. They resemble the caterpillars of butterflies and moths but sawfly larvae can be distinguished because they always have at least six pairs of abdominal legs. The caterpillars of butterflies and moths never have more than five pairs of these prolegs. Those sawfly larvae that tunnel in leaves and stems have no abdominal legs and look more like beetle larvae than caterpillars. Pupation takes place in a cocoon, either in the soil or leaf litter, or attached to the food plant.

The larva of a sawfly, distinguished from a lepidopterous caterpillar by the greater number of stumpy prolegs

prolegs

The European sawfly families, illustrated on Pl. 36, may be distinguished with the aid of the following key.

A Simplified Key to the Families of European Sawflies

1. Antennae inserted below eyes: hind wings without any enclosed cells   Orussidae, p. 253
    Antennae inserted between eyes: hind wings usually with at least one enclosed cell   2

2. Antennae with only three segments, of which the third is very long   Argidae, p. 254
    Antennae with more than three segments   3

3. Antennae with three segments of normal thickness, the third being very long and followed by a thread-like flagellum: insects under 5mm long   Xyelidae, p. 253
    Antennae not like this: insects usually over 5mm long   4

4. Cenchri present   5
    Cenchri absent: body very slender   Cephidae, p. 254

5. Antennae strongly clubbed   Cimbicidae, p. 254
    Antennae not strongly clubbed   6

6. Antennae branched or lightly toothed or with small flaps on the underside   7
    Antennae not branched or toothed or else only basal segments branched   8

7. Cross vein 2r present in front wing   Megalodontidae, p. 253

    Cross vein 2r absent from front wing   Diprionidae, p. 254

8. Antennae with 11 or more segments: insects usually over 10mm long   9
    Antennae usually with no more than 10 segments: if more than 10 segments are present insects are less than 10mm long and pronotum lacks a straight hind margin   Tenthredinidae, p. 254

9. Abdomen strongly flattened   Pamphilidae, p. 253
    Abdomen cylindrical   10

10. Vein Rs of front wing recurved at tip   Siricidae, p. 253

    Vein Rs not recurved at tip   Xiphydriidae, p. 254

The family **Blasticotomidae** has been omitted from the key because it has only one rarely found member, *Blasticotoma filiceti* (Pl. 36). It occurs mainly in Northern Europe and the larva tunnels in the stems of ferns. The insect may be recognised by its four-segmented antennae: the third segment is very long and the fourth is very short.

The **Orussidae** has only one European member, *Orussus abietinus* (Pl. 36). It has been recorded from the British Isles, but it is found mainly on the Continent. The unusual venation and the position of the antennae distinguish this family from all other sawflies, and some entomologists place it in a separate sub-order. The larva is a parasite of timber beetles.

The head and venation of *Orussus*. This sawfly is unusual in having its antennae inserted below the eyes

The **Xyelidae** contains only two British species, both under 5mm long. They can be recognised by the characteristic antennae, together with the rather broad stigma. *Xyela julii* (Pl. 36) is often found around birch and pine trees in spring. The larvae live in male pine cones, while the adults are attracted to birch flowers. These insects are weak fliers.

Members of the **Pamphilidae** are very flat, broad-bodied insects between 7 and 15mm long. They are generally fast fliers. Their larvae live on conifers and other trees, spinning or rolling leaves together to make shelters. There are about 20 British species, of which *Pamphilus sylvaticus* (Pl. 36) is one of the commonest. It feeds on hawthorn and other rosaceous trees. Parthenogenesis is common in this family and the males of several species are very rare. The **Megalodontidae**, found on the Continent but not in Britain, is a closely related family, distinguished by its flabellate antennae (Pl. 36). There are several European species, feeding on herbaceous plants.

The members of the **Siricidae** are known as wood wasps or horntails, names which refer to their wood-boring habits and to the long, stout ovipositor of the female. The insects are at least 14mm long and often much longer, and the family

Two views of the antenna of *Megalodontes*, showing how it is composed of overlapping flaps, giving it a toothed appearance on the underside

contains some of our most fearsome-looking insects because of the ovipositors which are often taken to be stings. The insects are quite harmless to man, however. Family characteristics also include the minute tegulae, slender antennae composed of 17–30 segments, and a notch on the hind margin of the pronotum. Our commonest species is the black and yellow *Urocerus gigas*, although it is probably not a native. Females are often seen but the males usually keep to the tree tops where they fly actively in the sunshine. The females bore into pine trees and other conifers – usually unhealthy trees are selected – and lay their eggs. The larvae have vestigial legs and spend their lives tunnelling through the wood. Another fairly common species is a dark metallic blue in colour. Foreign species are commonly introduced in timber.

The **Xiphydriidae** is similar to the Siricidae (see key) but the body is mainly black. The antennae normally have 13–19 segments. Our two species feed on birch and sallow.

The **Cephidae** contains slow-flying insects with rather slender cylindrical or laterally compressed bodies. They can be separated from all other sawflies by the absence of cenchri. The antennae are long and thread-like. The larvae of this family are stem-borers and several of them do damage to cereals and other crops. *Cephus pygmaeus* (Pl. 36) is important in this respect. There are 12 British species in the family, ranging up to 18mm in length.

The **Tenthredinidae** is the major family in this sub-order, especially in the Northern Hemisphere, and it contains about 400 British species. They range in size from 2.5mm to about 15mm long and most of them are either black or brownish yellow in colour. One of the commonest is the Gooseberry Sawfly (*Nematus ribesi*) whose larvae often defoliate gooseberry and currant bushes. Another common and interesting species is *Pontania proxima* which is responsible for the little red bean galls that form on willow leaves in summer (Pl. 36). Unlike most galls, this one starts to swell as soon as the insect lays its egg and it is almost fully developed before the egg hatches. The larva then proceeds to consume the contents of the gall before leaving to pupate in the soil. Parthenogenesis is again very common in this family and the males of some species are almost unknown.

Members of the **Argidae** (Pl. 36) range from 5mm to 11mm in length and are rather heavy, sluggish fliers. They are readily identified by the long, one-segmented flagellum (hairy in the male) and the unusually large cenchri. The larvae feed on leaves of various shrubs.

The **Cimbicidae** contains stout, fast-flying sawflies with strongly clubbed antennae. We have 12 species in Britain, ranging from 4mm to 28mm in length. The larvae feed on a variety of shrubs and trees and one of the commonest is the Hawthorn Sawfly, *Trichiosoma tibiale*. Its oval brown cocoon is a common sight on hawthorn twigs in winter.

Members of the **Diprionidae** can be recognised at once by the structure of their antennae. They are feathery in males and toothed in females. *Cladius* species, belonging to the Tenthredinidae, may possibly be confused with this family, although their antennae are toothed only near the base. The Diprionidae are rather stout, slow-flying insects whose larvae live on conifers. The adults range from 5mm to 10mm long. Our commonest species is the Pine Sawfly, *Diprion pini* (Pl. 36).

SUB-ORDER APOCRITA – BEES, WASPS, ANTS, ICHNEUMON FLIES, ETC.

This is by far the larger of the two sub-orders and it contains some of the most advanced of all insects. They can be distinguished from sawflies by their 'wasp waists'.

There are two sections within the sub-order – the **Parasitica** and the **Aculeata**. The Parasitica are nearly all parasites and their ovipositors are adapted for piercing the host tissues. In some species the ovipositor is two or three times the length of the body (Pl. 38) enabling the insect to reach a host that may be tunnelling inside a plant. Among the members of the Parasitica are the ichneumons and chalcids, both of which parasitise the young stages of other insects. The section also includes the gall wasps, which feed on plant material and induce gall formation in their hosts. Bees, wasps, and ants belong to the Aculeata, in which the ovipositor is usually modified as a sting. There is, however, no hard and fast division between the two sections and they merge into one another among the Bethyloidea and Proctotrupoidea. Some members of the Bethyloidea, for example, are parasitic although they are structurally closer to the Aculeata.

The larvae are always surrounded by food, provided by the host plant or animal or else provided by the parent insect. In consequence, the larvae are generally poorly developed. They have no legs and their heads are rather reduced.

True social behaviour, in which the insects live together in colonies and work together for the good of the community, is found only among the termites and the aculeate Hymenoptera. All the ants are social insects, but relatively few of the bees and wasps are social. Most of them are solitary insects and, apart from making some sort of nest and providing food for their offspring, they have much the same type of life story as the rest of the insect world.

The social Hymenoptera live in colonies which are headed by one or more mated females known as queens. These queens do little more than lay eggs and the work of collecting food, rearing the young, building the nest, and keeping it tidy is carried out by the workers. These are also female insects but they are not fully developed and only in exceptional circumstances can they lay eggs. The workers are generally smaller than the queens. Male insects, called drones among the bees, are much less common and appear late in the year. They do no work in the colony and their sole function is to mate with new queens. Drones are produced parthenogenetically, that is to say that the female lays unfertilised eggs when producing drones.

Ant colonies and the colonies of honey bees last for several years, with new queens replacing old ones from time to time. Bumble bees and wasps, however, start afresh every year, only the mated queens surviving winter. These hibernated queens wake up in the spring and start building nests. They must rear the first brood of workers themselves before they can hand over these duties and devote themselves to egg-laying.

Among the bees and wasps, and also some of the ants, the ovipositor has become the sting and is no longer concerned with egg-laying. Because the sting is a modified egg-laying tool, only female insects can sting. The sting apparatus has been fully studied in honey bees and the following brief account refers to that insect, although there are only slight variations in the other insects. The active, penetrating part of the sting is the shaft, consisting of three needle-like members – a stylet and two lancets. The stylet partially sheathes the lancets and the three together enclose the poison canal. The sting shaft, together with its muscles and the poison sac, is housed in the end of the abdomen when at rest. When the bee is about to sting, it arches its body and plunges the sting shaft perpendicularly into the victim. The lancets are barbed and, by moving them forward alternately, the bee sinks its sting deeper into its victim. This movement of the lancets also pumps venom down the canal and into the wound. The bee can withdraw its sting from the bodies of other insects but the barbs hold it tight in human skin: the bee has to tear herself away, leaving the sting be-

Plate 37   **ORDER HYMENOPTERA** (Contd.)

SUB-ORDER APOCRITA

Insects with a marked 'waist'

Family **Cynipidae** – gall wasps
Small winged or wingless insects: gaster flattened from side to side: characteristic venation in winged insects. The insects induce galls on a variety of plants, especially oaks

1a. *Andricus kollari* (Hartig) $\times 1\frac{1}{2}$
1b. in resting attitude
1c. marble gall on common oak

2a. *Andricus fecundator* (Hartig) $\times 1\frac{1}{2}$
2b. artichoke gall on common oak
2c. section of artichoke gall showing inner chamber

3a. *Neuroterus quercusbaccarum* (L.) $\times 3$
3b. spangle gall of asexual generation on common oak
3c. currant gall of bisexual generation on common oak

4a. *Diplolepis rosae* (L.) $\times 3$
4b. bedeguar gall or robin's pincushion on wild rose
4c. section of bedeguar gall to show chambers

5. smooth and spiked pea galls of *Diplolepis nervosa* (Curtis) on rose

6a. *Diastrophus rubi* (Bouché) $\times 3$
6b. gall on stem of bramble

7a. *Biorrhiza pallida* (Olivier) sexual form $\times 3$
7b. oak apple gall of sexual form
7c. asexual generation
7d. root galls of asexual generation

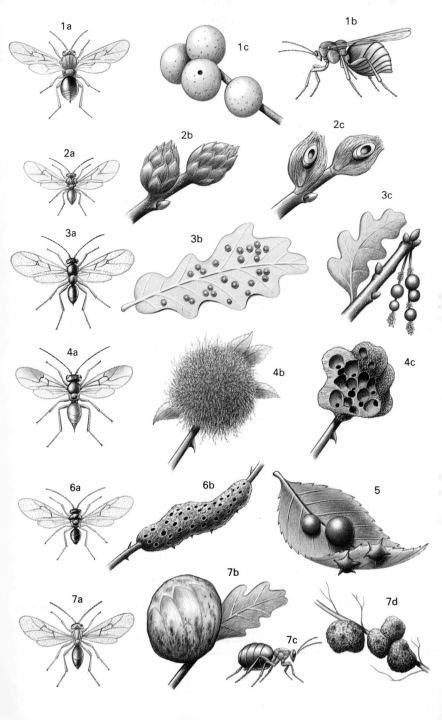

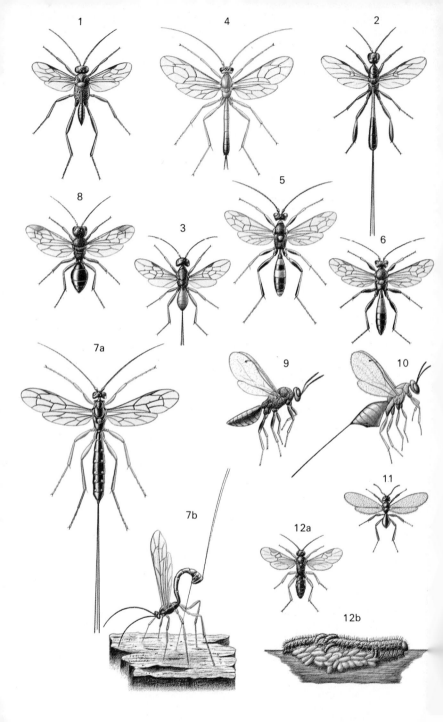

Evaniidae (Superfamily Evanioidea). Gaster attached near top of   p. 262
propodeum: petiole long
1. *Evania appendigaster* (L.) $\times 1\frac{1}{4}$

Side view of *Evania*

Gasteruptiidae (Superfamily Evanioidea). Gaster attached near   p. 262
top of propodeum: gaster long and narrow
2. *Gasteruption jaculator* (L.) $\times 1\frac{1}{4}$

Aulacidae (Superfamily Evanioidea). Gaster attached near top of   p. 262
propodeum: gaster pear-shaped with short petiole
3. *Aulacus striatus* Jurine $\times 1\frac{1}{4}$

Ichneumonidae. Antennae with over 16 segments: front wings with   p. 263
stigma and with cross vein 2m-cu: costal cell almost obliterated
4. *Netelia testacea* (Gravenhorst) $\times 1\frac{1}{4}$
5. *Amblyteles armatorius* (Forster) $\times 1\frac{1}{4}$
6. *Ichneumon suspiciosus* Wesmael $\times 1\frac{1}{4}$
7a. *Rhyssa persuasoria* (L.)
7b. *Rhyssa* in act of ovipositing

Front wing of ichneumon fly

2m–cu

Trigonalidae (Superfamily Trigonaloidea). Antennae with over 16   p. 262
segments: costal cell of front wing open
8. *Pseudogonalos hahni* (Spinola) $\times 2$

Pteromalidae. Metallic coloured chalcids, often with triangular   p. 266
gaster: hind coxa not conspicuously larger than others
9. *Pteromalus puparum* L. $\times 6$

Torymidae. Metallic chalcids with hind coxa very much larger than   p. 266
others: hind femur without a row of teeth beneath: ovipositor
very long
10. *Torymus nigricornis* Boheman $\times 6$

Platygasteridae. Minute insects with virtually veinless wings: p. 266
antennae usually with 10 segments and slightly clubbed
11. *Platygaster zosina* Walker $\times 8$

Braconidae. Antennae with over 16 segments: costal cell of front   p. 264
wing almost obliterated: cross vein 2m-cu absent
12a. *Apanteles glomeratus* (L.) $\times 5$
12b. larvae and pupae surrounding dead caterpillar

no 2m–cu

Front wing of braconid

hind. Wasps and other bees, however, have smaller barbs and can easily with-draw their stings and use them again. The venom injected is a complicated mixture of proteins, enzymes, and other substances, varying with the species. No antidote is known at present. Formic acid is the main ingredient of ant stings. The sting is used mainly for repelling invaders at the nest and, among the wasps, for paralysing prey prior to taking it back to the nest.

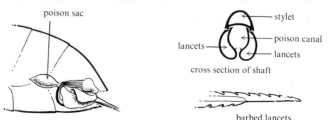

poison sac

stylet

lancets

poison canal

lancets

cross section of shaft

barbed lancets

The bee's sting is at the tip of the abdomen and the shaft consists of two barbed lancets running on 'rails' on the pointed stylet. The lancets move forward alter-nately and they penetrate deep into the victim. Poison is then pumped down the central canal and into the wound

As well as their stings, the bees and wasps have an acrid taste and/or a tough, hairy coat. All of these features make the insects unpleasant eating for birds and other predators and many species advertise their unpleasantness with bold, bright colour patterns. Black with yellow, orange, or red are the common com-binations and this is known as warning coloration. The theory of warning colora-tion, well supported by experimental evidence, is that the predator tries the unpleasant insects when young but rapidly learns to associate the bold pattern with unpleasantness.

These brightly or boldly marked, unpleasant insects are imitated by a number of harmless, good-to-eat insects which benefit from the resemblance because predators mistake them for the unpleasant ones. This phenomenon is known as mimicry and is easily explained on the basis of natural selection. Any chance resemblance between a harmless insect and an unpleasant one will be increased as predators 'weed out' the poorest imitators in each generation: only the best will survive and, over the course of many generations, offspring will get more and more like the unpleasant insect they resemble. One of our hover-flies, *Volucella bombylans* (Pl. 32), exists in several different forms, each resembling a different species of bumble bee.

The mimicry described so far should really be called Batesian mimicry – after H. W. Bates who first described it in 1862 – because there is another form of mimicry in which two or more species look alike and are all unpleasant. This is known as Müllerian mimicry – after Fritz Müller who described it in 1878. All the species sharing the common pattern benefit from the arrangement because a predator has only one pattern to learn before it avoids all the species.

Müllerian mimicry is particularly common among South American butterflies but there are no definite examples of it in Britain. Batesian mimicry, however, is well established in the British fauna. The bees and wasps are by far the commonest models and their commonest mimics are the Diptera – hover-flies and others. Mimics also occur among the moths, beetles, and other Hymenoptera.

A Simplified Key to the Superfamilies of the Apocrita

This key can be used to distinguish the winged adults. Of the wingless forms in this sub-order – and there are many – the only ones likely to come to the notice of the non-specialist are the ants – recognisable by their elbowed antennae and the shape of the petiole (Fig. p. 267) – and the velvet ants. The latter are recognised by their hairy bodies.

1. Gaster attached near the top of the propodeum   Evanioidea, p. 262

     Gaster attached near the bottom of the propodeum   2

2. Antennae long and with more than 16 segments: stigma present on front wing   3
    Antennae shorter, with less than 16 segments: stigma often absent   4

3. Costal cell wide (Pl. 38)   Trigonaloidea, p. 262
    Costal cell almost or quite obliterated   Ichneumonoidea, p. 263

4. Anal or vannal lobe absent from hind wing, except in some Proctotrupoidea where the rest of the venation is characteristic (Fig. p. 266): mainly small or minute insects   5
    Anal or vannal lobe usually present in hind wing, although sometimes indistinct: generally medium-sized or large insects, including bees and wasps   8

5. First one or two segments of gaster very narrow and scale-like   Formicoidea, p. 267
    Gaster not so constructed   6

6. Gaster laterally compressed: antennae with a short scape and not elbowed   Cynipoidea, p. 264
    Gaster not laterally compressed: antennae usually with a long scape and elbowed   7

7. Pronotum extending back to tegulae   Proctotrupoidea, p. 266
    pronotum →
    Pronotum not extending back to tegulae   tegula   Chalcidoidea, p. 265

8. Hind wing with no closed cells   Bethyloidea, p. 266

    One or more closed cells in hind wing   9

Plate 39   **ORDER HYMENOPTERA**

SUB-ORDER APOCRITA (Contd.)

Family **Mutillidae** – velvet ants   p. 267
     Hairy insects with short stout legs: females wingless:
     pronotum reaching back to tegulae
1a. *Mutilla europaea* L. – male $\times 1\frac{1}{2}$
1b. female $\times 1\frac{1}{2}$

Family **Tiphiidae** (Superfamily Scolioidea)   p. 266
     Smooth-bodied insects with pronotum reaching back to
     tegulae: female often wingless
2a. *Methocha ichneumonoides* Latreille – male $\times 1\frac{1}{2}$
2b. female $\times 1\frac{1}{2}$

△ Family **Scoliidae**   p. 267
     Large hairy insects with dark wings: legs stout
▲ **3.** *Scolia flavifrons* Fabr.

Family **Sapygidae** (Superfamily Scolioidea)   p. 266
     Pronotum reaches back to tegulae: both sexes winged: anal
     lobe on hind wing
4. *Sapyga quinquepunctatum* (Fabr.) $\times 2$

Family **Chrysididae**   p. 266
     No closed cells in hind wing: body usually metallic
▲ **5.** *Stilbum cyanarum* Forster $\times 2$
6. *Chrysis ignita* (L.) $\times 2$

Family **Formicidae** – the ants   p. 267
     Front part of abdomen slender with one or two scale-like
     outgrowths: antennae normally elbowed: winged or wingless
7a. *Formica rufa* L. – male $\times 2$
7b. queen $\times 2$
7c. worker $\times 2$

▲ **8a.** *Messor barbara* L. – male $\times 1\frac{1}{2}$
8b. soldier $\times 1\frac{1}{2}$
8c. queen $\times 1\frac{1}{2}$
8d. worker $\times 1\frac{1}{2}$

scale or node

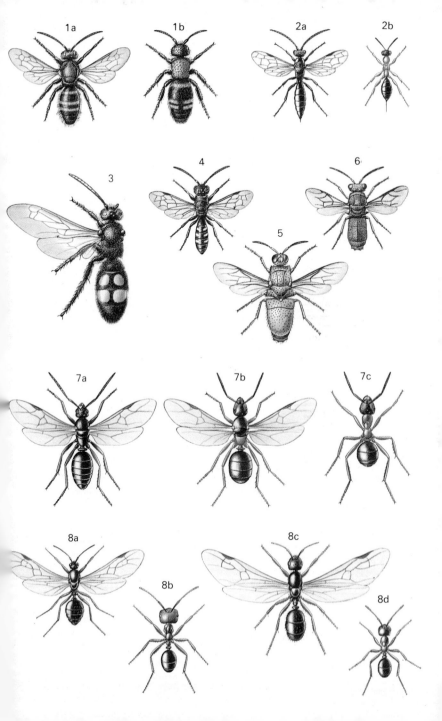

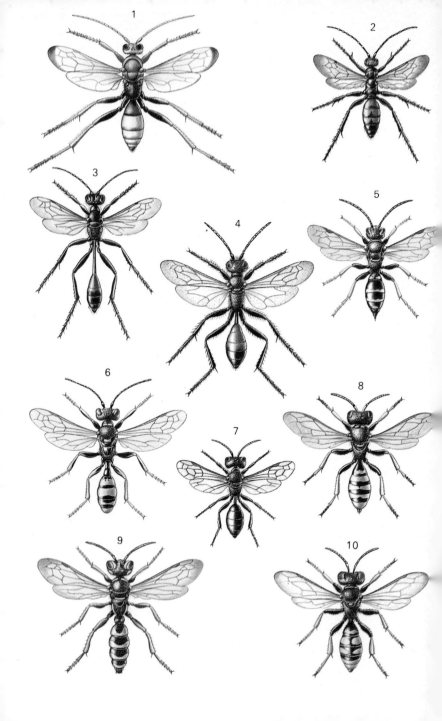

SUB-ORDER APOCRITA (Contd.)

Family **Pompilidae**   p. 275
     Pronotum reaching back to tegulae: wings laid flat at rest:
     hind femur relatively long

▲   **1.** *Cryptocheilus spectabile* (Morawitz)

    2. *Anoplius viaticus* (L.)   ×1½

Thorax from above

Family **Sphecidae**   p. 275
     Pronotum not reaching back to tegulae: hind tarsi slender

    3. *Ammophila sabulosa* (L.)   ×1½

    4. *Ammophila hirsuta* (Scopoli)   ×1½

    5. *Gorytes mystaceus* (L.)   ×1½

    6. *Mellinus arvensis* (L.)   ×2

    7. *Pemphredon lugubris* Latreille   ×2

    8. *Ectemnius quadricinctus* (Fabr.)   ×2

    9. *Cerceris arenaria* (L.)   ×2

  10. *Crabro cribarius* (L.)   ×2

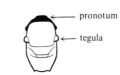

Thorax from above

The black and yellow members of Sphecidae are likely to be confused with the social wasps (Vespidae) at first, but they can be distinguished by the pronotum and by the fact that they (the Sphecidae) lay their wings flat when at rest. The social wasps all fold their wings lengthwise and the wings thus appear very narrow (Plate 41).

9. Pronotum reaching back to tegulae   10

pronotum
tegula

Pronotum not reaching back to tegulae,   12
but forming a lobe over first thoracic
spiracle   pronotum
tegula
lobe over 1st spiracle

10. Front wings folded lengthwise   Vespoidea, p. 271
    at rest: eyes emarginate (Pl. 42)
                      wings folded
                      lengthwise

    Front wings not so folded: eyes not usually emar-
    ginate   11

11. Legs long, especially hind femur   Pompiloidea, p. 275
    Legs usually short and stout   Scolioidea, p. 266

12. Hind tarsi broad and often very hairy   Apoidea, p. 278
    Hind tarsi not broadened   Sphecoidea, p. 275

Superfamily Evanioidea

The members of this group are medium-sized parasitic insects, generally black, or black with red abdomens. They are all recognisable by the way in which the gaster is attached near the top of the propodeum (Pl. 38). There are three families – all represented in Britain – differing mainly in the venation, the shape of the gaster, and the host insects. The three main host groups are various wood-boring beetles, solitary bees and wasps, and the egg purses of cockroaches.

Side view of *Evania*, showing how the gaster is
attached to the top of the propodeum

Superfamily Trigonaloidea

The only British member of this group is the rare *Pseudogonalos hahni* (Pl. 38) which has been recorded as a parasite of various wasps and also as a hyperparasite, attacking ichneumons and other parasites already living inside caterpillars.

Superfamily Ichneumonoidea

This is a very large group of parasitic insects, playing an important role in controlling insect numbers and responsible for the destruction of huge numbers of insect pests. A few species attack spiders but the majority parasitise other insects, especially Lepidoptera. The group can be recognised by the long antennae, the stigma usually present in the front wing, and the almost or completely obliterated costal cell. Two families occur in Britain – the Ichneumonidae and the Braconidae. They differ mainly in the venation.

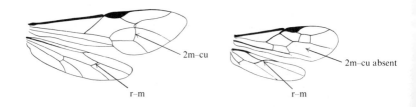

Wings of Ichneumonidae (*left*) and Braconidae, showing the presence and absence of cross vein 2m-cu in the front wing, and the different positions of cross vein r-m in the hind wing

Members of the **Ichneumonidae** are mainly parasites of the larvae of butterflies and moths. Sawfly and beetle larvae are the other major hosts but many ichneumons are hyperparasites. The parasites are not usually confined to any one host species, although they generally keep to their own particular group of hosts. Adult ichneumons may often be seen on flowers or running about on the herbage, searching for suitable hosts with their ever-moving antennae. Having found such a host, the female ichneumon prepares to lay her egg or eggs with the aid of her slender ovipositor. This arises from the underside of the abdomen, just in front of the tip. Although often small, it is always visible externally. This is so in all the Parasitica. Only among the Aculeata does the ovipositor (sting) emerge from the tip of the abdomen.

The ichneumon usually pierces the host body with its ovipositor and lays the egg or eggs inside the host body. Some species, however, merely lay their eggs on the outside of the host. From there, the larvae may make their own way inside, or they may simply attach themselves to the host and feed from the outside. The ichneumon larvae concentrate on the non-essential organs of the host at first, draining its reserves but allowing it to go on living. Parasitised larvae are usually smaller than healthy ones and rather 'lazy': they will often sit exposed on leaves whereas healthy larvae will always conceal themselves. When the ichneumon larvae are nearly fully grown they turn their attention to the essential organs of the host and kill it. They then pupate in little silken cocoons. These cocoons may be formed inside or outside the host body, which by this time is little more than an empty skin. The host may or may not pupate before the parasites are fully grown. The number of parasites to a host depends upon the relative sizes of host and parasite and ranges from 1 to 100 or more.

The ichneumons may overwinter in the host larvae or pupae, or else they may hibernate as adults, having emerged from their hosts in late summer. It is usually only the mated female ichneumons that hibernate: the males die in the autumn.

One of our commonest ichneumons is the yellowish brown *Netelia testacea* (Pl. 38). It parasitises a variety of noctuid moth larvae and the adult parasite often comes to lighted windows. Certainly one of our most striking ichneumon flies is the female *Rhyssa persuasoria* (Pl. 38), whose ovipositor is in the region of 40mm in length. This insect parasitises the horntail *Urocerus gigas* (p. 253) and is not uncommon in pine woods. *Rhyssa* is able to detect the host larvae tunnelling in the tree trunks and then it performs the seemingly impossible feat of driving its slender ovipositor into the wood. The two halves of the ovipositor rotate backwards and forwards very rapidly and they drill down into the wood like a minute auger. One egg is laid next to each horntail larva and the larval *Rhyssa* feeds externally on its host.

Some of the larger ichneumons can pierce human skin with their ovipositors and produce a slight stinging sensation. They are unlikely to do this, however, unless they are held.

The members of the **Braconidae** are essentially similar in habits and appearance to the ichneumon flies. One of the commonest is *Apanteles glomeratus*, a parasite of the cabbage white butterflies (*Pieris* spp.). A large *P. brassicae* larva may contain over 150 parasites and their cocoons are often seen surrounding dead larvae and pupae (Pl. 38). One group of the Braconidae attacks aphids. Species of *Aphidius* cement the host body down to the plant before they pupate in it. The empty aphid skins remain on the plants long after the parasites have left through a neat little hole in each one.

Superfamily Cynipoidea

The members of this group are small or minute insects with a rather characteristic wing venation (Pl. 37). The gaster is laterally compressed, more so in some species than in others, and the insects are generally dark in colour, although some are yellowish or reddish brown. The most important family, and the one to which most of our species belong, is the **Cynipidae**. Its members are of special interest because most of them induce gall formation on plants and many of them alternate between sexual and non-sexual generations. They are called gall wasps. Each species induces formation of its own characteristic gall on the plant. Most of them are found on oaks but a few species attack roses and certain herbaceous plants.

Neuroterus quercusbaccarum is a typical example, its reddish spangle galls being abundant on oak leaves in late summer (Pl. 37). Inside each gall is a tiny grub feeding on the gall tissue. The galls fall from the leaves in October but continue to grow for a while. The larval gall wasps complete their growth during the winter and pupate. The adults emerge in February and March and they are all asexual females. They lay their eggs parthenogenetically in oak buds and the resulting larvae induce the formation of little spherical galls on the leaves or male catkins (Pl. 37). These galls are known as currant galls and adult gall wasps emerge from them in May and June. There are both males and females in this summer generation and, after pairing, the females lay their eggs in the tissues of the leaves. These eggs give rise to the asexual generation again and the spangle galls.

Diplolepis rosae, the insect responsible for the familiar robins' pincushion galls on roses (Pl. 37), has no alternation of generations. Males are extremely rare and the species, like several of its relatives, reproduces almost entirely by parthenogenesis.

The mechanisms of gall formation are not fully understood but the essential factor seems to be that the presence of the larvae causes the plant tissues to grow in a particular way and provide abundant food for the larvae. Each species has its own special effect and even closely related gall wasps may produce very different galls (Pl. 37).

Many other insects take advantage of the food and shelter to be found in plant galls and the rightful inhabitant is often starved to death or even actually killed by these uninvited guests. Among the latter there are several species of gall wasp that induce no galls of their own but lay their eggs in the developing galls of other species. These inquiline species do no direct harm to the original gall wasp larva but it may starve to death if there are too many inquilines sharing its food. Parasites are also common in galls, attacking both the original inhabitants and the inquilines. The most frequent parasites are ichneumon flies and chalcids which use their long ovipositors to reach the host larvae within the galls.

Superfamily Chalcidoidea

This is probably the largest superfamily of insects. There are more than 1,500 known British species and because of their small size, many more undoubtedly remain to be discovered. They are common insects, often found walking on window panes and rarely absent from the sweep net in summer, but their small size deters many people from studying them. Most chalcids are less than 3mm long but many of them are brilliantly coloured with metallic greens and blues and they are extremely beautiful insects (Pl. 38). Almost all of them are parasites or hyperparasites, attacking eggs, larvae, and pupae of other insects. A few species are phytophagous, however, feeding on seeds or causing gall formation in other parts of the plant. The parasitic species usually pupate inside their hosts.

| Mymaridae | Trichogrammatidae | Pteromalidae |

Three types of chalcid wing, showing the very reduced venation in this superfamily

As a group, the Chalcidoidea can usually be recognised by their elbowed antennae and (in the winged forms) the characteristic venation. There are many families – 14 in the British fauna – but they are not at all easy to separate. The **Mymaridae** can be recognised by its stalked, linear wings. These tiny creatures, which parasitise the eggs of various other insects, are called fairy flies. They include the smallest of all insects, some of them being under 0.25mm long. The

Trichogrammatidae is another family of minute egg parasites, recognisable by their 3-segmented tarsi and distinct lines of hairs on the wings. Several species in this family have been used in the biological control of injurious Lepidoptera. Other families worth mention are the **Pteromalidae**, in which the abdomen is often more or less triangular in profile (Pl. 38), and the **Torymidae**. Members of the latter family are rather elongate insects, often a brilliant metallic green. Most of them parasitise gall-living insects and the.females have relatively enormous ovipositors which allow them to reach their hosts inside their galls.

Superfamily Proctotrupoidea

The members of this superfamily and the next exhibit certain features that link the Parasitica and the Aculeata. The Proctotrupoidea, for example, are all small or minute parasites, but they have certain structural similarities with wasps. They are nearly all slender, black insects and they attack a variety of other insects,

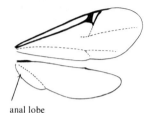

Wings of *Phaenoserphus* (family Proctotrupidae), showing the anal lobe of the hind wing and the characteristic venation. The anal lobe is missing in most proctotrupids

anal lobe

including the egg stages. The wing venation is often very reduced and many wingless species are known. Some species have a stigma in the front wing. Several species exhibit polyembryony, with one egg being laid in the host but developing there into numerous larvae. The largest of our six families is the **Platygasteridae**, whose members mainly affect gall midges (Diptera: Cecidomyidae). The Hessian-fly – a serious pest of wheat – is kept in check by the parasite *Platygaster zosina* (Pl. 38).

Superfamily Bethyloidea

Although all the members of this rather diverse superfamily are parasites, they show a great many affinities with the non-parasitic Aculeata and the systematic position of the group is not really clear. Best known members are the ruby-tailed wasps of the family **Chrysididae**. These insects are brilliantly coloured with metallic greens, blues, and ruby (Pl. 38), and they parasitise various solitary bees and wasps. *Chrysis ignita* is a common British species, while *Stilbum cyanurum* is widespread on the Continent.

Superfamily Scolioidea

Although included in the Aculeata, many members of this group are parasites and there are obvious affinities with the Parasitica, particularly with the Bethyloidea. There are only eight British species, none of them common, distributed in three families. The British species parasitise various bees and wasps. Most of them have hard bodies and potent stings. The **Mutillidae** are commonly called velvet ants, although they are not ants at all. The name arose from the fact that most females – the sex most frequently met with – are wingless and the insects are more or less covered with soft hair (Pl. 39).

The family **Scoliidae**, unrepresented in the British Isles, contains some of the largest Hymenoptera. They are hairy insects, generally dark in colour and marked with red or yellow. Unlike the velvet ants, both sexes are fully winged, the wings often being dark and with a metallic sheen. The larvae feed ectoparasitically on the larvae of various beetles. *Scolia flavifrons* (Pl. 39) is a large European member of the family.

Superfamily Formicoidea – The Ants (Pl. 39)

This group contains just one very large family – the Formicidae – with probably something like 10,000 species in the world. There are about 36 British species, arranged in several sub-families. All ants are social insects, living in colonies and usually having female (queen), male, and worker castes. A number of species are social parasites, however, and rely on the workers of other species to do some or all of their work.

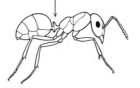

Side view of an ant, showing the characteristic scale-like section of the petiole

Ants, whether winged or not, can be distinguished from other insects by the structure of the petiole. This consists of one or two segments which usually bear little nodes or scales. The elbowed antennae of the ants will also help to separate them from other insects. Some sub-families possess well developed stings but many ants have no sting, although they can often defend themselves by squirting formic acid at their attackers. The ant's jaws are tough and sharp and many of the larger species can give painful bites.

The bulk of the ants in a colony are workers. These are all wingless females and, although they can sometimes lay eggs, they are not sexually fully developed. The workers are not always all the same: several species have two or more worker castes. Large-headed workers are quite common in certain non-British species, such as *Messor* (Pl. 39). These are called soldiers and their job is to guard the colony. Another remarkable worker caste is the replete, found among some honey-gathering species. The repletes hang themselves up on the roof of the nest chamber and gorge themselves on honey brought in by other workers. The honey distends their bodies enormously and they are unable to move about. They discharge honey when required. These honey ants are not found in Britain.

A replete honey ant – a living larder swollen with food. The ant normally hangs motionless from the roof of the nest chamber

Family **Sphecidae** (Contd.)

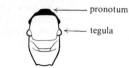

▲   **1.** *Sphex maxillosus* Fabr.

▲   **2.** *Sceliphron destillatorium* Illiger

▲   **3.** *Bembex rostrata* L.   Thorax from above

▲   **4.** *Liris praetermissa* Richards   ×2

▲   **5.** *Pison atrum* Spinola   ×2

Family **Vespidae** p. 271
    Pronotum extends back to tegulae: eyes deeply notched, almost crescent-shaped: wings folded lengthwise when at rest

                    Thorax from above

▲   **6.** *Eumenes unguiculata* Villers

     7a. *Eumenes pedunculatus* (Panzer)   ×1½
     7b. clay nest or pot made by *pedunculatus*

     8. *Odynerus spinipes* (L.)   ×1½

▲   **9.** *Polistes gallicus* L.   ×1½

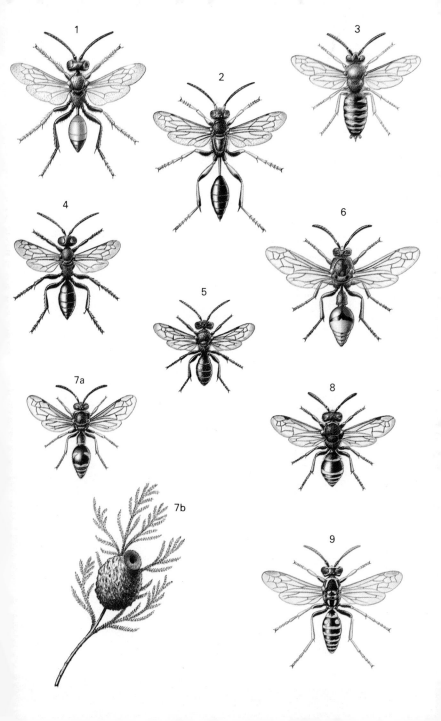

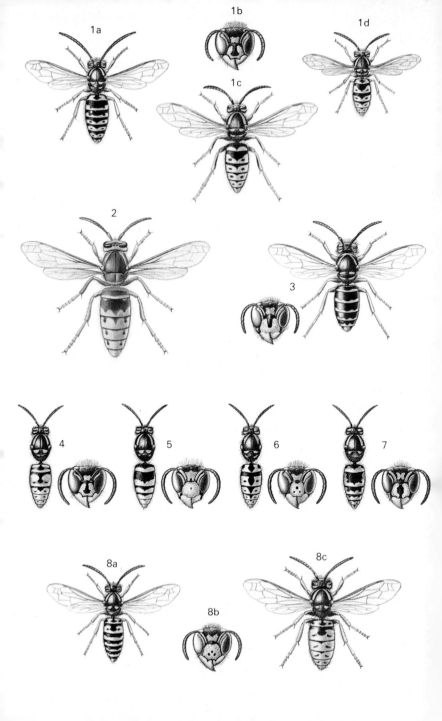

Family **Vespidae** (Contd.)
> The various species of *Vespula* differ mainly in the patterns of the face and abdomen, although the abdominal patterns vary somewhat within a species. The faces of all the British species are illustrated

1a. Common wasp – *Vespula vulgaris* (L.) – male
1b. Face of worker
1c. Queen
1d. Worker

2. Hornet – *Vespa crabro* L.

▲   **3.** *Vespula media* DeGeer

4. Red wasp – *Vespula rufa* (L.)

5. Tree wasp – *Vespula sylvestris* (Scopoli)

6. German wasp – *Vespula germanica* (Fabr.)

7. Norwegian wasp – *Vespula norvegica* (Fabr.)

8a. Cuckoo wasp – *Vespula austriaca* (Panzer) – male
8b. Face
8c. Female

Important things to look for include the colour of the basal segment of the antenna and the length of the cheek between the eye and the jaw. There are also differences in the number of yellow thoracic spots.

Male and fully developed female ants are produced at certain times of the year. Both sexes are usually fully winged and they go off on their marriage flights. Every neighbourhood usually has one day a year in which all the common garden ants emerge and everyone is plagued by 'flying ants'. Climatic conditions control the emergence of the ants and this ensures that all the nests in one area will erupt at one time. Each nest seems to produce mainly males or females and so there is a good chance of cross-breeding. After mating, which usually takes place in the air, the ants return to earth and the males soon die. The females break off their wings and seek a suitable nesting site, although only a small percentage of them escape the attention of birds.

The mated females may enter an existing nest, in which case the nest then continues with more than one queen. Alternatively, the new queen may find a place of her own. She then seals herself up until the spring, keeping going on the food reserves in her body and on the degenerating wing muscles she no longer needs. Her eggs mature and she lays them in spring, feeding the young ants on her own saliva. As soon as these first young ants become adult, they take over the building and running of the colony and the queen devotes herself to egg-laying.

The workers build the nest around the queen's chamber, making a number of 'rooms' and a maze of tunnels. The nesting site varies from species to species and may be under the ground, in hollow trees, or in mounds made up by the ants themselves. The queen remains in her chamber, laying eggs and being tended by the workers. Her eggs are taken away from the 'royal chamber' and hatched elsewhere in the nest. The eggs themselves are very tiny – the 'ants' eggs' sold for feeding goldfish are really the ant pupae. The larvae are reared on honey and insect grubs and are often transported from room to room in the nest as they grow. There is much 'mutual feeding' between workers and larvae, the latter giving up sweet saliva in return for food. The pupae are usually kept near the surface of the nest where they get some warmth from the sun and this helps them to mature more quickly. There is a remarkable co-operation between the workers in the colony, aided by an apparently continual exchange of information between them by rubbing heads and antennae together. The colonies are remarkably stable and long-lasting. Individual ants come and go but the queens live for several years and the 'community spirit' between the workers ensures that new queens are reared when necessary to ensure continuance of the colony.

Among the ants, one can trace an evolution of feeding habits very similar to that seen in man. The most primitive ants, like the earliest men, are hunters. They are mainly carnivorous and they raid their surroundings for food. Some of these hunters make no permanent nests and simply 'camp' from time to time to raise new broods of workers. Those that do make permanent nests do not have very large colonies. The next stage is represented by the herders and harvesters – the ants that look after aphids for the honeydew they provide and also collect nectar and other vegetable food. Several species of ant actually rear aphids in their nests, bringing in the aphids and attaching them to plant roots growing through the nests. Most of our British ants belong to the herding and harvesting group. The highest division is represented by the farmers, particularly the Attini or parasol ants of Tropical America. These ants are fungus eaters and they actually grow their own food on specially prepared beds of leaf fragments, just as man grows mushrooms.

The ants exhibit many degrees of social parasitism and slavery. A number of foreign species practise what is called temporary social parasitism. The mated queen seeks out the nest of some closely related species in which she will be accepted and then she lays her own eggs. These are looked after and the young are reared by the workers of the host species. The host queen is usually killed at some stage and the host workers gradually die out, leaving the nest completely to the parasitic species. The latter species is quite able to look after itself and its early parasitic behaviour enables it to get a nest without making one.

One of the best-known of the slave-making ants is *Formica sanguinea*, a red ant found in Britain. Workers of this species raid the nests of related species, such as *Formica fusca*, and bring back pupae. These are tended in the *sanguinea* nest and the workers emerging work for their captors. *F. sanguinea* can manage without slaves but there are several species that cannot. The first batch of workers goes out to collect slave pupae and no nest building takes place until the slave ants emerge. Another British species, *Anergates atratulus*, is even more specialised and has no workers of its own at all. The young queen enters the nest of *Tetramorium caespitum* and her young, which are all sexual forms, are raised entirely by the host species.

A great many other creatures find suitable food and shelter inside an ant nest and the study of these 'guests' is a subject in itself. Space will not allow discussion of it here, other than to point out the three main groups of guests. These are: (a) various scavenging and predatory beetles which are definitely not welcomed by the ants; (b) numerous small scavengers, including beetle and fly larvae, springtails, and the white woodlouse *Platyarthrus hoffmannseggi*, which are more or less ignored by the ants; (c) welcome guests, sometimes invited or brought by the ants, that repay the hospitality by providing the ants with sweet secretions. The larva of the Large Blue butterfly is an example (p. 175).

Superfamily Vespoidea – The True Wasps

These insects are called true wasps in order to distinguish them from the 'digger wasps' of the other superfamilies. There is only one family – the **Vespidae** – and it contains all the social wasps as well as many solitary species. The most useful characteristics of the family as far as identification is concerned are the deeply notched, almost crescent-shaped eyes (Pl. 41), the lengthwise folding of the wings at rest (Pl. 41), and the backward extension of the pronotum to reach the tegulae (Fig. p. 249).

All wasps feed their young on meat – insect larvae, scraps of carrion, and so on – and in this respect they differ very much from bees which feed their larvae on nectar (honey) and pollen. Although the adult wasps are fond of nectar and other sweet things, they do not have the nectar-sucking mouth-parts of the bees: they have very powerful jaws and a short 'tongue' (Fig. p. 248). Wasps possess no pollen-gathering apparatus and they are generally less hairy than bees. Their colours are due mainly to the colours of the body plates or sclerites and not to the colours of the hairs as in bees.

We have only two genera of solitary vespid wasps in Britain. These are *Eumenes*, with one species, and *Odynerus*, with 19 species. These wasps have no worker caste, just male and female, and they do not live in colonies, although the female does build a nest for her offspring. *Eumenes pedunculatus* is the Potter Wasp of sandy heathland. It is about 15mm long and of a very characteristic shape (Pl. 41). The common name refers to the nest made by the female. It is in the form of a little flask, made of fine sand grains cemented together with the insect's saliva

Plate 43

BEES – Order Hymenoptera

SUB-ORDER APOCRITA (Contd.)

Superfamily **Apoidea** p. 278

Pronotum not reaching back to tegulae: hind tarsi usually broad: insects generally hairy

Family descriptions are omitted because the features used in separating the families of bees are not easily observed. A key to the British genera appears on page 280

1. *Prosopis signata* (Panzer) × 2

2. *Colletes succincta* (L.) × 2

3. *Panurgus banksianus* (Kirby) × 2

4. *Dasypoda hirtipes* (Fabr.) × 1½

5. *Macropis labiata* (Fabr.) × 1½

6. *Stelis punctulatissima* (Kirby) × 1½

7a. *Coelioxys inernis* (Kirby) – male × 2
7b. female × 2

8. *Chelostoma florisomne* (L.) × 1½

9. *Anthidium manicatum* (L.) × 2

▲ 10. *Anthidium florentinum* Fabr. × 1½

▲ 11. *Anthidium variegatum* Latreille × 2

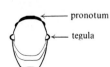

pronotum

tegula

Thorax from above

SUB-ORDER APOCRITA (Contd.)

Superfamily **Apoidea** (Contd.)
Family descriptions are omitted because the features used
in separating the families of bees are not easily observed. A
key to the British genera appears on page 280

1a. *Megachile centuncularis* (L.) – male   ×2
1b. female   ×2
1c. insect in flight carrying leaf fragment

2a. *Eucera longicornis* (L.) – male   ×1½
2b. female   ×1½

▲ **3.** *Chalicodoma muraria* L.

4a. *Osmia rufa* (L.) – male   ×1½
4b. female   ×1½

5. *Sphecodes spinulosus* von Hagens   ×1½

6a. *Andrena armata* (Gmelin) – male   ×1½
6b. female   ×1½

7. *Nomada lineola* Panzer   ×1½

▲ **8.** *Halictus scabiosa* (Rossi)   ×2

9. *Halictus malachurus* (Kirby)   ×2

10. *Ceratina cyanea* (Kirby)   ×3

Gaster of *Megachile* showing
how it is hollowed out in front

Bees belonging to the genera *Andrena* and *Halictus* are often confused, although
the *Halictus* species rarely have such flat abdomens as the *Andrena* species.
The groove at the hind end of the abdomen in female *Halictus* bees is a useful
guide, and the genera can also be separated by looking at the basal vein near
the middle of the front wing. In *Andrena* this vein is almost straight, but in
Halictus (and *Sphecodes*) it is quite strongly curved.

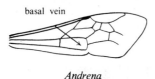

basal vein

Andrena

basal vein

Sphecodes

and attached to a plant (Pl. 41). The wasp stocks the flask with caterpillars paralysed by her sting and then lays a single egg, suspended from the roof above the caterpillars. She then seals the nest and flies off to build another one. The wasp larvae feed on the caterpillars through the autumn and winter and emerge as adults in the following summer. *E. unguiculata* is a larger European member of the genus.

The mason wasps of the genus *Odynerus* (Pl. 41) have a similar life history but their nests are built in sand or in the cavities of walls, especially those whose mortar is on the soft side. The nest usually has three or four cells or chambers and each is stocked with caterpillars and a single egg. Although their cells are close together, the larvae live independent lives and there is no co-operation or social activity. The parents never see their offspring.

The social wasps – all in the sub-family **Vespinae** – live in fairly large colonies and have a worker caste as well as the males and females (queens). Males and queens are much larger than workers (Pl. 42) and the males can be identified by their longer antennae – 13 segments to the female's 12. The wasp colonies are always annual affairs and only the mated queens survive the winter. Wasps never store up food in their nests and in temperate climates they never swarm to increase the number of colonies.

We have seven species of social wasps in Britain (Pl. 42) and all but one of them have the same sort of life history. The mated queens hibernate in some sheltered corner and wake up in the spring to look for a nesting site. The Common Wasp, German Wasp, and Red Wasp all make their nests under the ground as a rule – taking over old mouseholes and similar cavities which they enlarge. The Tree Wasp and Norwegian Wasp nest in trees and bushes and hang their nests from suitable branches. The Hornet (*Vespa crabro*) prefers hollow trees, upright or fallen. Our seventh species is the Cuckoo Wasp and it is the 'odd-man-out'. As its common name implies, it is a social parasite, having no workers. It lays its eggs in the nest of the Red Wasp where they are reared by the Red Wasp workers.

Having selected their sites, the queens start to collect building material. Unlike bees, the wasps have no wax glands and they cannot build wax combs. They use paper which they make from wood pulp, just like we make our paper from wood pulp. The wasps use their powerful jaws to scrape wood from trees and fence posts. They chew it up and mix it with saliva and then spread it out to make combs. The first part of the nest to be made is a little umbrella-shaped dome, suspended from the nesting cavity or branch. The cells are on the underside and open downwards. The queen fixes an egg in each cell and rears the resulting larvae on pulped insects. These larvae produce workers which take over building work and food collection while the queen gets down to egg-laying. More tiers of cells are formed below the first one, each attached to the one above by a number of slender paper stalks. The completed nest has about eight tiers and is ball-shaped. It is covered with a thin sheet of wasp paper, made up of shell-like lobes. Each lobe is banded, each band being the work of one wasp and one load of wood pulp. The entrance to the nest is usually near the bottom.

The internal structure of a wasp nest, showing the tiers of paper cells

A complete wasp nest may contain 20,000 individuals and all of these will have been reared on insects – many of them harmful. So it is not such a good idea to kill queen wasps in the spring. The adult wasps like sweet things and are certainly interested in our fruit and jam, but for most of the summer they are far too busy getting food for their young to bother us. They satisfy their craving for sweet things by occasional visits to flowers – although their short tongues do not allow them to get nectar from many flowers – and by taking saliva from the larval wasps in the nest. This saliva contains sugar over and above the needs of the sedentary larva and provides energy-giving carbohydrates for the active adults.

At the end of the summer, the wasps rear males and females in special large cells. When once these wasps have reached maturity, the colony begins to break up. The workers have no more larvae to feed and they can then turn their attention to fruit and other sweet substances. It is at this time that the wasps make a nuisance of themselves but as soon as the weather turns cold they die, leaving only the mated queens to carry on the race next year.

There are many additional species on the Continent. The Paper Wasp (*Polistes gallicus*) (Pl. 41) builds small nests, usually with less than 100 cells and without any surrounding envelope. It is a rather more delicate insect than the Common Wasp. *Vespula media* (Pl. 42) is another very common continental species. Heavily marked with black or dark brown, it is somewhat intermediate in appearance between a Hornet and a Common Wasp.

Superfamily Pompiloidea – The Spider-hunting Wasps (Pl. 40)

These insects are represented in Britain by about 40 species, all members of the family **Pompilidae**. They can be recognised by the pronotum, which extends back to the tegulae, and by their long, slender legs. Many of them have orange and black abdomens (Pl. 40). They are all solitary insects and all of them provision their nests with spiders. Most of them live in sandy areas and, like the Sphecoidea, they make their nests in the ground. This habit is responsible for the name digger wasps which is often applied to the members of both superfamilies.

The life history of all species follows the same pattern. The adults emerge in the summer and, after mating, the female sets about looking for spiders. She chases them with a very agile run, and, having caught one, she paralyses it with her sting. The next thing is to make a burrow and she does this by digging with her mandibles and legs. The spider is then dragged into the nest chamber and is sometimes followed by a second and third if they are small spiders. The wasp then lays an egg in one of the spiders, seals up the burrow, and goes off to repeat the process. The wasp larvae feed on the paralysed spiders until winter, which they pass as larvae or pre-pupae. Then they pupate and the adults emerge in the summer. Male pompilids have no interest in spiders and spend their days visiting flowers. They are generally slimmer than the females.

Superfamily Sphecoidea (Pl. 40)

This is by far the largest group of our solitary wasps, having about 230 British representatives. They share with the Pompiloidea the common name of digger wasps, although not all of them actually dig – some make their nests in hollow stems and similar places. There is only one family – the **Sphecidae** – but it is divided into many sub-families. The members of the sub-family **Sphecinae** are

Plate 45   **BEES** – **Order Hymenoptera**

SUB-ORDER APOCRITA (Contd.)

Superfamily **Apoidea** (Contd.)
Family descriptions are omitted because the features used in separating the families of bees are not easily observed. A key to the British genera appears on page 280

1. *Epeolus cruciger* (Panzer)   × 3

2. *Melecta luctuosa* (Scopoli)   × 1½

3a. Honey bee – *Apis mellifera* L. – drone   × 1½
3b. Honey bee – queen   × 1½
3c. Honey bee – worker   × 1½

4a. *Anthophora acervorum* Fabr. – male   × 1½
4b. *Anthophora acervorum* – female   × 1½

▲   **5.** *Anthophora hispanica* Fabr.   × 1½

▲   **6.** *Xylocopa violacea* (L.)

   *****7a.** Buff-tailed humble bee – *Bombus terrestris* L. – drone
   7b. Buff-tailed humble bee – worker
   7c. Buff-tailed humble bee – queen

*These are of the British race: Continental specimens have white 'tails'

Plate 46
BUMBLE BEES AND CUCKOO BEES – Order Hymenoptera

SUB-ORDER APOCRITA (Contd.)

Superfamily **Apoidea** (Contd.)   p. 278

1. *Bombus lucorum* L. $\times 1\frac{1}{4}$

2. *Bombus lapidarius* L. $\times 1\frac{1}{4}$

3. *Bombus pratorum* L. $\times 1\frac{1}{4}$

4. *Bombus agrorum* Fabr. $\times 1\frac{1}{4}$

▲ 5. *Bombus argillaceus* Scopoli $\times 1\frac{1}{4}$

▲ 6. *Bombus consobrinus* Dahlbom $\times 1\frac{1}{4}$

▲ 7. *Bombus hyperboreus* Schönherr $\times 1\frac{1}{4}$

▲ 8. *Bombus mastrucatus pyrenaicus* Gerst. $\times 1\frac{1}{4}$

9. *Psithyrus rupestris* Fabr. – female $\times 1\frac{1}{4}$

10a. *Psithyrus vestalis* Geoffroy – male $\times 1\frac{1}{4}$
10b. *Psithyrus vestalis* – female $\times 1\frac{1}{4}$

All are queens unless otherwise stated

The species of Psithyrus are 'cuckoo bees', laying their eggs in the nests of other species. Each species of Psithyrus is very similar to its normal host species and difficult to separate from it. The main differences are the much less hairy abdomen in Psithyrus, with the shiny body plates showing through, and the lack of pollen baskets on the females of this genus.

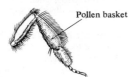

Pollen basket

Hind legs of *Bombus* (left) and *Psithyrus*

commonly called sand wasps because they excavate their burrows in sandy places. Our four species, typified by *Ammophila sabulosa* (Pl. 40), are readily recognised by the shape of the abdomen – very narrow in front and ending in a 'club'. The middle part of the abdomen is always orange in our species.

Unlike the spider-hunting pompilids, *Ammophila* digs its burrow before getting its prey. The burrow has a narrow neck and widens out at the bottom to form a flask-shaped cavity. When it is complete, the wasp closes it and flies up around it to get her bearings of its position. She then goes in search of a caterpillar – always a non-hairy one – which she will paralyse and then drag or air-lift back to the burrow. Having got the caterpillar into the burrow, *Ammophila* lays an egg on it, and then withdraws, closing the entrance with a grain of sand. The young wasp feeds on the caterpillar and emerges in the following summer. *Ammophila pubescens* exhibits a slight advance towards social behaviour in that the parent female replenishes the larval food supply several times. She often attends to several larvae in different burrows. None of our other *Ammophila* species carries out this progressive provisioning.

The rest of our Sphecoidea are more in keeping with the general idea of wasps, being either black or black and yellow in the main (Pl. 40). They can be distinguished from the true wasps because the pronotum does not reach the tegulae and the wings are not folded lengthwise when at rest. The prey of these solitary wasps varies from group to group and includes aphids, flies, beetles, and froghopper nymphs. Some of them make burrows with several cells and, although they are all mass-provisioned and independent of each other, we can consider this to be a first stage in the evolution of social behaviour.

Superfamily Apoidea – The Bees (Plates 43-46)

All the bees, both social and solitary, are included in this superfamily, although the social species, comprising less than 30 of our 250 or so kinds of bees, are confined to just two families – the **Halictidae** and the **Apidae**. All bees, whether social or solitary, feed on pollen and nectar and they rear their young on the same diet. In this respect they differ from all the wasps, whose young are fed entirely on a meat diet. Visibly, the bees differ from the true wasps and the spider-hunting pompilids because the pronotum does not reach back to the tegulae (Fig. p. 249). Bees can be separated from the other digger wasps (Sphecoidea) by their broad and usually hairy back legs. The microscope will also reveal that many of the bees' hairs are feathery – an adaptation for collecting pollen – whereas those of the wasps are unbranched.

The glossa or 'tongue' is usually well developed, usually pointed and often very long, although bees of the genera *Prosopis* and *Colletes* have very short, wasp-like tongues, wider at the front than behind. *Andrena* and related genera have pointed tongues but they are still relatively short and broad. These bees are very important pollinators of many flowers but they cannot reach nectar concealed in deep-throated flowers. Here, the important pollinators are the long-tongued bees such as the Honey Bee (*Apis*), the bumble bees (*Bombus*), and the flower bees (*Anthophora*). Despite the great development of the glossa for sucking up nectar, the bees still retain their mandibles or jaws and they use them mainly for building their nests and cells, often cutting wood and leaves in the process.

The feathery hairs of the bees have already been mentioned. Pollen adheres to these hairs very well and one often sees bees almost yellow with pollen as they wander over the flowers. Apart from the parasitic bees, which rely on the pollen and nectar stored by other bees, female and worker bees usually possess special pollen-carrying equipment, either on the back legs or on the underside of the abdomen. In its simplest form, this equipment is a 'brush' of hairs to which the pollen is attached as it is periodically combed from the body. The pollen baskets formed on the hind tibiae of bumble bees and honey bees are rather more complicated structures. The outer surface of the tibia is smooth and shiny but it is

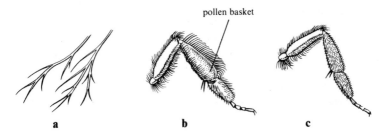

a, highly magnified bee hairs; **b,** hind leg of *Bombus*, showing the pollen basket; **c,** hind leg of *Psithyrus*

bordered on both sides by stout, curved hairs which form a flexible cage or basket (Pl. 46). Pollen is combed from the body with the front legs and then moistened and passed to the back legs where it is packed into the baskets. A good deal of pollen can be carried in this way – some bumble bees have been known to carry as much as 60 per cent of their own weight in pollen, although the average is probably about 20 per cent – and bulging yellow pollen baskets are a common sight on bees returning to the nest.

There are quite a number of families in the Apoidea but their separation is a difficult task, involving many minute and often obscure features. There are, however, less than 30 genera in Britain and these are relatively easy to separate on the basis of shape, size, colour, and certain other reasonably visible features. The sub-marginal cells mentioned in the following key are the cells just behind vein Rs in the distal half of the front wing.

Front wings of *Megachile* (*left*) and *Bombus*, showing the sub-marginal cells

A Simplified Key to the Genera of British Bees (Apoidea), excluding a few rather uncommon genera. Parasitic genera are marked with an asterisk

1. Tongue short and bilobed, broadest at front   2

    Tongue pointed at the front   3

2. Insects black and hairless   *Prosopis*, p. 281
    Insects hairy, banded with black and yellow or white   *Colletes*, p. 278

3. Front wing with two sub-marginal cells   4
    Front wing with three sub-marginal cells   13

4. Tongue short and ovate   5

    Tongue long and slender   7

5. Bees at least 12mm long: conspicuous tufts of golden
    hair on hind tibiae, especially in female   *Dasypoda*
    Bees no more than 10mm long   6

6. Tibiae with tawny hairs   *Panurgu$_s$*
    Tibiae with white hairs   *Macropi$_s$*

7. Hard, black, almost hairless bees   *Stelis**
    Bees more or less hairy, although hair may be sparse   8

8. Body very narrow and black: grey hairs on thorax:
    greyish bands on abdomen   *Chelostoma*
    Insects not like this   9

9. Gaster framed with golden hair   *Anthidium*
    Gaster not so adorned   10

10. Gaster black with white marks: tip very pointed in
    female and spiny in male   *Coelioxys**
    Insects not like this   11

11. Front of gaster scooped out on   *Megachile*, p. 283
    dorsal surface

    Front of gaster not scooped out   12

12. Female with pollen basket on legs: male with very long
    antennae   *Eucera*
    Female without pollen basket on legs: male antennae
    not unusually long   *Osmia*

13. Tongue short and ovate   14
    Tongue long and slender   17

14. Bees more or less hairless, especially on the abdomen:
    abdomen black with red or yellow   15
    Bees hairy and not usually marked with red or yellow   16

15. Antennae usually completely black: insects never with
    yellow markings   *Sphecodes**, p. 287
    Antennae usually at least partly red: insects often with
    wasp-like colouring   *Nomada**, p. 287

16. Abdomen very flattened   *Andrena*, p. 282
    Abdomen more cylindrical: female with prominent
    groove at tip of abdomen   *Halictus*, p. 283

17. Small metallic blue insects   *Ceratina*
    Insects not blue   18

18. Gaster black with whitish spots   19
    Gaster not so coloured   20

19. Insects less than 10mm long: legs not hairy   *Epeolus**
    Insects more than 12mm long: legs hairy   *Melecta**

20. Bees more or less densely hairy   21
    Bees less hairy, especially on abdomen   *Apis*, p. 286

21. Eyes reaching down the side of   *Anthophora*
    the face and meeting
    the mandibles

    Eyes not reaching down to mandibles   22

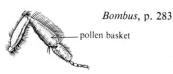

    cheek

22. Outer surface of hind tibiae covered with hairs: ab-
    dominal hairs relatively sparse and tergites shining
    through   *Psithyrus**, p. 287

    Outer surface of hind tibiae not   *Bombus*, p. 283
    covered with hairs but fringed
    with long hairs which form the   pollen basket
    pollen basket in the female:
    abdominal hairs dense and covering
    tergites

There is not room in this book for descriptions of all the bee genera, although all those mentioned in the key are illustrated (Pls. 43 to 46). We must make do with a brief survey illustrating the various degrees of social behaviour.

Bees of the genus *Prosopis* (Pl. 43) are rather small, almost hairless insects, black with yellow faces – hence their common name of yellow-faced bees. In fact, they do not look much like bees at all but they feed their young with pollen and nectar. They are all solitary insects and they make small nests – only half a dozen or so cells – in hollow stems and similar places. The cells are constructed with a secretion from the female bee's mouth. This secretion soon hardens into a transparent membrane which forms the walls of the cells. The short, blunt tongue – which distinguishes *Prosopis* and *Colletes* from all other bees – plays a major part in the formation of the cells. *Prosopis*, being almost hairless, cannot collect

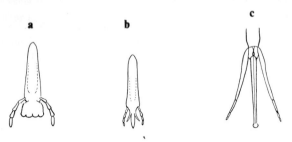

Tongues of bees: **a,** broad wasp-like tongue of *Prosopis*; **b,** short and ovate tongue of *Andrena*; **c,** long slender tongue of *Apis*

pollen in the usual way and the female fills her crop with both nectar and pollen. She provisions her nest cells with this mixture – the so-called 'bee-bread' – and lays an egg in each. The cells are then closed and the parent bee dies. There is no contact between parent and offspring. *Prosopis* has only one generation each year, the bees emerging in the summer and being particularly common at bramble flowers in July and August. The short, wasp-like tongue and the absence of any pollen-gathering equipment in *Prosopis* lend support to the idea that bees evolved from wasp-like ancestors and gradually evolved pollen-gathering equipment to go with their vegetarian habits. *Prosopis* is certainly one of the most primitive bees.

Members of the genus *Andrena* (Pl. 43) – with some 60 species in Britain – are rather variable as far as size and colour go. They are generally quite hairy and they look very much like honey bees, although they can be distinguished quite easily by their short tongues (Fig. above). The most constant feature of all these bees is the marked flattening of the abdomen. *Andrena* species are all solitary and they make their nests in the ground – usually selecting light, sandy soil. There may be many nests close together, giving the impression of communal life, but each female is working alone to excavate a small burrow with perhaps half a dozen earthen chambers. *Andrena* species, together with *Halictus*, are often called mining bees because of their burrowing habits. There is no contact between parent and offspring, the female bee showing no interest in her burrow after she has made and provisioned the cells. She is probably dead before her progeny emerge. Most of the species emerge from their nests in the spring and, after mating, the females go about making fresh burrows. Many species produce a second generation about July but others take a whole year to complete their life cycles and adults are found only for a short period each year. *Andrena* bees are favourite hosts of stylopid parasites (p. 320).

Leaf-cutting bees of the genus *Megachile* are quite well known on account of their activities on our rose bushes. These bees nest mainly in dead wood and their cells are constructed from pieces of leaf cut neatly from the plant with the bees' large mandibles. The bees are not unlike honey bees in some ways but they can always be distinguished because they have only two sub-marginal cells (Pl. 44). They are all solitary species.

Bees of the genus *Halictus* are hairy, although not markedly so, and they are generally rather small. Females of this genus are easily identified by the groove at the tip of the abdomen (Pl. 44) but the males are less easily recognised and may often be confused with *Andrena*, although they are less flattened than *Andrena*. Another difference, although not always obvious, is the strongly curved basal vein of *Halictus* (Pl. 44). In *Andrena*, this vein is almost straight. Most species of *Halictus* are solitary bees with nesting habits very similar to those of *Andrena*, but there are some sub-social and social species. Several species guard their nests after stocking them and laying their eggs, and the parent females often remain around long enough to make contact with their offspring. Progressive provisioning is practised by some foreign species, although there is not necessarily any co-operation between parent and offspring. *Halictus malachurus* (Pl. 44), not uncommon in the southern half of Britain, has reached the stage of social co-operation, although it retains mass provisioning of its cells. This species – in fact the whole genus – differs from *Andrena* in that the adult females hibernate after mating. They come out of their winter quarters in the spring and make their nesting burrows which they provision in the normal way. The females – or queens as they can rightly be called – stay in and around the nest and guard it. So far, things are just as they are in some of the solitary species, but here comes the difference: the bees that emerge from the first cells are all worker females. They set to work building more cells and provisioning them ready for the queen to lay more eggs. This next batch of eggs gives rise to normal male and female bees which mate and then only the mated females survive – usually hibernating gregariously in their old nests. By producing a first brood of workers – although there are not more than a dozen or two – this *Halictus* species is able to raise a larger family than any of the solitary bees which have to rely on the efforts of one female. *H. malachurus* therefore is a clear intermediate between solitary bees such as *Andrena* and the more highly developed social species such as the bumble bees and hive bees.

The large, hairy bumble bees (or humble bees) familiar to everyone are usually species of *Bombus*. They are usually black with a greater or lesser amount of yellow banding (Pl. 45), and their common names – Red-tailed Bumble Bee, Buff-tailed Bumble Bee, and so on – often refer to the colouring. All of these bees are social insects and they usually make their nests under the ground, although some – often called carder bees – nest in the dense vegetation and leaf litter at the bottom of hedgerows and so on. The mated queens (Pl. 46) are the only ones to survive the winter and the bumble bee story is very much like that of the wasp. The queen comes out of hibernation in the spring and looks for a suitable site, such as a mousehole. She does not seem to be in much of a hurry to start her nest – perhaps she waits until there are sufficient flowers for her to feed her offspring – and spends much of her time at rest. Dried grass and moss are collected for the nest – these materials are often already present in the hole if it has been used by a mouse or vole – and made into a light ball. Then the bee flies off for a load of pollen and nectar. On returning to the nest, the queen bee

Plate 47 **BEETLES – Order Coleoptera**

Insects in which the front wings are tough and horny, covering the hind wings and normally covering the abdomen as well. Front wings (elytra) meet in mid line   p. 290

Family **Cicindelidae** – Tiger Beetles   p. 294
Antennae attached to top of head: elytra without striae

1. Green tiger beetle – *Cicindela campestris* L. ×1½

2. Wood tiger beetle – *Cicindela sylvatica* L. ×1½

Family **Carabidae** – Ground Beetles   p. 295
Antennae attached to side of head: elytra usually striated

3. *Feronia cuprea* (L.) ×1½

4. *Feronia nigrita* (Fabr.) ×1½

5. *Leistus spinibarbis* (Fabr.) ×1½

6. *Elaphrus cupreus* Dufts. ×1½

7. Bombardier beetle – *Brachinus crepitans* (L.) ×3

8. *Dromius quadrimaculatus* (L.) ×3

9. *Dyschirius globosus* (Herbst) ×6

10. *Amara aulica* (Panzer) ×3

11. *Carabus granulatus* L.

12. *Carabus nemoralis* Mueller

13. *Carabus violaceus* L.

△ Family **Rhysodidae**   p. 294
Stout, beaded antennae

▲ **14.** *Rhysodes sulcatus* (Fabr.) ×3

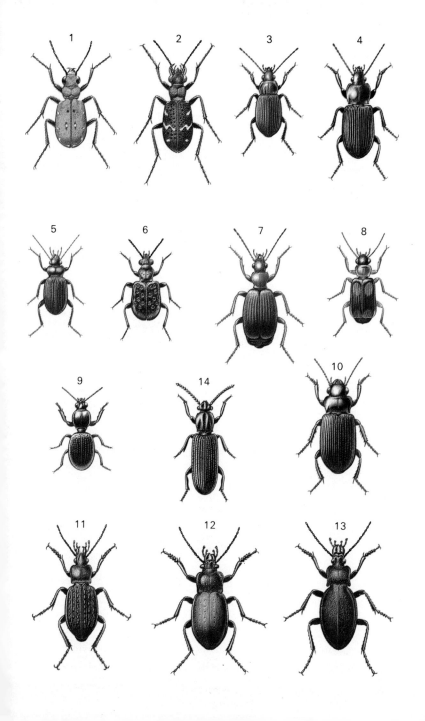

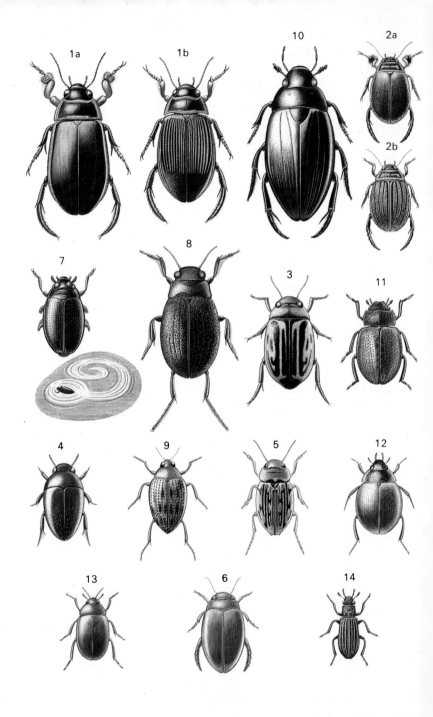

Family **Dytiscidae**   p. 296
   Elytra without rows of distinct punctures: often large beetles

1a. *Dytiscus marginalis* L. male
1b. *Dytiscus marginalis* L. female

2a. *Acilius sulcatus* (L.) male
2b. *Acilius sulcatus* (L.) female

3. *Platambus maculatus* (L.) × 3

4. *Noterus capricornis* (Herbst) × 4

5. *Deronectes depressus* (Fabr.) × 4

6. *Laccophilus minutus* (L.) × 4

Family **Gyrinidae** – Whirligig beetles   p. 295
   Middle and hind legs short and paddle-like

7. *Gyrinus natator* (L.) × 3

Family **Hygrobiidae**   p. 296
   Prominent eyes

8. *Hygrobia hermanni* (Fabr.) × 3

Family **Haliplidae**   p. 295
   Small beetles with distinct elongate punctures on elytra: hind coxae forming large plates

9. *Haliplus fulvus* (Fabr.) × 4

Family **Hydrophilidae**   p. 300
   Clubbed antennae and long palps

10. *Hydrous piceus* (L.)

11. *Spercheus emarginatus* (Schaller) × 3

12. *Laccobius sinuatus* Mots. × 4

13. *Enochrus testaceus* (Fabr.) × 4

14. *Hydrochus elongatus* (Schaller) × 4

manufactures a small plate of 'bee-bread' with the nectar and pollen and places it in the centre of the nesting material. She then lays up to a dozen eggs on this plate and surrounds them with a wall of wax which she produces from special glands on her abdomen. This cell is roofed over with wax too and the bee also builds a wax honey pot in which she stores honey to keep her and her brood going in bad weather. The queen sits on the cell and keeps the eggs warm. They hatch within about five days and the larvae grow rapidly on the bee-bread. The queen adds more food from time to time and, within a fortnight, the young bees have pupated and are ready to emerge. The new bees are, of course, all workers and they are somewhat smaller than the later workers. The queen continues to build wax cells for her eggs but the workers take over the job of feeding later batches of grubs. Male and female bumble bees appear later in the year and, after mating, the new queens take a few meals and find somewhere to hibernate.

The Honey Bee, or Hive Bee (*Apis mellifera*) is probably the most widely and deeply studied insect in the world and numerous lengthy books have been written on its social behaviour and on the wonderful ways in which the workers communicate with each other and pass on information about good sources of nectar. It is not really a native of Britain, although it has been here for some time. The perennial nature of the honey bee colony suggests that it comes from warmer parts and it almost certainly comes from South-East Asia.

The three castes – queen, drone, and worker – are more easily distinguished among the honey bees than among the other species (Pl. 45). The queen honey bee does nothing in the way of household work or food collecting because she never founds a colony alone – she always comes into an existing colony or else takes some workers off to start a new one. The queen therefore has no pollen baskets, no wax glands for building cells, and she has a shorter tongue than the workers.

Honey bee cells are formed on large vertical sheets hung from the roof of the nesting cavity – usually the hive, although bees do sometimes nest in hollow trees if a swarm escapes the attention of the bee-keeper. Each cell is perfectly hexagonal and the cells are used for rearing the young and for storing pollen and honey. Drone cells tend to be slightly larger than the normal brood cells and they occur mainly near the edges of the comb. Eggs are usually laid in them towards the end of the summer and the size of the cells somehow causes the queen to lay unfertilised, drone-producing eggs. Queen cells are irregular cone-shaped chambers hanging downwards from the edges of the comb. They are produced when the colony is about to swarm or when the workers feel that the queen is failing. The eggs laid in the queen cells are just the same as those laid in the worker cells and the future of the egg is controlled by the workers. For the first three days of their lives all bee grubs are fed on 'royal jelly' – a protein-rich secretion from the salivary glands of the workers. After three days, the grubs destined to become workers are fed on pollen and nectar but the budding queens continue to receive royal jelly. Transferring eggs and young larvae from queen cells to worker cells and vice versa clearly shows that it is the feeding and not the genetic make-up of the egg that controls queen production. Bee-keepers actually transfer eggs from the comb to artificial queen cells in order to get more queens and so more colonies. Colonies that have lost their queen for some reason or other quickly set about increasing the size of some worker cells to produce 'emergency queens'. The loss of the original queen very soon becomes apparent in the colony because the workers miss the 'queen substance' which she gives out and which is passed from worker to worker when they feed each other and communicate with each other.

The first new queen to emerge from her cell usually goes around and stings her rivals while they are still in their cells and then she goes off on her marriage flight. She normally returns to her own hive and the workers kill off the old queen if she is failing. Alternatively, the old queen may take off with a swarm of workers to found another colony. Very occasionally, a colony may swarm again in the same year. If so, it is the new virgin queen that goes off with the swarm and not the established queen.

A well-formed honey bee colony may contain more than 50,000 bees, almost all of them workers. The queen lives for several years but the drones and the workers are short-lived, especially in summer when there is much work to do. Summer workers rarely live more than a few weeks. Drones are tolerated in summer but they do no work and they are thrown out in the autumn when the somewhat depleted colony settles down to rest, feeding on stored pollen and honey collected in the previous summer.

Mention has already been made of the parasitic bees. They do not actually feed on their hosts but merely take food which was intended for the host larvae. They are therefore social parasites and they are often called cuckoo bees. Some entomologists prefer to call them inquilines, retaining the word parasite for those animals that actually feed on their hosts. The genus *Nomada* contains many rather wasp-like bees with black and yellow or brown and yellow markings (Pl. 44). Most of them parasitise *Andrena* or *Halictus*. As with other cuckoo bees, *Nomada* has no pollen collecting equipment. Bees of the genus *Sphecodes* also parasitise *Halictus*. Our *Sphecodes* species never have any yellow but some species are likely to be confused with the black and brown species of *Nomada*. One useful distinction is that the antennae of *Sphecodes* are hardly ever tipped with red, whereas those of *Nomada* usually are. Another distinction is that the basal vein of *Nomada* is almost straight, whereas that of *Sphecodes* is strongly curved (Pl. 44).

As a final example of bees, we will look at *Psithyrus*, a genus of cuckoo bees that parasitise bumble bees. We have six species of *Psithyrus* and each sticks pretty well to one (sometimes two) host species, which it resembles quite closely (Pl. 46). Females are quite easily distinguished – those of *Psithyrus* have no pollen baskets (Pl. 46) – but the males are not so easy. One of the best guides is the hairiness of the abdomen. The abdominal tergites show through the coat of *Psithyrus* as shiny plates, but those of *Bombus* are almost always hidden by hairs.

The female *Psithyrus* hibernates just like the *Bombus* queen but she does not awake until some weeks after *Bombus* has started work. By this time, the nest has been made and a few smallish workers are in attendance. *Psithyrus* now makes her appearance and enters the host's nest. She may be attacked by the workers but there are not many of them and they are relatively small. Their stings are unable to penetrate the tough coat of the cuckoo bee and she is able to kill some of the workers quite easily if need be. After the initial unrest, the *Psithyrus* is tolerated and she starts to lay her own eggs. These are reared by the *Bombus* workers but few, if any, *Bombus* young are reared from now on – the invader either kills the *Bombus* queen or eats her eggs as soon as they are laid.

The continental fauna has many more species than we have in Britain, and many of them are considerably larger (Pl. 45). There are also some additional genera. Mention can be made of *Xylocopa*, a widespread genus many of whose

Plate 49   BEETLES – Order Coleoptera (Contd.)

Family **Silphidae** – burying beetles   p. 301
  Strongly clubbed antennae: hind part of abdomen exposed
1. *Necrophorus humator* (Goeze) ×1¼
2. *Necrophorus vespilloides* Herbst ×1¼
3. *Necrophorus investigator* Zett. ×1¼
4. *Phosphuga atrata* (L.) ×2

Family **Staphylinidae** – rove beetles   p. 301
  Antennae not clubbed: very short elytra: six abdominal
  segments usually exposed
5. Devil's coach horse – *Ocypus olens* Mueller ×1¼
6. *Tachyporus hypnorum* (Fabr.) ×3
7. *Stenus bimaculatus* Gyll. ×2
8. *Paederus littoralis* Grav. ×2
9. *Philonthus marginatus* (Fabr.) ×2
10. *Emus hirtus* (L.) ×2
11. *Creophilus maxillosus* (L.) ×2

Family **Sphaeritidae**   p. 300
  Shiny beetles with strongly clubbed but not elbowed
  antennae: front tibia not toothed: one abdominal segment
  exposed
12. *Sphaerites glabratus* (Fabr.) ×3

Family **Histeridae**   p. 300
  Shiny beetles with strongly clubbed elbowed antennae:
  front tibia strongly toothed: two abdominal segments
  exposed
13. *Hister cadaverinus* Hoff. ×2

Family **Buprestidae**   p. 307
  Metallic insects with head sunk deep into thorax: eyes often
  large
14. *Agrilus pannonicus* (Piller) ×3
▲ **15.** *Buprestis aurulentus* (L.) ×2

Family **Byrrhidae**   p. 306
  Rounded or oval beetles which can withdraw appendages
  into grooves on the underside of the body
16. *Byrrhus pilula* L. ×2

Family **Dascillidae**   p. 306
  Conical front coxae: tarsal segments strongly lobed
17. *Dascillus cervinus* (L.) ×2

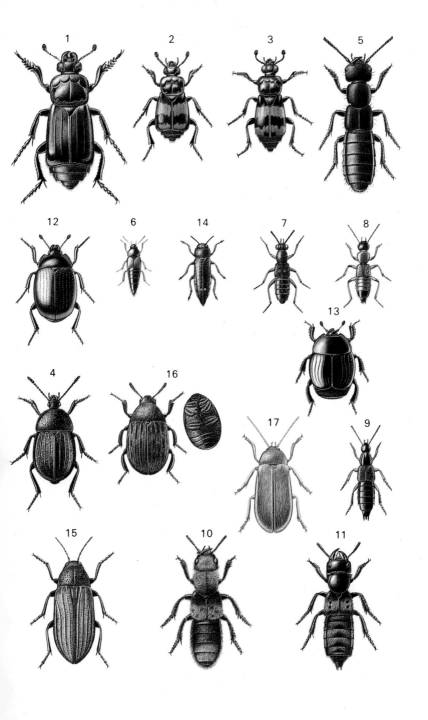

BEETLES – Order Coleoptera (Contd.)

Plate 50

Family **Lucanidae**   p. 302
Antennae more or less elbowed: last few antennal segments
expanded into flattened lobes
1a. Stag beetle – *Lucanus cervus* (L.) male
1b. female
2. Lesser stag beetle – *Dorcus parallelopipedus* (L.)
3. *Sinodendron cylindricum* (L.)   × 1½

Family **Geotrupidae**   p. 303
Antennae with 11 segments and not elbowed: last few
antennal segments expanded into leaf-like flaps which can
be drawn together to form a club: jaws visible from above
4. Dor beetle – *Geotrupes stercorarius* (L.)   × 1½
5a. *Typhaeus typhoeus* (L.) – male   × 1½
5b. female   × 1½
6. *Odontaeus armiger* (Scopoli)   × 1½

Family **Trogidae**   p. 303
Antennae not elbowed: last 3 antennal segments expanded
into leaf-like flaps which can be drawn together to form a
club: elytra roughly sculptured and often hairy
7. *Trox scaber* (L.)   × 2

Family **Scarabaeidae**   p. 303
Antennae with 9 or 10 segments and not elbowed: last few
antennal segments expanded into leaf-like flaps which can
be drawn together to form a club: jaws not normally visible
from above
8. *Copris lunaris* (L.)   × 1½
9. *Aphodius rufipes* (L.)   × 2

members have violet-tinged wings (Pl. 45). *Chalicodoma muraria* is a large relative of *Megachile*, but it makes its nest cells with mud instead of with leaves.

Collecting and Preserving
The larger species, including many of the bees and wasps, ichneumons, and sawflies, can be taken on the wing. It is often an easy matter to box them while they are feeding at flowers as well. The smaller insects can be obtained by beating and sweeping vegetation and also by collecting the hosts of the parasitic species.

All normal killing agents are suitable for Hymenoptera. The method of display depends largely on the size of the insect. Large ones can be pinned and set. Staging and pointing are both suitable for some of the smaller species but a lot of practice is necessary before one can arrange the wings neatly. The smallest species, together with some of the rather soft-bodied ichneumons, are best preserved in spirit.

Order Coleoptera – Beetles

Recognition features Minute to large insects, normally with two pairs of wings of which the front ones are hard or leathery and meet neatly along the mid-line of the dorsal surface. The hind wings are membranous and usually folded away out of sight beneath the front wings. Hind wings are sometimes absent, while a few species have no wings at all. The prothorax is normally large and mobile. Mouthparts are always of the biting type.

Most beetles can be recognised as such by the form of the front wings (elytra). The most frequent confusion is with heteropteran bugs but these have overlapping front wings, usually with a membranous portion at the tip, and tubular, sucking mouth-parts. Some of the beetles with short elytra look like earwigs but they never have the abdominal pincers of earwigs.

A typical beetle, showing the large prothorax and the hard elytra covering the whole of the abdomen

With more than 250,000 known species, this is the largest of all insect orders. More than 4,000 species are found in Britain. In the tropical Hercules and Goliath beetles, with weights in the region of 100 grams, the Coleoptera contains the bulkiest of all insects. But such is the range of form and size within the order that it also contains some of the smallest insects, less than 0.5mm long. Beetles are abundant as individuals as well as in terms of species, although this may not be apparent to the casual observer because of the small size and secretive or nocturnal habits of many species. Most beetles can and do fly well but relatively little time is spent in flight: beetles are very much insects of the ground and low vegetation.

Within the limitations imposed by their biting mouth-parts, the beetles have invaded all available habitats – including the sea – and exploited all possible food sources. The order includes plant-feeders – with many important wood-borers – scavengers, predators, and parasites: few natural organic materials escape the attentions of one or other of these groups. Many species are serious pests: chafers and many other beetles damage our growing crops; several species infest stored grain and flour; carpets and other fabrics are eaten by carpet beetles; and timber is weakened by woodworm and other beetles. Most of the damage is done by the larvae but the adults often do their share, although many prefer pollen or nectar. On the credit side, many beetles are useful allies in combating other insect pests. The aphid-eating ladybirds are especially important. Other useful beetles include the dung beetles and burying insects that consume animal dung and carrion and are an important link in the nitrogen cycle.

The success of beetles is due largely to the tough elytra and the hardness of the cuticle in general. The elytra allow the beetles to live under stones and in litter, thus making use of the shelter provided, yet still retain the delicate wings necessary for dispersal. The hard cuticle makes the beetles resistant to injury and desiccation, thus allowing them to live in drier places than most insects – granaries for example. The elytra also enable the beetles to live in water: the space between the elytra and the body is filled with air and acts as an air tank for the water beetle. The biting jaws, although primitive in themselves, have also contributed to the beetles' success because they have remained adaptable and usable for a wide variety of functions, not only feeding.

The beetle head is a heavily sclerotised capsule and, with a few notable exceptions, it is fairly constant in structure throughout the order. The main exception concerns the weevils, in which the head is extended forwards to form the rostrum or snout. The antennae are then inserted at some point along the rostrum. Beetle antennae themselves are basically 11-segmented, although this number is often reduced (rarely increased). The form of the antennae varies considerably and is an important feature in classification. Many species have clearly 'elbowed' antennae. Compound eyes are usually present, although often small, but ocelli are found only in a few groups. The mouth-parts are all fully developed, usually with prominent, biting mandibles. This does not mean, however, that beetles take only solid food: many of them macerate their food and moisten it with digestive juices before ingestion. Others lap up nectar and sap oozing from trees, while the larvae of several other species have tubular mandibles with which they suck up liquid food.

The prothorax is large and usually quite mobile, with the whole of the pronotum visible from above. The mesothorax – largest of the three segments in most flying insects – is the smallest in beetles because there are no functional wings on this segment. It is fused with the metathorax which is relatively large in all flying beetles. All but the mesoscutellum is covered by the elytra when the beetle is at rest.

The elytra themselves are highly modified front wings, horny or leathery and usually rather tough. The name Coleoptera refers to the elytra and means 'sheath wings' (Greek *koleos* = sheath). In some flightless weevils and other beetles in which the hind wings are absent the two elytra have become fused together, forming a single protective shield. The elytra are usually long enough to cover the whole of the abdomen when the beetle is at rest but in some families they are shorter and leave a greater or lesser part of the abdomen exposed. Normally only the last two or three segments are exposed in this way but the rove beetles of the family Staphylinidae reveal as many as seven segments (Pl. 49). There is often a delicate pattern of furrows or rows of pits on the elytra and this ornamentation is of great value when identifying beetles, especially below the family level. Other decorations include hairs, scales, and metallic sheens.

In flight, the elytra play no active part in propulsion and are held rigid at an angle to the body. They may provide some lift but the propulsion comes entirely from the membranous hind wings. At rest, these hind wings are folded neatly beneath the elytra and are not often seen. The venation is reduced but is sometimes of use in classification.

The legs are of normal construction but exhibit great variation according to the habits of the beetles and we find modifications for digging, swimming, and walking. The shape and arrangement of the coxae and their cavities is important in classification. The coxae may be longer than they are broad, in which case they project from their cavities, or they may be broader than long (transverse). If the two measurements are about the same, the coxae are rounded. The hind coxae are often hollowed out behind (excavate) to receive the femur when the

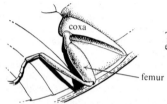

The underside of a beetle, showing the excavate hind coxa, into which the femur fits when the leg is folded

legs are folded. The normal number of tarsal segments is five on all legs, giving a tarsal formula 5, 5, 5, but there is often some reduction from this. The most frequent variation is the reduction of the 4th segment to a minute structure visible only under high magnification and the legs are then said to be 'apparently 4-segmented'. When the 4th segment is reduced in this way the 3rd segment is normally enlarged and it is this enlargement that conceals the small 4th segment There are other apparently 4-segmented legs, however, in which it is the basal segment that is minute.

The apparently 4-segmented tarsus of a leaf beetle (Chrysomelidae), showing how the minute fourth segment is concealed within the third segment

There is nothing unusual about the beetle abdomen, although certain features are used in the classification of these insects. The two main sub-orders are separated by the structure of the 1st abdominal sternite (p. 293) and several smaller divisions depend upon the number of visible abdominal sternites.

Beetle eggs are generally quite plain and typically egg-shaped, without fancy decoration. The number laid by each female depends on the species and varies from a dozen or so to several thousand. Some species lay theirs carefully where the young will find food; others simply scatter their eggs. Very few beetles care for their eggs and most of them perish before the eggs have hatched, but there are a few species that exhibit some form of parental care by watching over the eggs and young larvae. The larval head is always well developed and carries biting jaws very much like those of the adult. Adult and larva often eat the same type of food. Thoracic legs are usually present in the larvae but most weevil larvae, living in seeds, buds, etc., are legless. Other beetle larvae may be campodeiform, scarabaeiform, or eruciform, the campodeiform larvae being typical of the more primitive beetles.

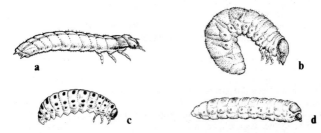

Beetle larvae: **a**, campodeiform larva of ground beetle; **b**, scarabaeiform larva of cockchafer; **c**, eruciform (caterpillar-like) larva of leaf beetle; **d**, apodous larva of weevil

The pupa is normally of the exarate type, with the appendages free. Boring larvae usually pupate in their larval quarters after tunnelling to a point near the surface of the stem or whatever they are in. Others pupate in the soil or in a flimsy cocoon above ground.

Most of our beetle species probably have only one generation each year, spending the winter as young larvae, pupae, or adults. Relatively few species seem to overwinter in the egg stage.

British and European beetles belong to two sub-orders – the **Adephaga** and the **Polyphaga**. A third sub-order – the **Archostemmata** – is not represented in Europe. The European sub-orders may be separated by the following characteristics:

Hind coxae immovably articulated to metasternum and completely dividing the 1st visible abdominal sternite: antennae 11 segmented usually filiform or moniliform

Adephaga, p. 294

Hind coxae usually movably articulated to metasternum and very rarely completely dividing 1st visible abdominal sternite: antennae of various types

Polyphaga, p. 296

SUB-ORDER ADEPHAGA

This is the more primitive of the two sub-orders and contains predominantly carnivorous species living on land and in fresh water. The name Adephaga presumably refers to the habit of going after food (Latin *ad* = towards). The larvae are campodeiform and are generally predatory like the adults. Both stages are generally very active. There is only one superfamily – the *Caraboidea* – and it has seven families, separable with the aid of the following key, based upon that given by Crowson in the RES Handbook.

Key to the Families of European Adephaga

1. Terrestrial insects with projecting sensory bristles on various parts of the body: hind coxae not extending laterally to meet elytra 2
   Aquatic insects without such sensory bristles and with the hind coxae extending laterally to meet the elytra 4

2. Antennae stout and hairy .... Rhysodidae, p. 294
   Antennae more slender 3

3. Elytra without regular striae: antennae inserted on top of head, just in front of eyes .... Cicindelidae, p. 294
   Elytra usually with regular striae: antennae inserted at side of head, between eyes and jaws .... Carabidae, p. 295

4. Compound eyes each completely divided into upper and lower halves: mid and hind legs forming short broad paddles .... Gyrinidae, p. 295
   Insects not like this 5

5. Elytra with rows of distinct elongate punctures: hind coxae forming large plates: insects under 6mm long ... Haliplidae, p. 295
   Elytra not so marked: hind coxae not forming large plates: insects often over 6mm long 6

6. Beetles with prominent bulging eyes (Pl. 48) ... Hygrobiidae, p. 296
   Eyes not bulging: head more rounded .... Dytiscidae, p. 296

The family **Rhysodidae** is found mainly in the tropics, but a few species are found in southern Europe. The beetles have a deeply grooved prothorax and stout moniliform antennae (Pl. 47). Both adults and larvae live in rotten wood.

Members of the **Cicindelidae** are commonly called tiger beetles. They are closely related to the Carabidae and often treated as a sub-division of that family, but they differ in the position of the antennae and in the ornamentation of the elytra, there being no obvious striation in the tiger beetles. Our five species, of which the commonest is the Green Tiger Beetle, *Cicindela campestris* (Pl. 47), are all long-legged, fast-running beetles fond of sunning themselves on the ground. When disturbed they take off in a noisy buzzing flight but they rarely fly far at one go and soon return to earth. Both adult and larva are fierce carnivores, the larva making a little burrow in which it lies in wait for prey. In association with this burrowing habit, tiger beetles are found mainly in areas of light, well-drained soil.

The **Carabidae** is a large family with about 350 British species. They are commonly known as ground beetles because they spend much of their time on or under the ground. Like the tiger beetles, these insects are good runners, but many of them lack wings and the elytra are fused together in several species. The fused elytra give the beetles added protection as they scramble about. Most ground beetles are nocturnal and they can be found hiding under logs and stones during the daytime. Both adults and larvae are mainly carnivorous but the larvae do not burrow: they go out and actively hunt for worms, slugs, and insect prey. The elytra normally have nine longitudinal ridges apiece, separated by furrows or rows of dots. This ornamentation is important in identifying the species. Black is the main colour among the ground beetles but many of them have beautiful metallic sheens (Pl. 47). The shape of the body is fairly constant throughout the family and many ground beetles, especially the larger ones, can be recognised as such on sight.

Two sub-families are represented in Britain (three if the tiger beetles are included here) and these are the **Carabinae** and the **Harpalinae**. They are easily distinguished because the Harpalinae, with about 290 of our ground beetles, all have notched front tibiae. Our largest ground beetles belong to the genus *Carabus*, whose members may reach a length of 25mm. This genus, typified by the

The notched front tibia of the sub-family Harpalinae

notch

Violet Ground Beetle (*C. violaceus*), is recognisable by the backward extension of the sides of the prothorax and sometimes by the flattened rim that runs around the edge of the elytra (Pl. 47). Most of our other common ground beetles are quite small, less than 12mm long, although the genus *Feronia* (still often called *Pterostichus*) contains some very common black species up to about 18mm long (Pl. 47). This genus belongs to the Harpalinae.

Members of the **Gyrinidae**, typified by the common *Gyrinus natator* (Pl. 48), are known as whirligig beetles because they spend most of their adult lives skimming round and round on the surface of still or slow-moving water. They are all small, shiny, black insects in which the middle and back legs are flattened and hair covered – ideal for skating over the surface and also for swimming. Each eye is divided into two parts – an upper part for seeing over the surface and a lower part for seeing down into the water. Whirligig beetles feed mainly on small insects that fall on to the water surface but they may occasionally dive after something. They also dive when disturbed. The beetles can be seen in huge numbers in late summer but then they disappear down into the mud for the winter. Eggs are laid on water plants when the beetles reappear in spring.

The **Haliplidae** contains a number of small beetles that are often called crawling water beetles because they do not swim much and prefer to creep about the masses of *Spirogyra* and other algae which is their main food. The beetles are easy to recognise because they all have a distinctive pattern (Pl. 48) and because the hind coxae form very broad plates.

The Screech Beetle (*Hygrobia hermanni*) is our only member of the **Hygrobiidae**. It is about 12mm long and has a convex body. The rather prominent eyes are
the most distinguishing features (Pl. 48) but the living insect will identify itself
when picked up by squeaking. It does this by rubbing the tip of the abdomen
against the undersides of the elytra. The larva is a strange looking creature, with
three feathery 'tails', found in muddy ponds.

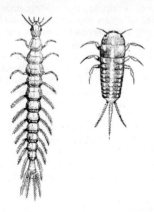

Larvae of whirligig beetle (*left*) and
screech beetle

The **Dytiscidae** is a fairly large family of water beetles, containing about 107
British species which range in length from 2mm to 38mm. The largest are the
diving beetles of the genus *Dytiscus*, *D. marginalis* (Pl. 48) being the most
common species. Most members of the family are rather dark in colour and they
are well streamlined, with the head drawn back into the prothorax to give a clean
outline to the body. The hind legs are used for swimming and they are broad and
hairy. Both adults and larvae are fierce carnivores and it is unwise to put the
larger species in an aquarium with anything else, even fair-sized fishes. The diving
beetles can make short work of frogs, newts, and sticklebacks and if they get
into a garden pond they will have goldfish too. The larvae are even more ferocious
than the adults but they feed in a different way. The larval mandibles are sharply
pointed and they each enclose a narrow canal. The mandibles are thrust into the
larva's prey and the larva then proceeds to suck its victim dry.

The genus *Noterus* (Pl. 48) stands a little apart from the rest of the Dytiscidae
because its members (two British species) have rather dilated antennae. Their
body shape also differs from that of the other genera because it is very convex
dorsally and yet almost flat ventrally. The rest of the family are usually less convex
dorsally and always somewhat rounded beneath. *Noterus* is therefore sometimes
placed in a separate family, the **Noteridae**.

SUB-ORDER POLYPHAGA

This is by far the largest sub-order of beetles and, as might be guessed from the
name (Polyphaga means 'eating many things'), it contains a very varied assortment of insects. Apart from all being beetles, there is little to link them together
and, although the families are fairly well defined, the higher groupings are far

from settled. Research during the last 20 years or so has led to the splitting up of such unsatisfactory groupings as Diversicornia – beetles with diverse antennae – but even now there are large and rather heterogeneous superfamilies such as the Cucujoidea whose diversity is illustrated on Pls. 52 and 53.

We have not room in this book to deal adequately with all the families and we are limiting our descriptions to the superfamilies and some of their more interesting or important members. The superfamilies given are those listed by Crowson in the RES Handbook and these differ quite considerably from the groupings used in many of the older works on beetles. To make life a little easier for readers brought up on the older books, the description of each superfamily includes mention of its position in the older classification.

The following key is a very much simplified one and ignores a number of 'odd-men-out'. Nevertheless, a large proportion of British beetles should be correctly placed with its aid.

A Simplified Key to the Superfamilies of British Polyphaga, based upon that given by Crowson in the RES Handbook

1. Head more or less prolonged into a beak, or else small cylindrical insects, often with elytra hollowed out at back (Pl. 56): antennae generally clearly clubbed and elbowed, the 1st segment (scape) retractable into a groove in the beak — Curculionoidea, p. 318
   Insects not fitting this description — 2

2. Antennae with 9–11 segments, the last 3–7 being expanded on one side to form a lamellate club — Scarabaeoidea, p. 302
   Antennae not like this but if last 3 segments form a club segment 8 is smaller than segment 7 or else hind coxa is excavate — 3

3. Antennae small, usually less prominent than maxillary palps and terminating in a small club — Hydrophiloidea, p. 300
   Antennae not so built and nearly always larger than palps — 4

4. Tarsi all apparently 4-segmented: antennae not clubbed — Chrysomeloidea, p. 315
   Tarsi not all apparently 4-segmented, or if so antennae clubbed — 5

5. Head nearly or quite as broad as thorax: antennae 10-segmented, the last 2 forming a club: minute insects <1.5mm long — Dascilloidea, p. 306
   Insects not fitting this description — 6

6. Rather elongate insects with long legs and soft bodies: tarsi always 5, 5, 5: antennae filiform or pectinate: sometimes wingless — 7
   Insects not fitting these descriptions — 10

7. Projecting bristly hairs on thorax and elytra mar-
gins: elytra often banded or spotted or metallic
(Pl. 52): always fully winged   Cleroidea, p. 312
No such hairs or coloration   8

8. Tarsi very long and thin: body more or less cylindrical: antennae short and toothed: male with
characteristic maxillary palps (Pl. 52)   Lymexyloidea, p. 312
More flattened insects with shorter tarsi, the penultimate segment being somewhat lobed below   9

9. Very narrow insects with the apices of elytra more
or less truncated   Cantharoidea, p. 310
More rounded insects with apices of elytra slightly
pointed   Dascilloidea, p. 306

10. Elytra truncate, with at least 3 abdominal segments
exposed: antennae rarely clubbed: tarsi without
lobed segments   Staphylinoidea, p. 301
Elytra usually exposing less than 3 segments, if
more than 3 then antennae are strongly clubbed   11

11. Hard black shiny insects with truncated elytra exposing 1 or 2 abdominal segments: antennae usually
elbowed and strongly clubbed: tarsi without lobed
segments   Histeroidea, p. 300
Insects not completely fitting these descriptions:
if only 1 or 2 abdominal segments exposed, tarsi
usually with penultimate segment lobed   12

12. Hind coxae clearly excavate behind: 13
antennae rarely clubbed

Hind coxae not clearly excavate behind, or if so
antennae strongly clubbed   18

13. Front coxae projecting: hind angles of prothorax
not acute   14
Front coxae transverse or rounded: hind angles of
prothorax usually acute   15

14. Prothorax strongly hooded   Bostrychoidea, p. 311
over head: last 3 antennal
segments differ from rest

Prothorax not so humped: last 3 antennal segments
not distinguished   Dascilloidea, p. 306

15. Insects very short and broad, with broad antennae   Dryopoidea, p. 306
    Insects not fitting this description   16

16. Short ovate insects, very convex and hairy on top   Byrrhoidea, p. 306
    Insects not like this: if similar in shape they are not
    hairy   17

17. Head strongly deflexed: antennae very short and
    toothed: insects generally more or less glabrous
    above   Buprestoidea, p. 307
    Head less strongly deflexed: antennae longer:
    insects pubescent above but not always clearly   Elateroidea, p. 307

18. Hind coxae excavate behind: antennae strongly
    clubbed   19
    Hind coxae not excavate behind, or if so the insects
    <1.5mm long   20

19. Middle coxae widely separated   Byrrhoidea, p. 306
    from each other: elytra usually
    distinctly striated

    middle coxae

    Middle coxae not widely separated: elytra not
    usually striated   Dermestoidea, p. 310

20. Prothorax usually forming a hood part way over
    the head: tarsi 5, 5, 5   Bostrychoidea, p. 311
    Prothorax not so formed, or if so tarsi actually or
    apparently 4, 4, 4   21

21. Antennae filiform: tarsi 5, 5, 5, with segment 5 and
    claws large   Dryopoidea, p. 306
    Antennae not usually filiform, if so then tarsi not
    as above   22

22. Front coxae projecting: prominent bristly hairs on
    some part of body: elytra covering abdomen   Cleroidea, p. 312
    Front coxae not projecting, or if so elytra shorter
    than abdomen or without prominent hairs   23

23. Front coxae distinctly projecting: antennal club
    often involving 4 or 5 segments   Staphylinoidea, p. 301
    Front coxae often transverse or rounded, if pro-
    jecting the hind tarsus has 4 segments: antennal
    club, if present, rarely with more than 3 segments   Cucujoidea, p. 312

Superfamily Hydrophiloidea

The members of this group were once included in a group called Clavicornia – 'beetles with clubbed antennae' – but were later separated and named Palpicornia. This name, referring to the prominent palps, is perhaps more descriptive of the group than the modern name Hydrophiloidea because, although most of the species are aquatic, there are several terrestrial ones. The adults are almost all vegetarians, feeding mainly on decaying plants, but many of the larvae are carnivorous. Although most of them live in stagnant water, these beetles are not good swimmers and have no flattened, oar-like legs. They spend most of their time crawling on water plants. As a group, they are sometimes called silver water beetles because the underside of the insect is covered with fine hairs that hold a layer of air and give the beetle a silvery appearance. The true colour of these insects, however, is usually black or dark brown. As well as the air film carried on the underside, these insects carry a bubble under their elytra but the method of replenishing this air supply is peculiar. Whereas most water beetles come up tail-first to take in air, the hydrophilids come up head-first and use their hairy antennae to break the surface film. The hairs are water-repellent and so there is a continuous tract of air from the surface, along the antenna, and into a groove along the side of the thorax. This groove leads along the body and connects with the spiracles and both dorsal and ventral air reservoirs. There is, of course, a groove along each side of the insect, but the beetle normally comes to the surface slightly on one side and only one antenna is involved at any one time. ·The enlarged palps of these beetles take over the normal functions of the antennae.

We have about 120 species. Some entomologists recognise five British families, whereas others consider all our members to belong to one family – the **Hydrophilidae**. The best known species is the Great Silver Beetle (*Hydrous piceus*) (Pl. 48). Reaching almost 50mm in length, this is our largest water beetle and, next to the Stag Beetle, our second largest beetle of any kind. Although vegetarian, it is capable of inflicting a nasty wound on unwary fingers through a sharp spine on the underside.

Superfamily Histeroidea

The members of this group were originally placed in the Clavicornia and Staphylinoidea but they are now separated on the basis of their strongly clubbed and usually elbowed antennae. All but one of our 40 or so species belong to the family **Histeridae**. The exception is the rather rare *Sphaerites glabratus* (Pl. 49) which is distinguished by its non-elbowed antennae. It belongs to the **Sphaeritidae**. The **Histeridae** are generally hard, shiny insects, black or black with red markings (Pl. 49). The elytra are short and leave two abdominal tergites exposed. When disturbed, the insects withdraw their appendages into grooves on the underside of the body and appear quite dead. They are scavenging insects, found in dung, carrion, rotting vegetation, and so on, but they appear to feed as much on other scavenging insects as on the refuse itself. The larvae are nearly all predatory.

Superfamily Staphylinoidea

These insects were originally placed in the Clavicornia, although many of them have thread-like antennae, but they have been known as Staphylinoidea for some time and are described as such in many of the older books. The only major change recently has been the removal of the Histeridae from this superfamily. Joy used the name Brachelytra for this group in view of the short elytra possessed by the majority of the species. This is a very large superfamily with 10 British families. The best known are the Silphidae – burying beetles and other non-burying carrion feeders – and the Staphylinidae – the rove beetles. Most of the species are scavengers or predators and they almost all have short elytra, exposing between three and six abdominal tergites.

The **Silphidae** includes the larger members of the group and all its members (60 British species) have strongly clubbed antennae. They are commonly called burying beetles or sexton beetles from the habit of some species of burying small carcasses. The beetles are mainly dark in colour but some of the larger and better-known species (genus *Necrophorus*) are marked with orange (Pl. 49). These beetles have a good sense of smell and they are attracted to carrion. The first individuals of each sex to arrive at a carcass appear to fight later arrivals and turn them away. Sexton beetles are therefore most often found singly or in pairs at a carcass. After mating, the insects set to work to bury the carcass – bird, mouse, mole, or what-have-you – by removing the soil beneath it. The jaws and spined tibiae are used in this operation, grass roots and other small obstacles being no problem for the strong jaws. The beetles have even been known to amputate limbs of the carcass to ease its passage down through the soil. They have also been seen dragging a dead animal from its original site to one where the soil was easier to dig. When the carcass is buried, the female beetle excavates a small passage leading off from the burial chamber and lays her eggs there. She then returns to the carcass and feeds. The male may or may not remain there but the female remains and feeds her offspring with regurgitated food during the early part of their life before they start to feed on the carcass themselves. The larvae undergo hypermetamorphosis, there being three distinct larval forms, starting with a typical campodeiform larva and ending with an almost legless 'maggot'. They pupate in individual cells hollowed out near the feeding chamber.

Although these insects are usually regarded as scavengers, there is not universal agreement on this point. Some species *do* eat carrion, but others are definitely carnivorous, feeding on fly larvae and other insects in the carcass.

We have nearly 1,000 species of rove beetles (**Staphylinidae**) in Britain, varying in size from the Devil's Coach Horse (Pl. 49) at about 25mm to minute beetles only about 1mm long. The antennae are not clubbed and the elytra are almost always small, giving the insects a superficial similarity to earwigs although, of course, they have no pincers. Despite the short elytra, however, the hind wings are large and flight is good in most species. Many of them can be found in and around animal dung but it is probable that most of them are predatory, feeding on the scavenging fly larvae and other insects. Ant nests also shelter a good many species of staphylinid beetles, or 'staphs' as they are often called by the entomologist. Some of these guests are welcomed because they produce sweet liquids which are enjoyed by the ants; others are merely tolerated and live as scavengers in the nest, sometimes taking the ants' eggs or larvae.

The **Pselaphidae** contains numerous small beetles, most of which inhabit ants' nests. The insects are very often ant-like themselves and they can usually be recognised by their clubbed antennae and relatively long clubbed palps.

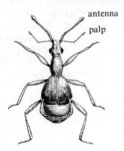

Pselaphus hesei, a member of the Pselaphidae, many of which are ant-like. The long palps are not found in all the species

Superfamily Scarabaeoidea

Called the Lamellicornia in older books, this superfamily is one of the easiest to recognise because of the structure of the antennae. The last three to seven antennal segments are expanded on one side to form a number of flat blades or lamellae which are usually capable of being folded together to form a conspicuous club (Fig. p. 18). The Scarabaeoidea is also a very large superfamily with well over 20,000 species, although only 92 are found in Britain. Its members are strong, heavy insects and they spend a lot of their time burrowing in the ground, in dung, or in rotten wood. Nevertheless, they are almost all very strong fliers. The males of many species possess bizarre outgrowths of the head and thorax. The larvae of this group are of the typical scarabaeiform type – soft-bodied, stout, and permanently curved (Fig. p. 293). They are usually surrounded by plenty of food – plant roots, dung, or rotting wood – and do not move much, although their thoracic legs are well developed.

Four families are recognised and they may be distinguished with the following key.

1. Antennae more or less elbowed: antennal lamellae unable to form a club — Lucanidae
   Antennae not elbowed: antennal lamellae can be drawn together to form a club — 2

2. Elytra roughly sculptured, with hairs, scales, or tubercles — Trogidae
   Elytra not so sculptured — 3

3. Antennae 11-segmented: jaws fully visible from above — Geotrupidae
   Antennae 9-10 segmented: jaws often concealed from above — Scarabaeidae

Best known of the three British members of the **Lucanidae** is the Stag Beetle (*Lucanus cervus*) (Pl. 50) which gets its name from the huge, antler-like mandibles of the male. Reaching 50mm in length, it is our largest beetle, but there is much variation in size and some specimens may be only half this length. Although the male may look rather frightening with its large 'horns', it is quite harmless. The jaws are so large that the muscles cannot move them with any power. The small mandibles of the female can give a much stronger nip. It would seem that the male mandibles are largely ornamental. This species breeds in rotting tree stumps and other suitable wood but it seems to be getting rarer.

The **Trogidae** and **Geotrupidae** are often treated as sub-families of the Scarabaeidae but modern practice is to give them family status. Our only members of the **Trogidae** are four not very common species of *Trox*. These beetles can be recognised by their rough sculpturing (Pl. 50) and they feed largely on small carcasses. They do not have the broad, digging legs found in the Geotrupidae. The latter family, whose members are commonly known as dor beetles, contains eight British species, mainly dung feeders. The antennae end in a dull pubescent, 3-jointed club. The common *Geotrupes stercorarius* (Pl. 50), called the Lousy Watchman because it is often infested with mites, frequents cow dung. Male and female beetles work together and excavate shafts under the dung. They then haul the dung down and lay eggs in it. The adults also feed on the dung themselves and they usually bury far more than they ever use. These beetles thus perform a very useful service in removing dung and hastening the return of nitrates to the soil. A related beetle, *Typhaeus typhoeus*, is associated with the dung of rabbits and sheep. The male of this species has prominent thoracic horns (Pl. 50) and, although he provides the dung pellets, he does none of the digging. This is in keeping with general observation that males with exaggerated horns do little of the work.

The family **Scarabaeidae** is one of the largest of all insect families, with over 19,000 species. There are 77 British members. As well as being one of the largest insect families, the Scarabaeidae also contains the largest species – the tropical Goliath and Hercules beetles. This family is also noted for the extraordinary 'horns' that develop on the head and thorax of some species. These horns are usually fully formed only in the male, although some species are horned in both sexes. The mandibles are not out of the ordinary and are usually concealed from above. The family can be divided into two main groups – the dung beetles or scarabs proper and the plant-eating chafers – although these are further divided into sub-families. The main genera of our scarabs are *Copris* and *Aphodius*, both illustrated on Pl. 50. *Copris lunaris* is of special interest because both parents excavate and burrow under cow dung and both tend the larvae, right up until the larvae leave the burrow.

Whereas the scavenging dung beetles are generally useful, the chafers, distinguished by the exposed tips of their abdomens, are positively harmful. The largest and commonest of our chafers is the Cockchafer or Maybug (*Melolontha melolontha*) (Pl. 51) which often comes crashing into lighted windows in early summer. Its large size – up to 35mm long – and buzzing flight make it a little frightening but it is quite harmless – harmless to us that is. These beetles do untold damage to trees and crops by eating foliage and flowers. The fat, white larvae are even more destructive. They live underground for three or four years and consume a great amount of plant roots during that time – particularly cereals and other grasses. It is said that rooks are particularly fond of both adult and larval cockchafers and the larvae are often called rookworms. Other important chafers include the brilliant green Rose Chafer (*Cetonia aurata*) and the Garden

Plate 51   BEETLES – Order Coleoptera (Contd.)

Family **Scarabaeidae** (Contd.)   p. 303
1. Common cockchafer – *Melolontha melolontha* (L.)   ×1¼
2. Rose chafer – *Cetonia aurata* (L.)   ×1¼
3. Garden chafer – *Phyllopertha horticola* (L.)   ×1¼
4. *Hoplia philanthus* Fuessly   ×1¼

Family **Cantharidae**   p. 310
Elongated, soft-bodied beetles with hairy elytra
5. *Cantharis rustica* Fallen   ×1¼
6. Soldier beetle – *Rhagonycha fulva* (Scopoli)   ×3

Family **Lampyridae**   p. 310
Elongated: elytra (when present) soft and hairy: light-
producing organs in ♂, ♀ or both: head covered by pronotum
7a. Glow-worm – *Lampyris noctiluca* L. – male   ×1¼
7b. female   ×1¼
7c. larva   ×1¼

Family **Elateridae**   p. 307
Elongated: hard elytra and sharply pointed angles at back of
prothorax: antennae often toothed or feathered
8. *Corymbites cupreus* Fabr.   ×1¼
9. *Athous haemorrhoidalis* Fabr.   ×1¼
10. *Elater balteatus* L.   ×1¼
11. *Agriotes lineatus* (L.)   ×3
12. *Hypnoidus quadripustulatus* (Fabr.)   ×3

Family **Dermestidae**   p. 310
Distinctly clubbed antennae and rather downy elytra:
usually a single large ocellus on top of head, although
absent in *Dermestes*
13. *Attagenus pellio* (L.)   ×5
14. *Anthrenus fuscus* Olivier   ×5
15. *Dermestes maculatus* DeGeer   ×3
16. Larder beetle – *Dermestes lardarius* L.   ×3
17. *Trogoderma granarium* Everts   ×3

Family **Melyridae**   p. 312
Bristly: teeth or other appendages on tarsal claws
18. *Anthocomus fasciatus* (L.)   ×5

Family **Heteroceridae**   p. 306
Short thick antennae and heavily spined front legs
19. *Heterocerus flexuosus* Stephens   ×5

△ Family **Cebrionidae**   p. 310
Antennae inserted close to eyes: mandibles very prominent
▲ **20.** *Cebrio gigas* Fabr. – male   ×1¼ Female is wingless

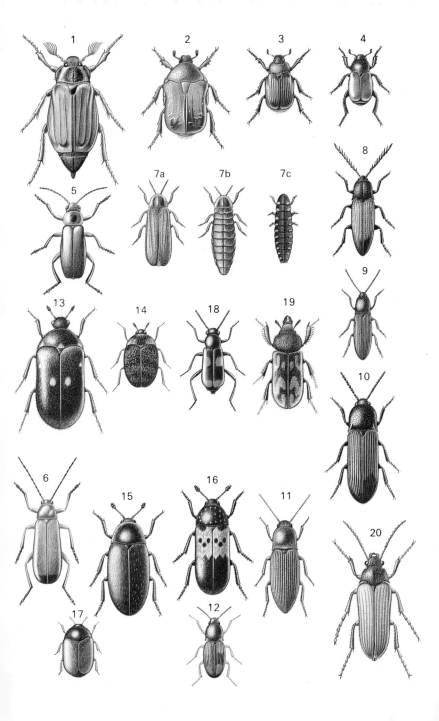

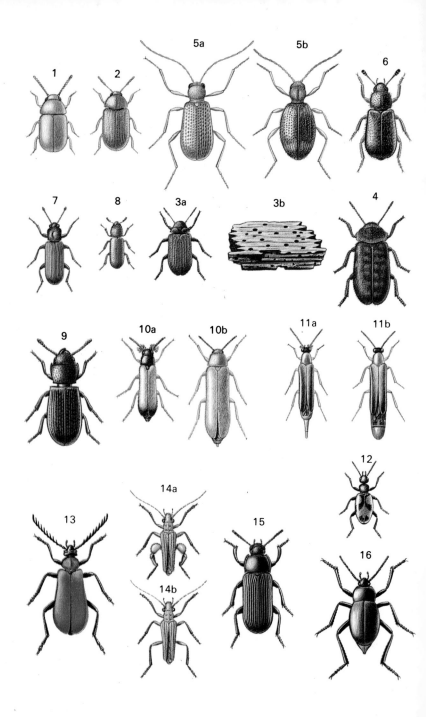

BEETLES – Order Coleoptera (Contd.)

Plate 52

Anobiidae. Head often covered by a prominent hood formed by the pronotum: antennae more or less toothed p. 311
1. Cigarette beetle – *Lasioderma serricorne* (Fabr.) ×5
2. Drug-store beetle – *Stegobium paniceum* (L.) ×5
3a. Furniture beetle – *Anobium punctatum* (DeGeer) ×3
3b. Typical damage by *Anobium* larvae – the woodworm
4. Death-watch beetle – *Xestobium rufovillosum* (DeGeer) ×3

Ptinidae – spider beetles. Small: long antennae and legs: head often concealed by thorax: abdomen often globular p. 312
5a. *Ptinus fur* (L.) – male ×5
5b. *Ptinus fur* – female ×5

Cleridae. Hairy: strongly clubbed antennae: tarsi with membranous flaps or lobes on one or more segments p. 312
6. *Necrobia rufipes* (DeGeer) ×5

Lyctidae – powder post beetles. Slender: antennae end in a large 2-segmented club: last joint of tarsi very long p. 311
7. *Lyctus fuscus* (L.) ×3

Bostrichidae. Thorax forming hood over head: antennae with 3-segmented club p. 311

Rhizopertha

8. Lesser grain borer – *Rhizopertha dominica* (Fabr.) ×3

Trogositidae. Last tarsal segment relatively long and bearing small lobe between claws p. 312
9. *Tenebroides mauritanicus* (L.) ×3

Lymexylidae. Slender, downy beetles in which the males have elaborately branched palps p. 312
10a. *Hylecoetus dermestoides* (L.) – male ×3
10b. *Hylecoetus dermestoides* – female ×3
11a. *Lymexylon navale* (L.) – male ×3
11b. *Lymexylon navale* – female ×3

Anthicidae. Small: rounded heads distinct from thorax p. 313
12. *Anthicus antherinus* (L.) ×3

Pyrochroidae – cardinal beetles. Rather flattened beetles with a broad neck and usually with pectinate antennae: generally red p. 313
13. *Pyrochroa coccinea* L. ×1½

Oedemeridae. Soft: often metallic: penultimate segment of tarsus bilobed: often swollen hind femora on ♂♂ p. 313
14a. *Oedemera nobilis* (Scopoli) – male ×1½
14b. *Oedemera nobilis* – female ×1½

Tenebrionidae. Rather dark and generally stout beetles of variable appearance: often with elytra fastened down p. 314
15. *Tenebrio molitor* L. ×1½
16. *Blaps mucronata* Latreille

Chafer (*Phyllopertha horticola*), illustrated on Pl. 51. All have much the same sort of life history as *M. melolontha*.

Superfamily Dascilloidea

This is a relatively small group of beetles with only three British families, drawn from the older Diversicornia and Staphylinoidea. The three families are rather different in appearance – they all crop up separately in the key to superfamilies on page 297 – but agree in having more or less conical, projecting front coxae and excavated hind coxae. The **Clambidae** are all minute insects, less than 1.5mm

A typical clambid beetle

long, with broad heads and clubbed antennae. We have five species, all found in rotting vegetation. *Dascillus cervinus* (Pl. 49) is our only member of the **Dascillidae** and is usually found in flowers. The **Helodidae** contains 13 British species which are all soft-bodied and rather fragile. Most of them are between 2 and 5mm long and they are found around ponds and streams. The larvae are aquatic.

Superfamily Byrrhoidea

This superfamily contains only one family – the **Byrrhidae** which was formerly included in the Diversicornia. There are 10 British species, in six genera, and they are all very rounded insects ranging in length from 1.5 to 10mm. Legs and antennae can be withdrawn into grooves on the underside of the body and the insects feign death in this manner. *Byrrhus pilula* (Pl. 49) is one of our commonest species. Most of them live among mosses and grasses.

Superfamily Dryopoidea

The beetles in this group are nearly all aquatic and are all of minute size, being less than 5mm long. There are about 30 British species, in five families. Although

Heterocerus (*left*) and *Elmis*, two members of the superfamily Dryopoidea. The enlargement shows the strong tarsal claws of *Elmis*

aquatic, these beetles do not really swim. Members of the family **Heteroceridae** (Pl. 51) burrow in mud at the edges of ponds and streams and their front tibiae are strongly spined in association with this habit. The **Dryopidae** and **Elmidae** spend their time crawling on aquatic vegetation and they are without spined tibiae. Instead, they have strong tarsal claws with which they cling to the plants. Many of them live in fast-moving water and some of the elmid beetles have developed plastron respiration (p. 26).

Superfamily Buprestoidea

This superfamily, originally part of the Diversicornia, contains but one large family – the **Buprestidae**. This is mainly a tropical family and there are only 12 species in Britain, none of them really common. They are shiny, metallic insects ranging from 1 to 12 mm long. The head is sunk deeply in the thorax, the eyes are unusually large, and the antennae are short and toothed. The larvae are mainly wood-borers, tunnelling just under the bark, and many species are serious timber pests. Others, however, tunnel in herbaceous plants and several species induce galls. *Agrilus* (Pl. 49) is the commonest of our five genera. The large and striking *Buprestis aurulentis* (Pl. 49) is an American species but it sometimes appears here, having been imported as a larva in timber. Some records suggest a larval life of nearly 30 years is possible.

Superfamily Elateroidea

The members of this group – part of the old Diversicornia – are generally rather elongated insects with hard skeletons. The head is sunk deeply into the thorax and bears toothed or comb-like antennae (Pl. 51). The hind angles of the prothorax are sharply pointed and often extended. Most important of our three families is the **Elateridae**, whose members are generally known as click beetles or skip-jacks from their ability to flick themselves into the air and right themselves when they fall on to their backs. This ability is associated with a very mobile joint between the first and second thoracic sternites. Under normal circumstances, a projection on the prosternum rests on the edge of a cavity in the mesosternum. When the insect falls upside-down it begins to arch its back and the 'peg' slips off the edge and springs down into the cavity. This produces the familiar click and also causes the insect to bounce up in the air. While airborne, the insect usually manages to right itself. All the click beetles – 65 species in Britain

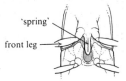

The underside of a click beetle (family Elateridae), showing the 'spring'

– are similar in shape and colour, being generally brownish and rather dull, although several species have a metallic sheen (Pl. 51). Under a lens they can be seen to have a coating of fine, often greyish hairs. Click beetle larvae – known as wireworms – are responsible for a considerable amount of crop damage

Plate 53   **BEETLES** – **Order Coleoptera** (Contd.)

Family **Meloidae**   p. 313
  Soft-bodied beetles with a narrow neck and often with short
  elytra
  1. *Meloë proscarabaeus* L. ×1¼
  2. *Lytta vesicatoria* (L.) ×1¼

Family **Tenebrionidae**   p. 314
  Often wingless, with elytra fastened down
  3. *Tribolium confusum* Duval ×4
  4. *Gnathocerus cornutus* (Fabr.) ×4

Family **Nitidulidae**   p. 314
  Antennae with distinct 3-segmented club: abdomen often
  exposed
  5. *Carpophilus hemipterus* (L.) ×4

Family **Cucujidae**   p. 314
  Antennae with an indistinct club: thorax often toothed at
  edge
  6. Saw-toothed grain beetle – *Oryzaephilus surinamensis* (L.)
    ×6

Family **Cryptophagidae**   p. 314
  Very small and rather hairy beetles with distinctly clubbed
  antennae
  7. *Cryptophagus saginatus* Sturm ×6

Family **Coccinellidae** – ladybirds   p. 315
  Generally rounded insects with head partly concealed from
  above: often brightly coloured: tarsi with 4 segments, but
  3rd minute and tarsi therefore appear 3-segmented
  8. Eyed ladybird – *Anatis ocellata* (L.) ×2
  9. Seven-spot ladybird – *Coccinella 7-punctata* L. ×2
  10. *Coccidula rufa* (Herbst) ×5
  11. *Rhyzobius litura* (Fabr.) ×5
  12. *Psyllobora 22-punctata* (L.) ×5
  13. *Propylea 14-punctata* (L.) ×5
  14. *Subcoccinella 24-punctata* (L.) ×5
  15 a, b, c, d. Two-spot ladybird – *Adalia bipunctata* (L.) ×4
  16 a, b, c, d. *Adalia 10-punctata* (L.) ×4

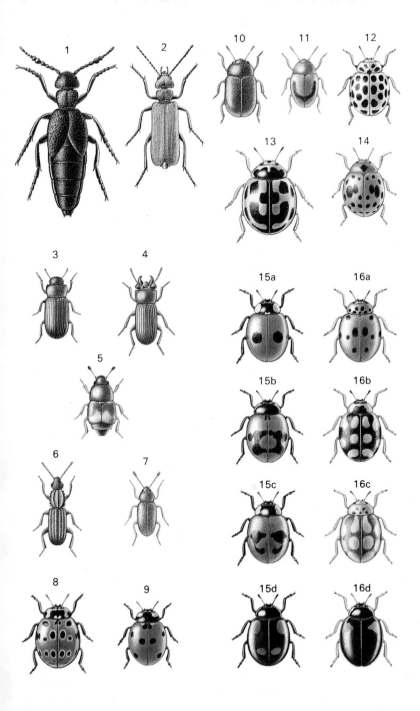

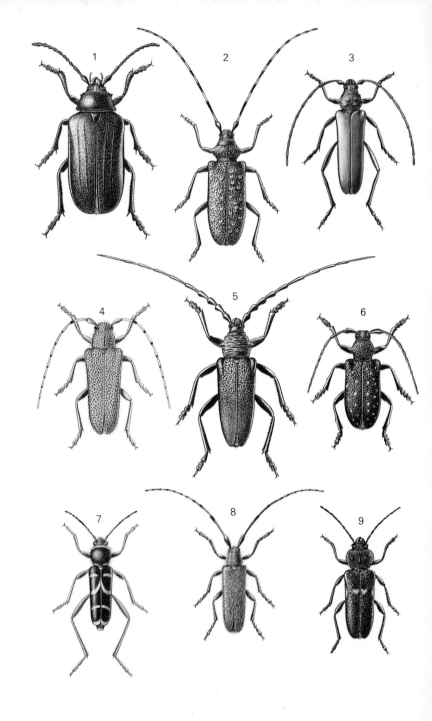

Family **Cerambycidae**   p. 315
   Antennae usually very long: tarsi apparently 4-segmented,
   with the 3rd segment bilobed

1. *Prionus coriarius* (L.)

▲ **2.** *Monochamus galloprovincialis* (Olivier)

3. *Aromia moschata* (L.)

4. *Saperda carcharias* (L.) × 1¼

▲ **5.** *Cerambyx cerdo* L. × 1¼

6. *Lamia textor* (L.) × 1¼

7. Wasp beetle – *Clytus arietis* (L.) × 1¼

▲ **8.** *Agapanthea villosoviridescens* DeGeer × 1¼

9. House longhorn – *Hylotrupes bajulus* (L.) × 1¼

for many of them feed on plant roots. The adult beetles feed on pollen and nectar, and also on the tissues of flowers and leaves.

The **Cebrionidae** contains some relatively large beetles related to the click beetles. The larvae are like wireworms and live in the soil. Females are sometimes wingless. A few species are found in Southern Europe. *Cebrio gigas* (Pl. 51) is a typical example.

Superfamily Cantharoidea

These insects – yet another division of the old Diversicornia – are generally rather narrow, elongate beetles with soft bodies. The elytra are also rather soft and they are covered with short, downy hair – often sufficient to give them a dull, matt appearance. Our largest family – with 41 species – is the **Cantharidae**. The elytra bear little in the way of striations – a feature that separates the Cantharidae from the Lycidae. Cantharid beetles are frequent flower visitors, being especially attracted to umbellifers, although they are carnivorous insects and probably feed on other flower-visiting species. The family is typified by the Soldier Beetle, *Rhagonycha fulva* (Pl. 51). On account of its reddish colour, this beetle has earned itself the misleading name of 'Blood-sucker' in many parts of the country.

The family **Lampyridae** contains one of the most famous of all insects – the Glow-Worm (*Lampyris noctiluca*). The common name is unfortunate but derives from the appearance of the female which, while not really like a worm, is not much like a beetle either (Pl. 51). The male is more typical of beetles, being fully winged and able to fly. In both sexes, the prothorax is extended forwards and completely covers the head. All stages of the life history, including the eggs, give out light but it is the adult female that emits the strongest light. The underside of her last three abdominal segments bears the light-producing organs, which consist of a layer of luciferin backed by a reflector of minute crystals. Light is produced by enzymatic oxidation of the luciferin and the process requires both oxygen and water. The luciferin layer is well supplied with tracheae in this connection. The light emitted is a pale greenish blue and almost all the chemical energy is converted into light – there is very little heat produced. The function of the light is to attract males and the females merely sit in the grass and raise their abdomens. A verge or hedgebank full of glow-worms is a sight worth seeing. The male beetles have much more efficient eyes than the females and a glowing female soon attracts a mate. The light can be shut off when required – probably by reducing the oxygen supply to the luciferin – and the insects glow mainly at dusk. They may also 'go out' if suddenly disturbed, although they will often continue glowing if picked up gently and put in a box.

Adult glow-worms do not feed much, if at all, but the larva is predatory and feeds on small snails and slugs. It grabs these with its jaws and injects a digestive juice which reduces the prey to liquid for ingestion. It is partly the importance of snails in the diet that restricts glow-worms mainly to areas of chalk and limestone – the snails are so restricted by the need for shell-building calcium.

Superfamily Dermestoidea

The **Dermestidae** is the only important family in this group – another division of the old Diversicornia. Its members range from 1.5 to 10mm in length and are generally rather sombre in colour. They are covered with downy hairs or scales.

Most species possess a large, single ocellus on the top of the head, although this is missing in *Dermestes* species. The antennae are distinctly clubbed and, together with the legs, they can be withdrawn into the underside of the body. In this position, the insects feign death. The Dermestidae (Pl. 51) are basically scavengers but many species are of considerable economic importance. *Dermestes maculatus* and *D. lardarius* (the Bacon Beetle or Larder Beetle) damage hides and dried meat and are more common in warehouses than out-of-doors, although they can be found in dried out carcasses. These insects can be usefully employed in cleaning animal skeletons for preservation. Other important genera include *Attagenus* and *Anthrenus* (carpet beetles) (Pl. 51) which damage furs, fabrics, and stored food. The larvae, which do the damage, are covered with hairs and are commonly called 'woolly bears'. Many species, because of their association with stored products, are of world-wide distribution.

Superfamily Bostrychoidea

The members of this group – a division of the old Clavicornia – can generally be recognised by the 'hooded' pronotum which covers all or much of the head from above. This feature does occur in a few other beetles, however. Most of the species are wood borers and some are serious pests of timber. The larvae are soft and white and more or less scarabaeiform.

The family **Lyctidae**, typified by *Lyctus fuscus* (Pl. 52), are commonly called powder-post beetles because the boring larvae produce a very fine dust, quite unlike that produced by the Furniture Beetle (see below). The Lyctidae differ from the other families in the group because the pronotum does not conceal the whole head from above and they have distinct 2-segmented antennal clubs. Members of the other three families have 3-segmented clubs or no distinct clubs at all.

Our native species of the **Bostrychidae** – recognised by the 3-segmented antennal club – are all very rare but mention should be made of *Rhizopertha dominica*, the Lesser Grain Borer (Pl. 52), which often finds its way to this country in stored grain and sometimes establishes itself.

Lateral and dorsal views of *Rhizopertha dominica* (family Bostrychidae), showing the hooded pronotum

The **Anobiidae** (Pl. 52) contains two notorious pests – the Woodworm or Furniture Beetle (*Anobium punctatum*) and the Death Watch Beetle (*Xestobium rufovillosum*). The larvae of these insects tunnel into dead wood – rafters, furniture, or simply dead trees – and can quickly reduce it to dust. The beetles lay their eggs in any small crevice – well-polished furniture is relatively safe from attack – and the larvae tunnel in. Not until the adults leave through their 'worm holes' do we learn of their presence, although the adult Death Watch Beetle can sometimes be detected by its knocking. The beetles bang their heads against whatever they are standing on and, by doing this several times in quick succession, they produce a noise not unlike a scaled-down pneumatic drill. This is believed to be a 'mating call'. Other important members of this family, illustrated on Pl. 52, include the Cigarette Beetle (*Lasioderma serricorne*) and the Drug-Store Beetle (*Stegobium paniceum*), both of which attack a variety of stored products, including tobacco. The members of this family have no distinct antennal clubs and the bases of the antennae are fairly well separated.

The **Ptinidae**, or spider beetles, are closely related to the Anobiidae but their antennae are inserted close together. They also tend to be much rounder – hence their name of spider beetles (Pl. 52). They are scavenging insects and none is a wood borer. Several of them are pests of stored produce – grain, dried fruit, and fabrics. Their natural habitats would seem to be the nests of birds and other animals.

Superfamily Cleroidea

Another division of the old Clavicornia, this group contains a number of predatory and scavenging beetles – most of them in the **Cleridae**. The members of this family are rather hairy insects and often brightly coloured (Pl. 52). The antennae are either strongly toothed or else they end in distinct clubs. As larvae, many of them feed on bark beetles and other wood borers, but *Necrobia rufipes* attacks stored bacon and hams. The Cadelle (*Tenebroides mauritanicus*) belongs to the closely related **Trogositidae** and is not hairy (Pl. 52). It is an introduced species but firmly established in granaries and other food stores where it partly offsets its damage by destroying other insect pests. The family **Melyridae** is a large one, although only poorly represented in the British Isles. Its members are very variable, but generally possess long bristly hairs on the head. The tarsal claws also have teeth or other outgrowths on them. One of our commoner species is *Anthocomus fasciatus* (Pl. 51).

Superfamily Lymexyloidea

There is only one family in this group – the **Lymexylidae** – and it contains but two British species – *Hylecoetus dermestoides* and *Lymexylon navale*. Both are narrow-bodied, wood-boring insects (Pl. 52), characterised by the extraordinary development of the male palps.

Superfamily Cucujoidea

This is a very large group of insects with many diverse families and little to link them all together. The Cucujoidea contains all the members of the old Heteromera, together with most of the species from the old Clavicornia. There are, therefore, two fairly distinct groups within the superfamily – the old Heteromera, in which the tarsal formula is 5, 5, 4 in both sexes and the antennae have, at most, a weak club; and the old Clavicornia, in which the female tarsi are never 5, 5, 4 and in which the antennal club is always well developed. Only the main families in each section are described here.

SECTION HETEROMERA

Members of the family **Oedemeridae** are rather elongated insects, soft-bodied and often with a metallic sheen (Pl. 52). The adults are generally flower-feeders but the larvae are wood borers. There are seven British species.

The **Pyrochroidae**, or cardinal beetles, have only three British representatives but they deserve mention because of their bright red colour (Pl. 52) which gives them their common name and makes them quite conspicuous insects. The larvae live under bark and the adults are generally to be found there or on herbaceous plants.

Members of the **Anthicidae** look rather like small ground beetles on first sight (Pl. 52) although, with lengths in the region of 3–4mm, they are much smaller than most of our ground beetles. Apart from size, the unstriated elytra and four tarsal segments in the hind leg will distinguish the Anthicidae. The beetles live in decaying material and can often be found on the compost heap and in rotting seaweed.

The beetles of the family **Meloidae** are of particular interest because of their complex life cycles. The young stages of the British species are all parasites of solitary bees, but grasshoppers are the main hosts in other parts of the world. The female beetles lay large numbers of eggs in the soil – several thousand eggs per female, deposited in a number of separate batches. Egg-laying takes place in the

The life cycle of the oil beetle *Meloë proscarabaeus*

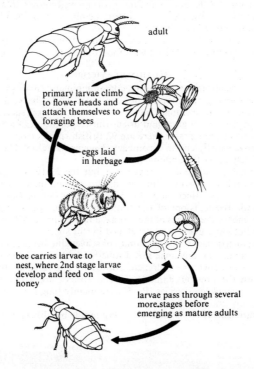

adult

primary larvae climb to flower heads and attach themselves to foraging bees

eggs laid in herbage

bee carries larvae to nest, where 2nd stage larvae develop and feed on honey

larvae pass through several more stages before emerging as mature adults

spring and the eggs soon hatch into tiny louse-like larvae, endowed with strong claws. These larvae crawl up on to the heads of dandelions and other spring flowers and await the arrival of their host insects. Only a small proportion find the right host and the others perish. The lucky ones are carried to the host's nest where they detach themselves and seek out an egg to eat. After this, the larvae turn to eating the bees' food reserves of pollen and nectar and the larvae undergo a series of moults at each of which they become more and more grub-like, with soft bodies and reduced legs.

Lytta vesicatoria, the Blister Beetle or Spanish Fly, is a typical beetle but our other representatives of this family, exemplified by the Common Oil Beetle, *Meloë proscarabaeus*, are far from typical (Pl. 53). The short, soft elytra gape open at the back and the insects are clumsy almost to the point of being comical. The common name is derived from the oily secretion produced when these beetles are disturbed. This is really the insect's blood and its discharge is an example of reflex bleeding (p. 318).

The family **Tenebrionidae** is a large one, although there are only about 35 species on the British list. The members are commonly called nocturnal ground beetles or darkling beetles, names which reflect their habits and general colour. Most of the species are black or deep brown and the majority are flightless, even wingless. The elytra are often soldered down. There is considerable variation within the family as far as shape and size go, but the antennae are often thickened or more or less clubbed at the ends. Two common species, *Tenebrio molitor* and *Blaps mucronata*, are shown on Pl. 52. *T. molitor* lives in flour and other cereal products and its larva is the mealworm – well-known to animal lovers as food for birds, lizards, etc. Many other members of the family are pests in granaries and warehouses. These include *Tribolium* species, *Gnathocerus cornutus* (both Pl. 53), and *Latheticus oryzae*. Many of our species are probably not native and have been introduced with food materials.

SECTION CLAVICORNIA

The family **Nitidulidae** is a large one, containing many small scavenging beetles, most of them under 5mm long. They are found under bark, in decaying plant and animal material, in fungi, and at oozing sap. Several species have become stored product pests, in grain and dried fruits especially. *Carpophilus hemipterus* (Pl. 53) is one of these pests. There are 92 British species (some introduced) and their antennae usually end in a compact, 3-segmented club. The elytra often do not completely cover the abdomen.

The **Cucujidae** also contains scavengers but the 23 British species are rarely met with outside food stores. They are flat insects and their antennae never have more than an indistinct club (Pl. 53). *Oryzaephilus surinamensis*, the Saw-toothed Grain Beetle, is one of our commoner granary pests. It gets its common name from the toothed edges of the thorax, a feature present in many members of the family but particularly well developed in this species.

The **Cryptophagidae** is another family of scavenging beetles, most of them less than 3mm long. The antennae are distinctly clubbed and the somewhat hairy elytra completely cover the abdomen. Loose bark and fungi are the main habitats but, as with the previous families, several species are associated with stored products. *Cryptophagus* species (Pl. 53) are mainly fungus feeders and are often found in damp grain.

The **Lathridiidae** is very similar to the last family but differs in having only three tarsal segments (4 or 5 segments in Cryptophagidae). Fungi, decaying material, dried carcasses, and stored foods are the likely places for these beetles, of which there are about 50 British species.

The **Coccinellidae** is certainly the best known family of the Cucujoidea because it contains the familiar and brightly coloured ladybirds (Pl. 53). All but one of our 45 species are predatory and they destroy vast numbers of greenfly and other pests, feeding on them in both larval and adult stages. The bright colours – generally black with red or yellow – are of a warning nature, advertising the bitter taste of these insects. When handled, they exude drops of pungent blood which stain the hand and smell for quite a time afterwards. This is an example of reflex bleeding.

The vegetarian of the family is *Subcoccinella vigintiquatuorpunctata*, the 24-spot Ladybird. The specific name here, and in other species, is usually abbreviated to numerals: 24-*punctata*. This is a very variable species, one of the few constant things being that it does not have 24 spots! There are from 16 to 20 irregular blotches. The genera *Coccidula* and *Rhyzobius* (Pl. 53) are not in keeping with the general idea of ladybirds in that they are rather elongate insects but the other genera are all of the typical hemispherical shape. Colours and patterns vary a good deal and cannot be relied on for identifying the species.

Superfamily Chrysomeloidea

The members of this superfamily are almost all plant-feeding insects and the group was and sometimes still is called the Phytophaga. None of the species has a really distinct antennal club and the tarsi are all apparently 4-segmented, segment 4 being very small. This is a very large group with some 40,000 species, arranged in three families.

The **Cerambycidae** are wood-feeding insects, usually recognisable by their very long antennae – hence the common name of longhorn beetles. The species, of which we have about 70 in Britain, are generally found in wooded regions where some of them do considerable damage to timber. Some of these beetles, many of which are large and brightly coloured, are shown on Pl. 54. The Wasp Beetle, *Clytus arietus*, is of special interest because of its mimetic resemblance to wasps. The actual pattern is only a little wasp-like but the resemblance is completed by the agitated way in which the beetle scuttles over tree trunks and vegetation, tapping its antennae just like a wasp. *Hylotrupes bajalus* larvae feed on dead wood and the species is sometimes found in house timbers. It is therefore known as the House Longhorn. Many additional species occur on the Continent and they are often larger than the British species. They often reach Britain in imported timber.

The **Bruchidae** is a family of seed-eating beetles, with only about 900 known species. The head is produced forward a little in front of the eyes but there is no true rostrum as in weevils, nor are the antennae elbowed (Pl. 55). The elytra are often shorter than the abdomen, leaving a small part of the latter exposed. Leguminous crops are the main food plants and many of the bruchids attack stored seeds such as beans and lentils.

The **Chrysomelidae** is the largest of the three families, with more than 25,000 species, more than 250 of them British. They are almost all leaf-feeders and are commonly called leaf beetles. Most of them are quite small and many are brightly coloured, often metallic (Pl. 55). *Timarcha tenebricosa* is our largest leaf beetle.

Plate 55   LEAF BEETLES – Order Coleoptera (Contd.)

Family **Chrysomelidae**   p. 315
Generally rather rounded beetles with shiny elytra: antennae
not excessivly long: third tarsal segment expanded and
concealing minute fourth segment, tarsi thus appearing
4-segmented

1. *Galerucella nymphaea* (L.) $\times 2\frac{1}{2}$

2. *Donacia vulgaris* Zschach $\times 2\frac{1}{2}$

3. *Chrysolina polita* (L.) $\times 2\frac{1}{2}$

4. *Cassida viridis* L. – a tortoise beetle $\times 2\frac{1}{2}$

5. *Cryptocephalus hypochaeridis* (L.) $\times 4$

6. *Chrysolina hyperici* (Forster) $\times 4$

7. *Clytra quadripunctata* (L.) $\times 2\frac{1}{2}$

8. *Gastrophysa viridula* (DeGeer) $\times 4$

9. *Phyllotreta nemorum* (L.) – a flea beetle $\times 4$

10. *Lema melanopa* (L.) $\times 4$

▲ **11.** Colorado Beetle – *Leptinotarsa decemlineata* Say $\times 1\frac{1}{2}$

12. Bloody-nose Beetle – *Timarcha tenebricosa* (Fabr.) $\times 1\frac{1}{2}$

13. *Melasoma populi* (L.) $\times 1\frac{1}{2}$

4th segment
5th segmen
3rd segment

Family **Bruchidae**   p. 315
Antennae distinctly thickened towards tip: neck usually
visible between head and thorax: elytra often short and
exposing abdomen: tarsi apparently 4-segmented

14. *Bruchus pisorum* (L.) $\times 4$

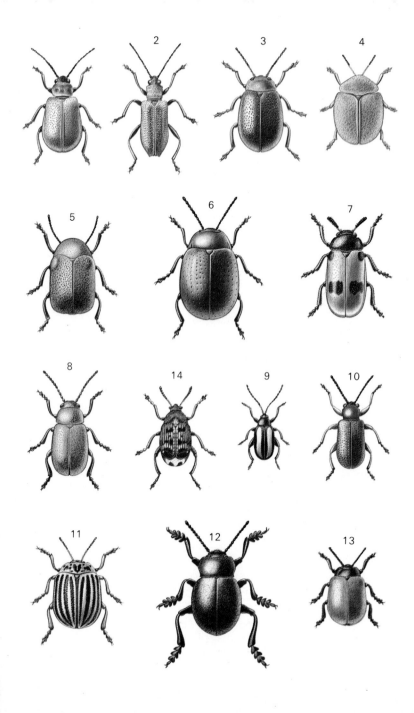

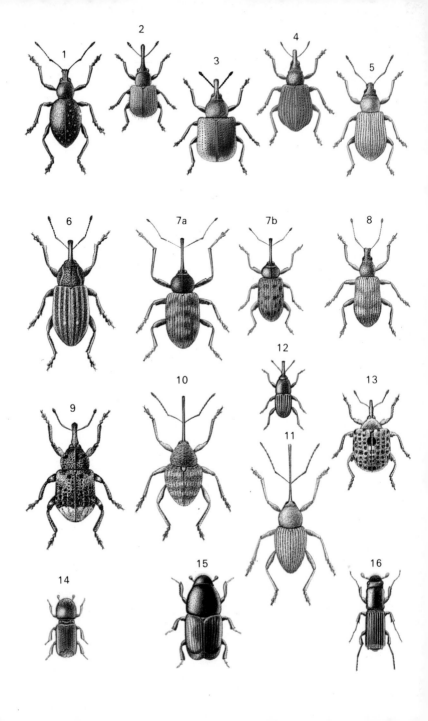

Plate 56
WEEVILS AND BARK BEETLES – Order Coleoptera (Contd.)

Family **Curculionidae**   p. 318
  Head produced into a prominent rostrum

1. *Otiorhynchus clavipes* (Bonsdorff) ×2

2. *Caenorhinus aequatus* (L.) ×4

3. *Byctiscus populi* (L.) ×4

4. *Apion miniatum* Germar ×4

5. *Phyllobius viridearis* (Laicharting) ×4

6. *Notaris bimaculatus* (Fabr.) ×4

7a. *Dorytomus longimanus* (Forster) – male ×4
7b. *Dorytomus longimanus* – female ×4

8. *Polydrusus tereticollis* (DeGeer) ×4

9. *Cryptorhynchidius lapathi* (L.) ×3

10. *Curculio nucum* L. ×4

▲ **11.** *Curculio elephas* Gyllenhal ×4

12. Grain weevil – *Sitophilus granarius* (L.) ×4

13. *Cionus hortulanus* (Geoffroy) ×4

Family **Scolytidae**   p. 319
  Dark cylindrical beetles with clubbed antennae and usually
  with the elytra scooped out at the back
14. *Pityogenes bidentatus* (Herbst) ×6

15. *Scolytus scolytus* (Fabr.) ×4

Family **Platypodidae**   p. 319
  Cylindrical beetles with thorax notched at sides: 1st tarsal
  segment very long
16. *Platypus cylindrus* (Fabr.) ×4

It is black, with a violet tinge, and may be found crawling among the grass in spring and early summer. It has no wings and the elytra are fused together. This insect is remarkable for its reflex bleeding when disturbed. It exudes deep red blood from its mouth, and from various other joints, and this has earned it the common name of Bloody-nosed Beetle. The bright red colour of the blood warns off the insect's attackers. As would be expected, many leaf beetles are crop pests. The flea beetles (genus *Phyllotreta*) are well-known enemies of young cabbages and other cruciferous plants. The Colorado Beetle (*Leptinotarsa decemlineata*) also belongs to this family, although we are lucky that we rarely see it in Britain. Other genera worth mention are *Donacia*, whose larvae feed on aquatic plants and whose adults run about on water lily and other floating leaves, and *Cassida* (the tortoise beetles) in which the elytra and thoracic terga completely cover the insect.

Superfamily Curculionoidea

This is a very large group containing the weevils (**Curculionidae**) and the bark beetles (**Scolytidae**), almost all of which are plant feeders. The weevils, which make up the bulk of the superfamily, have the head prolonged into a beak or rostrum carrying the mandibles at its tip and the antennae about half-way along it (Pl. 56). The group is sometimes still known by its old name of Rhynchophora (Greek *rhynchos* = a snout). The bark beetles do not have this snout but there are other features that link them to the weevils. For example, the antennae are nearly always elbowed and (in all British species) the tarsi are apparently 4-segmented.

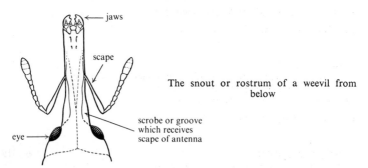

The snout or rostrum of a weevil from below

The **Curculionidae**, often now divided into several smaller families, is a vast assemblage of more than 40,000 species, over 500 of them British. All agree in the possession of a well-marked rostrum and clubbed antennae which are usually elbowed. The first segment of the antenna (the scape) is capable of being retracted into a groove along the side of the rostrum. Many of the species are covered with tiny scales and these are often responsible for the bright colours of many weevils. Several species are wingless and the elytra are fused together. The snout is thought in some species to be used as a boring tool, perhaps to make a hole for egg-laying or to reach a succulent inner layer of a plant. The larvae are legless and most of them feed enclosed in roots, stems, or seeds of plants. Many species, such as the

Grain Weevil, *Sitophilus granarius*, are serious pests in stored products, while others attack growing plants. *Curculio nucum*, for example, develops inside hazel nuts.

The bark beetles of the **Scolytidae** are all dark coloured insects with the rather typical cylindrical appearance of most wood-boring beetles (Pl. 56). The rostrum is virtually absent and the whole head is often concealed from above by the prothorax. The antennae are relatively short but they have a distinct scape and a solid club very like that of the weevils. The elytra are often scooped out at the back and are used as 'shovels' for removing debris from the tunnels. Bark beetle tunnels are, in fact, better known than the beetles themselves because these are the beetles that make radiating galleries just under the bark of many trees. Heavy infestations kill the trees and the bark falls to reveal the galleries. The beetles themselves are nearly all under 5mm long and it is usually easier to identify them from their galleries than from their own appearance because each species usually makes a distinctive pattern with its tunnels. Tunnelling starts with the adult

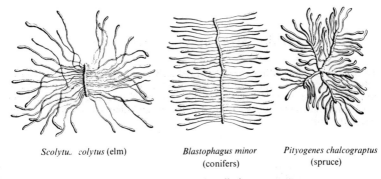

Scolytu... colytus (elm)   *Blastophagus minor*   *Pityogenes chalcograptus*
(conifers)   (spruce)

Some bark beetle galleries

beetles making an entrance hole through the bark. The female usually does the boring but the male is in attendance and helps by removing the debris. Once under the bark, in the nutritious cambium region, the male beetle usually excavates a nuptial chamber where mating takes place. The female (there may be one or several to each male) then starts to tunnel away from the chamber, keeping just under the bark, and lays her eggs at intervals along the gallery. When the larvae hatch they tunnel at right angles to the main gallery and so produce the well known pattern. When mature, the larvae pupate under the bark and the adults then emerge through their own exit holes. *Scolytus*, recognisable by the toothed front tibia (Pl. 56), is the typical genus of these bark beetles.

This family also includes species that bore right into the wood and feed on the sap and on fungi that grow in the tunnels. These beetles, exemplified by *Xyleborus* species, are known as ambrosia beetles. *Platypus* is also a wood borer and is usually considered to belong to a third family – the **Platypodidae**.

Collecting and Preserving

As can be gathered from the foregoing text, beetles can be collected anywhere at any time just by looking. Many of them are rather sluggish and are easily 'boxed'. Sweeping the vegetation will produce the biggest hauls of leaf beetles and weevils, while baits and pitfall traps (p. 33), or simply turning over stones will yield some of the ground-living species. Most normal killing agents are suitable for beetles, although these are not the easiest of insects to kill. Boiling water is very useful for those species that do not have hairs or scales on them. The insects can be preserved by direct pinning if large enough and it is conventional to pin through the right elytron to leave the coxae and other critical features of the underside available for study. The smaller species can be mounted on points and here, so that the underside remains visible for study, it is common practice to bend the tip of the point down and attach it to the right side of the beetle (Fig. p. 36). Carding is suitable for a display collection but the underside of the insect is then concealed. The smallest species are best preserved in spirit.

Order Strepsiptera – Stylopids

Recognition features Minute insects whose early stages are spent as parasites of other insects. Adult males are free-living and have the front wings reduced to tiny club-shaped structures rather like the halteres of true flies. The hind wings are broad and membranous. Adult females are grub-like and generally remain inside the host.

A male stylopid, showing the stout antennae and the large membranous wings

These tiny insects are quite common but they are rarely encountered by the non-specialist and therefore have no common name. There are about 400 known species, of which 18 are British. Almost all are parasitic, the most frequent hosts being plant hoppers (Homoptera) and various bees and wasps, especially bees of the genera *Andrena* and *Halictus*. Attack by stylopids normally causes sterility in the host, especially in the female, and the parasites must play some part in the natural regulation of the host population. It is unlikely, however, that stylopids will be suitable for biological control: breeding them in large numbers would be quite a problem.

As far as the adult insects are concerned, the stylopids are a very distinct group. A study of the larvae and metamorphosis, however, reveals a number of similarities with some beetle families and many entomologists treat the stylopids as Coleoptera.

The male insect is under 4mm long and is dark brown. The head is dominated by the protruding compound eyes and the abnormally thick antennae. These have between four and seven segments, some of which may bear projections giving the antennae a branched appearance. The mouth-parts are of the biting type but are very much reduced. The first two thoracic segments are small but the metathorax is well developed, in connection with the development of the hind wings, and may account for more than half of the body length. The club-shaped front wings act as balancers like the halteres of the true flies (p. 211). The name Strepsiptera means 'twisted wings' (Greek *strepsis* = a twist) and refers to the twisting of these organs. The hind wings are large but delicate and supported by a reduced venation.

In all the British species the female stylopids remain parasitic all their lives. They are grub-like, with no legs, eyes, or antennae, and remain inside the last larval skin. Only the head and thorax are visible, sticking out between two abdominal segments of the host.

The stylopid life history has been investigated in a number of hymenopterous hosts and the following account is fairly typical. The male parasites emerge from the hosts, usually while they are flying, and seek out a female. The complex male antennae presumably play some part in this. On the underside of the thorax of the female there is an opening which leads into the brood canal. This is simply the the space between the true female body and the surrounding larval skin. Male sperms are passed into the brood canal and they eventually find their way to the genital pore at the hind end. After fertilisation, the larvae hatch inside the host insect.

The larvae that come out on to the host surface are minute, active, woodlouse-shaped creatures and they pass to other host insects when they get a chance – possibly via flowers. But the stylopid larva is not interested in the adult host other than as a taxi. It must get into the nest and find a larva. Having entered the host larva, the parasite moults into a legless maggot which lives in the body cavity of the host, absorbing food from its blood. The parasite matures soon after the host emerges from its pupa.

Male stylopids are usually commoner than females but they most frequently attack female hosts. Male parasites have a greater effect than female parasites. Stylopids do not kill their hosts but they have a great effect on them, particularly on the reproductive system and the secondary sexual characters. Male hosts tend to become more female and vice-versa. Parasitised individuals are generally sterile. The size and proportions of the body also alter and stylopised individuals have often been described as new species because of these differences.

The entomological 'splitters' recognise five families among the British stylopids but the differences are very slight and other workers prefer to lump them all in one family, the **Stylopidae**. Our two main genera are *Stylops* and *Halictoxenos*.

Collecting and Preserving
The only way to collect stylopids is to search for stylopised host insects – recognisable by the swollen abdomen and other features – and try to keep them alive until the parasites emerge. The parasites must be preserved in spirit or mounted on microscope slides.

Glossary

Abdomen The hindermost of the three main body divisions of an insect

Acrostichal Bristles The two rows of hairs or bristles lying on either side of the mid-line of the thorax of a fly (Diptera) (Fig. p. 210)

Aculeate Possessing a sting (Hymenoptera)

Acuminate Tapering to a long point

Adeagus The part of the male genitalia which is inserted into the female during copulation and which carries the sperm into the female. Its shape is often important in separating closely related species

Alar Squama The middle one of three flap-like outgrowths at the base of the wing in various flies (Diptera) (Fig. p. 211)

Alùla The outermost of the three flap-like outgrowths at the base of the wing in various flies (Diptera): really a part of the wing membrane (Fig. p. 211)

Anal (*a*) concerning the anus or hind tip of the abdomen (*b*) concerning the hindermost region of the wing

Annulate With ring-like markings

Antennae The pair of sensory organs on the head – the 'feelers'. Their shapes vary enormously

Antenodal Veins Small cross veins in the front of the wing of dragonflies and damselflies (Odonata) between the wing base and the nodus (Fig. p. 64)

Anterior Concerning or facing the front

Apical At or concerning the tip or furthest part of any organ: apical cells, for example, are at the tip of the wing

Appendage Any limb or other organ, such as a wing, which is attached to the body by a joint

Appendix A short vein, especially a short continuation after the main vein has changed direction

Apterous Without wings

Apterygote Any member of the Apterygota – the primitive insects, such as the bristle-tails, which have never developed wings during their history

Aquatic Living in water

Arista A bristle-like outgrowth from the antenna of various flies (Diptera) (Fig. p. 208)

Aristate Bearing an arista or bristle

Arolium A small pad between the claws on an insect's foot. Usually very small, but well developed in grasshoppers and some other insects

Basal Concerning the base of a structure, that part nearest to the body. Basal cells (Diptera) are generally small cells near the base of the wing

Basitarsus The first segment of the tarsus, usually the largest

Bipectinate Feathery, with branches growing out on both sides of the main stem: applied mainly to antennae

Brachypterous With short wings

Bursa Copulatrix That region of the female genitalia which receives the adeagus and sperm during copulation. Its structure is often important in separating closely related species

Callus A rounded swelling: applied especially to swollen regions at the front or back of the thorax of various flies (Diptera) (Fig. p. 210)

Calypter The innermost of the three flap-like outgrowths that develop at the base of the wing in various flies (Diptera). Also known as the thoracic squama, the calypter generally conceals the halteres (Fig. p. 211)

Campodeiform (Applied to a larva) Flattened and elongated with well developed legs and antennae. Many beetle larvae are of this type, and so are the larvae of lacewings (Neuroptera) (Fig. p. 293)

Cardo The basal segment of the maxilla or secondary jaw

Carina A ridge or keel

Caste One of three or more distinct forms which make up the population among social insects. The three usual castes are: queen, drone (male), and worker. The termites and some of the ants have one or more soldier castes as well

Plate 57   Larvae of Lepidoptera – BUTTERFLIES

Family **Satyridae**
1. Meadow brown – *Maniola jurtina*
2. Grayling – *Hipparchia semele*
3. Large heath – *Coenonympha tullia*

Family **Nymphalidae**
4. Silver-washed fritillary – *Argynnis paphia*
5. White admiral – *Limenitis camilla*
6. Purple emperor – *Apatura iris*
7. Small tortoiseshell – *Aglais urticae*
8. Peacock – *Inachis io*

△ Family **Libytheidae**
▲ 9. Nettle-tree butterfly – *Libythea celtis*

Family **Nemeobiidae**
10. Duke of Burgundy fritillary – *Hamearis lucina*

Family **Lycaenidae**
11. Chalkhill blue – *Lysandra coridon*
12. Purple hairstreak – *Quercusia quercus*
▲ 13. Large copper – *Lycaena dispar rutila*

Family **Papilionidae**
14. Swallowtail – *Papilio machaon*
▲ 15. Apollo butterfly – *Parnassius apollo*

Family **Pieridae**
16. Small white – *Pieris rapae*
17. Large white – *Pieris brassicae*
18. Bath white – *Pontia daplidice*
19. Pale clouded yellow – *Colias hyale*
20. Brimstone – *Gonepteryx rhamni*

Family **Hesperidae**
21. Dingy skipper – *Erynnis tages*
22. Large skipper – *Ochlodes venatus*
23. Silver-spotted skipper – *Hesperia comma*

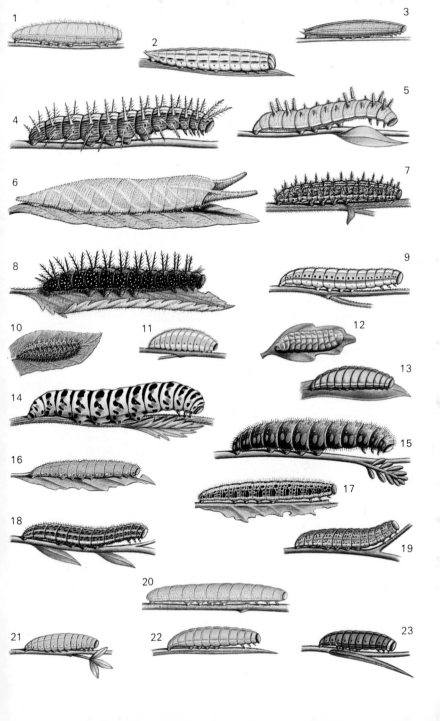

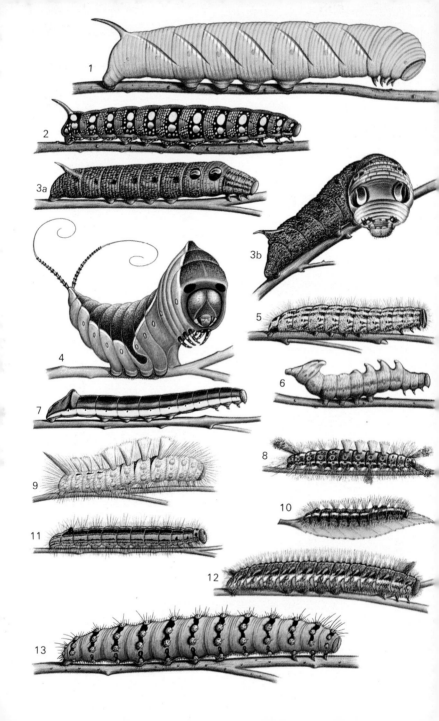

Family **Sphingidae**
1. Privet hawkmoth – *Sphinx ligustri*
2. Spurge hawkmoth – *Hyles euphorbiae*
3a. Elephant hawkmoth – *Deilephila elpenor*
3b. Threat or bluff attitude (p. 190)

Family **Notodontidae**
4. Puss moth – *Cerura vinula* – in threat posture
5. Buff-tip – *Phalera bucephala*
6. Iron prominent – *Notodonta dromedarius*
7. Lesser swallow prominent – *Pheosia gnoma*

Family **Lymantriidae**
8. Vapourer – *Orgyia antiqua*
9. Pale tussock – *Dasychira pudibunda*
10. Gold tail – *Euproctis similis*

Family **Lasiocampidae**
11. Lackey – *Malacosoma neustria*
12. Drinker – *Philudoria potatoria*

Family **Saturniidae**
13. Emperor – *Saturnia pavonia*

Caudal Concerning the 'tail' end of the insect

Cell An area of the wing enclosed by a number of veins. A cell is closed if it is completely surrounded by veins, while a cell which is bounded partly by the wing margin is said to be open

Cerci The paired appendages, often very long, which spring from the tip of the abdomen in many insects (singular: cercus)

Cervical Concerning the 'neck' region just behind the head

Chaetae Stiff hairs or bristles (singular: chaeta)

Chaetotaxy The arrangement of the bristles or chaetae on an insect: especially important in the classification of the flies (Diptera)

Cheek (see **Gena**)

Chitin The tough horny material, chemically known as a nitrogenous polysaccharide, which makes up the bulk of the insect cuticle

Ciliated Bearing small hairs (cilia)

Clavate Club-shaped, with the distal end swollen: most often applied to antennae

Clavus The posterior part of the front wing of a heteropteran bug (Hemiptera) (Fig. p. 115)

Clypeus The lowest part of the face of an insect, just above the labrum (Fig. p. 16)

Coarctate (applied to a pupa) Enclosed within the last larval skin, which therefore acts as a cocoon and protects the pupa. Such pupae are found in the flies (Diptera) of the sub-order Cyclorrhapha

Cocoon A case, made partly or completely of silk, which protects the pupa of many insects, especially the moths. The cocoon is constructed by the larva before it pupates

Contiguous Touching: the eyes of many dragonflies (Odonata), for example, are contiguous on the top of the head (see also **Holoptic**)

Corbicula The pollen basket found on the hind legs of many bees: formed by stout hairs standing on the borders of the tibiae (Fig. p. 279)

Corium The main part of the front wing of a heteropteran bug (Hemiptera) (Fig. p. 115)

Cornicle One of the pair of small tubular outgrowths on the hind end of the aphid abdomen (Hemiptera: Homoptera) (Plate 13)

Costa One of the major longitudinal veins of the wing, usually forming the front margin. The costal margin is the front margin of the wing. Abbreviated to C. (Fig. p. 22)

Costal Cell The cell between the costa and the sub-costal vein

Coxa The basal segment of the insect leg, often firmly attached to the body (Fig. p. 20)

Cremaster The little cluster of hooks at the hind end of a butterfly pupa (Lepidoptera). The hooks grip a little pad of silk and support the pupa (Fig. p. 167)

Cross Vein A short vein joining any two neighbouring longitudinal veins

Cubitus One of the major longitudinal veins of the wing, situated in the hind part of the wing and usually with two or three branches. Abbreviated to Cu. (Fig. p. 22)

Cuneus A more or less triangular region of the front wing of certain bugs (Hemiptera: Heteroptera), separated from the corium by a groove or suture (Fig. p. 115)

Cursorial Adapted for running

Dentate Toothed

Denticulate Bearing very small tooth-like projections

Depressed Flattened from top to bottom, as lice are (Fig. p. 108)

Diapause A period of suspended animation, a regular occurrence in the lives of many insects, especially in the young stages.

Discal cell Name given to a large and prominent cell near the middle of the wing. The discal cell of one group of insects may not be bounded by the same veins as that of another group of insects.

Distal Concerning that part of an appendage furthest from the body

Dorsal Concerning the back or upperside of an animal

Dorso-Central Bristles The two rows of bristles running along the thorax of a fly (Diptera) on the outer side of the acrostichal bristles (Fig. p. 210)

Dorso-Lateral Towards the sides of the dorsal (upper) surface

Dorso-Ventral Running from the dorsal (upper) to the ventral (lower) surface

Dorsum The upper side or back of an animal

Ecdysis The moulting process, by which an insect changes its outer coat

Ectoparasite A parasite which lives on the outside of its host. Fleas and lice are the most familiar examples among the insects

Elbowed Antennae Antennae in which the first segment (the scape) is much longer than the others and in which there is a distinct angle between the first and second segment

Elytron The hard and horny front wing of a beetle or an earwig (plural elytra). (See also Hemelytron)

Emarginate With a distinct notch or indentation

Embolium A narrow region along the costal margin of the front wings of certain bugs (Hemiptera: Heteroptera), separated from the rest of the corium by a groove or suture (Fig. p. 115)

Empodium An outgrowth between the claws on the last tarsal segment of flies (Diptera). It may be bristle-like or pad-like (Fig. p. 212)

Endoparasite A parasite which lives inside the body of its host. Most of the ichneumon flies (p. 263) are endoparasites

Endopterygote An endopterygote insect is one in which the wings develop inside the body of the young insect. It undergoes a complete metamorphosis, with a pupal stage occurring before the emergence of the adult

Epimeron The posterior part of the side wall of any of the three thoracic segments. According to the segment, the name may be prefixed by pro-, mes-, or met-

Epipharynx A component of many insect mouth-parts which is attached to the posterior surface of the labrum or upper lip. In chewing insects it is generally only a small lobe, but in the fleas it is greatly enlarged and used for sucking blood

Epiproct An appendage arising from the mid-line of the last abdominal segment, just above the anus. In the Thysanura and some mayflies (Ephemeroptera) it is long and forms the central of the three 'tails'

Episternum The anterior part of the side wall of any of the three thoracic segments. According to the segment, the name may be prefixed by pro-, mes-, or met-

Eruciform An eruciform larva is one with a more or less cylindrical body and with stumpy legs on the hind region as well as the true thoracic legs. The caterpillars of Lepidoptera are the typical examples

Exarate Pupa An exarate pupa is one in which the appendages are all free (Fig. p. 28)

Excavate Hollowed out. Many beetle coxae are excavate, hollowed out to receive the femur when the legs are folded (Fig. p. 292)

Exopterygote An exopterygote insect is one in which the wings develop gradually on the outside of the body. There is no pupal stage and the young insect is called a nymph

Exuviae The cast-off outer coat of an insect or other arthropod

Eye-Cap Hood partly covering the eye in certain small moths. Formed by the base of the antenna (Fig. p. 180)

Facet The surface of an ommatidium – one of the units making up the compound eye

Femur The third, and often the largest segment of the insect leg (Fig. p. 20)

Filament A thread-like structure, especially one at the end of the antenna

Filiform Thread-like or hair-like, applied especially to antennae

Flabellate With projecting flaps on one side, applied especially to antennae

Flagellum The distal part of the antenna, beyond the second segment (Fig. p. 18)

Fossorial Adapted for digging

Frenulum The wing-coupling mechanism found in many moths and some other insects. It consists of a bristle or a group of bristles arising from the 'shoulder' of the hind wing and passing under the front wing, where they are held in place by a hook or a group of bristles called the retinaculum

Frons The upper part of the insect face, between and below the antennae and usually carrying the median ocellus or simple eye. In flies (Diptera) it occupies almost all of the front surface of the head apart from the eyes

Frontal Bristles The two vertical rows of bristles running down the face of a fly (Diptera) from the ocelli to the antennae (Fig. p. 209)

Fronto-Orbital Bristles The short row of

bristles on each side of a fly head (Diptera) between the eye and the frontal bristles (Fig. p. 209)

Furcula The forked 'spring' of a springtail

Galea The outer branch of the maxilla, the inner one being the lacinia

Gall An abnormal outgrowth of a plant caused by the presence of a young insect or some other organism in the tissues. Aphids (Plate 13), gall wasps (Plate 37), and gall midges (p. 220) are among the most important gall-causing insects

Gaster That part of the abdomen in Hymenoptera which lies behind the 'waist' (see also Propodeum)

Gena The cheek, that part of the head below and behind the eye

Genal Comb A row of stout spines on the lower border of the cheek of certain fleas

Geniculate Abruptly bent or elbowed (see Elbowed Antennae)

Genitalia The copulatory organs of insects. The shape and arrangement of the genitalia is often the only way of distinguishing between closely related species

Genus A group of closely related species. The name of the genus is incorporated into the scientific names of all the member species: *Pieris napi* and *Pieris rapae*, for example, both belong to the genus *Pieris* (Plural: genera)

Gill Breathing organ possessed by many aquatic creatures, including numerous young insects. Insect gills are usually very fine outgrowths from the body and they contain numerous air tubes or tracheae. Oxygen passes into the air tubes from the water

Glabrous Without hairs

Glossa One of a pair of small lobes at the tip of the labium or lower lip. Usually small, but very long in honey bees and bumble bees, in which the two glossae are used to suck up nectar

Gynandromorph An individual creature with a mixture of male and female characteristics. One half of the body may be male, while the other half is female. This is particularly noticeable when it occurs among the blue butterflies (Lycaenidae), in which the males and females are differently coloured

Haltere One of the club-shaped 'balancers'

found among the true flies (Diptera). The halteres are the modified hind wings

Hamuli The minute hooks on the front edge of the hind wing of bees and other Hymenoptera. The hooks link the front and hind wings together. The hook which holds the springtail's 'spring' in place is also called the hamula

Haustellate Adapted for sucking liquids rather than biting solids

Hemelytron The front wing of a heteropteran bug (Hemiptera), differing from the elytron of a beetle in that the distal section is membranous. (Plural: hemelytra)

Hemimetabolous Having an incomplete metamorphosis, with no pupal stage in the life history. E.g. dragonflies, grasshoppers, etc.

Heteromerous (of beetles) Having unequal numbers of tarsal segments on the three pairs of legs – five on the first two pairs and four on the third, for example

Holometabolous Having a complete metamorphosis, with a pupal stage. E.g. butterflies and moths, bees and beetles

Holoptic With the eyes touching or almost touching on the top of the head (Diptera)

Holotype See type

Homonym A scientific name which has been given to two different species. When such an instance is discovered one of the species must be given another name

Honeydew The sweet liquid emitted from the anus of aphids and some other bugs (Hemiptera: Heteroptera) (p. 131)

Host The organism which is being attacked by a parasite

Humeral Angle The front basal part of the wing, close to the attachment to the body

Humeral Vein A small cross vein running from the costa to the sub-costa in the humeral portion (basal part) of the wing

Hyaline Clear and colourless, like the wings of most dragonflies

Hypermetamorphosis A type of life history which includes two or more different kinds of larvae (Fig. p. 313)

Hyperparasite A parasitic organism which attacks another parasite

Hypognathous Having a vertical head and face, with the mouth-parts at the bottom (Fig. p. 16)

Hypopharynx A component of the insect mouth-parts arising behind the mouth and just in front of the labium or lower lip. Usually short and tongue-like in species with biting jaws, but often drawn out to form a tube for the salivary duct in those species with sucking mouths (Fig. p. 209)

Hypopleural Bristles A curved row of bristles on the side of the thorax of certain flies (Diptera), just below and in front of the haltere and just above the base of the hind leg (Fig. p. 238)

Imago The adult stage in the insect life history (plural: imagines)

Inquiline A creature that lives in the home of another species without having any obvious effect on that other species

Instar The stage in an insect's life history between any two moults. An insect which has recently hatched from the egg and which has not yet moulted is said to be a first instar nymph or larva. The adult (imago) is the final instar

Integument The outer coat of the insect's body

Intercalary Vein An additional longitudinal vein in the wing, arising at the wing margin and running inwards but not directly connected to any of the major veins (Fig. p. 59)

Joint Strictly speaking, an articulation between two neighbouring parts, such as the tibia and femur of the leg. The word is commonly used, however, as a synonym of segment, meaning any of the divisions of the body or its appendages

Jugum A narrow lobe projecting from the base of the front wing in certain moths and overlapping the hind wing, thereby coupling the two wings together (Fig. p. 21)

Keel A narrow ridge. Also called a carina

Labellum The expanded tip of the labium, which is used by many flies (Diptera) to mop up the surface fluids (Fig. p. 209)

Labial Concerning the labium

Labium The 'lower lip' of the insect's mouth-parts, formed by the fusion of two maxilla-like appendages (Fig. p. 17)

Labrum The 'upper lip' of the insect's mouth-parts. Not a true appendage but a moveable sclerite on the front of the head

Lacinia The inner branch of the maxilla, the outer one being the galea

Lamella A thin leaf-like flap or plate, the name being applied to the outgrowths of certain antennae (Fig. p. 18)

Lamellate Possessing lamellae: applied especially to antennae (Fig. p. 18)

Larva Name given to a young insect when it is markedly different from the adult: caterpillars and fly maggots are good examples. The larvae must pass through a pupal stage before becoming adults (Fig. p. 28)

Lateral Concerning the sides

Ligula Name given to the lobes at the tip of the labium or lower lip: usually divided into glossae and paraglossae (Fig. p. 17)

Mandible The jaw of an insect. It may be sharply toothed and used for biting, as in grasshoppers and wasps, or it may be drawn out to form a slender 'needle', as in mosquitoes. The mandibles are absent altogether in most flies (Diptera) and Lepidoptera

Mandibulate Having mandibles suited for biting and chewing

Marginal Cell One of a number of cells bordering front margin of wing in outer region

Maxilla One of the two components of the insect mouth-parts lying just behind the jaws. They assist with the detection and manipulation of food and are often drawn out into tubular structures for sucking up liquids (plural: maxillae) (Fig. p. 17)

Maxillary Concerning the maxillae

Media The longitudinal vein running through the central region of the wing in most insects. Abbreviated to M (Fig. p. 22)

Membranous Thin and delicate, often transparent

Mesonotum The dorsal surface of the second thoracic segment – the mesothorax: usually the largest of the thoracic sclerites

Mesopleuron The sclerite or sclerites making up the side wall of the mesothorax

Mesoscutellum The hindermost of the three major divisions of the mesonotum, often more or less triangular or shield-shaped. Usually abbreviated to scutellum (Fig. p. 210)

Mesoscutum The middle, and usually major division of the mesonotum (Fig. p. 210)

Mesosternum The ventral surface or sclerite of the mesothorax

Mesothorax The second segment of the thorax

Metamorphosis Name given to the changes that take place during the insect's life as it turns from a young animal to an adult. These changes may be gradual and not too large, as in the grasshopper, and metamorphosis is then said to be partial or incomplete. On the other hand, the changes might be much greater and they may take place in one big step as in the Lepidoptera, which change from caterpillars to adults during the pupal stage. Metamorphosis of this kind is said to be complete

Metanotum The dorsal surface of the metathorax. It is often very small and its subdivisions are usually obscured

Metapleuron The sclerite of sclerites making up the side wall of the metathorax

Metasternum The ventral surface or sclerite of the metathorax

Metatarsus The basal segment of the tarsus or foot, usually the largest segment

Metathorax The third segment of the thorax

Moniliform Antennae composed of bead-like segments, each well separated from the next, are said to be moniliform (Fig. p. 18)

Moult To moult is to shed the outer covering of the body – the exoskeleton

Nodus A short but strong cross vein running back from the front margin of the wing in the Odonata. Its position is marked by a slight dent in the costal margin (Fig. p. 64)

Notaulix One of a pair of longitudinal grooves on the mesonotum of certain Hymenoptera, dividing the mesonotum into central area and two lateral areas (plural: notaulices)

Notopleuron A triangular area on the thorax of certain flies (Diptera), just behind the humeral callus and occupying parts of both dorsal and lateral surfaces

Notum The dorsal or upper surface of any thoracic segment: usually prefixed

by pro-, meso-, or meta- to indicate the relevant segment

Nymph Name given to the young stages of those insects which undergo a partial metamorphosis. The nymph is usually quite similar to the adult except that its wings are not fully developed. It normally feeds on the same kind of food as the adult (Fig. p. 27)

Obtect Pupa An obtect pupa is one in which the legs and other appendages are firmly fastened down to the rest of the body, as they are in the pupae of the Lepidoptera (Fig. p. 28)

Occiptal Suture A groove running around the posterior region of the head of some insects and separating the vertex from the occiput. On the sides of the head the same groove marks the posterior boundary of the cheeks or genae

Occiput Hindermost region of the top of the head, just in front of the neck membrane. In some insects it is separated from the vertex by the occipital suture, but it is not usually present as a distinct plate or sclerite

Ocellar Bristles Bristles arising from around or between the ocelli in various flies (Diptera)

Ocellar Triangle A triangular area, usually quite distinct from the rest of the head, on which the ocelli of Diptera are carried (Plate 34)

Ocellus One of the simple eyes of insects, usually occurring in a group of three on top of the head, although absent from some insects

Ommatidium One of the units which make up the compound eye (Fig. p. 19)

Ootheca An egg case, such as the purse-like structure carried around by cockroaches, or the spongy mass in which mantids lay their eggs

Oral Vibrissae The pair of large bristles just above the mouth in certain flies (Diptera). Usually simply called vibrissae (Fig. p. 209)

Oviparous Reproducing by laying eggs

Oviposit To oviposit is to lay eggs

Ovipositor The egg-laying apparatus of a female insect. Concealed in many insects, but extremely large among the bush crickets (p. 85) and some parasitic Hymenoptera (Plate 38)

Palp A segmented leg-like structure arising on the maxilla and the labium. The palps are sensory in function, playing a major role in 'tasting' food to determine its acceptability

Paraglossa One of a pair of lobes at the outer edges of the tip of the labium. With the central glossae, the paraglossae make up the ligula (Fig. p. 17)

Paraproct One of the two lobes which border the sides of the anus

Parasite An organism that spends all or part of its life in close association with another species, taking food from it but giving nothing in return. Ectoparasites live on the outside of their hosts, while endoparasites live inside the host's body

Parthenogenesis A form of reproduction in which eggs develop normally without having been fertilised. This is the usual method of reproduction among some stick insect species and among certain generations of gall wasps (p. 264) and aphids

Pecten A comb-like structure, such as is found at the base of the antenna in some insects (Fig. p. 164)

Pectinate Possessing branches which arise from the main stem like the teeth of a comb. Usually applied to antennae (Plate 53)

Pedicel Name given to the second segment of the antenna, and also to the narrow 'waist' at the front of the abdomen of an ant

Petiolate Attached by a narrow stalk

Petiole The narrow 'waist' of bees and wasps and other Hymenoptera: often known as the pedicel when referring to ants

Pictured A term used to describe wings, especially among the Diptera, which have dark mottlings on them (Plate 33)

Pilose Having a fairly dense coat of hair

Pleural Concerning the side walls of the body

Pleural Suture A vertical or diagonal groove on each of the thoracic pleura, separating the episternum at the front from the epimeron at the back

Pleuron The side wall of a thoracic segment

Plumose With numerous feathery branches, applied especially to antenna (Fig. p. 18)

Pollen Basket The pollen-carrying region on the hind legs of many bees, also known as the corbicula (Fig. p. 279)

Porrect Extending horizontally forward, applied especially to antennae

Posterior Concerning or facing the rear

Postmentum The basal region of the labium or 'lower lip'

Postscutellum A small division of the mesonotum just behind the scutellum: usually very small or absent, but well developed in certain Diptera (Fig. p. 238)

Post-vertical Bristles A pair of bristles – divergent, parallel, or crossing – which arise on the back of the head of various Diptera, some way behind the ocelli (Fig. p. 209)

Pre-apical Arising just before the tip: many flies, for example, have pre-apical bristles just before the tip of the tibia (Fig. p. 226)

Prementum The distal region of the labium or 'lower lip' of an insect, from which spring the labial palps and the ligula

Prepupa A resting stage through which many larvae pass before turning into pupae. The larvae are usually rather shrunken and deformed during this stage

Proboscis Name given to various kinds of sucking mouths in which some of the mouth-parts are drawn out to form a long tube (Fig. p. 155)

Prognathous Having a more or less horizontal head, with the mouthparts at the front

Proleg One of the stumpy legs on the hind region of the body of a caterpillar

Pronotal Comb A row of stout spines on the hind margin of the pronotum of certain fleas (Fig. p. 246)

Pronotum The dorsal surface or sclerite of the first thoracic segment

Propodeum The first abdominal segment of Apocrita (pp. 249, 254)

Prosternum The ventral surface of the first thoracic segment

Prothorax The first thoracic segment

Proximal Concerning the basal part of an appendage – the part nearest to the body

Pruinose Covered with a powdery deposit, usually white or pale blue (see Odonata, p. 63)

Pterostigma A small coloured area near the wing tip of dragonflies, bees, and

Plate 59   Larvae of Lepidoptera – MOTHS

△ Family **Amatidae**
▲ **1.** *Syntomis phegea*

Family **Arctiidae**
2. Garden tiger – *Arctia caja*
3. Jersey tiger – *Euplagia quadripunctaria*
4. Buff ermine – *Spilosoma lutea*
5. Cinnabar – *Callimorpha jacobaeae*

Family **Noctuidae**
6. Green silver lines – *Bena prasinana*
7. Alder moth – *Apatele alni*
8. Grey dagger – *Apatele psi*
9. Sycamore moth – *Apatele aceris*
10. Knotgrass – *Apatele rumicis*
11. Cabbage moth – *Mamestra brassicae*
12. Large yellow underwing – *Noctua pronuba*
13. Dot moth – *Melanchra persicariae*
14. Broom moth – *Ceramica pisi*
15. Old lady – *Mormo maura*
16. Small angle shades – *Euplexia lucipara*
17. Clay moth – *Leucania lythargyria*
18. Hebrew character – *Orthosia gothica*
19. Mullein moth – *Cucullia verbasci*

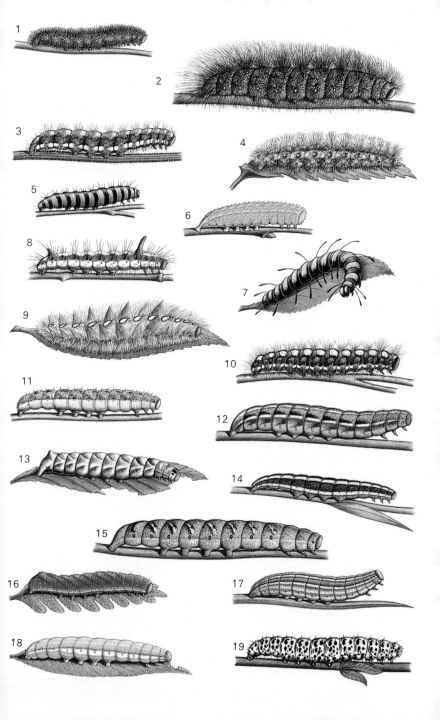

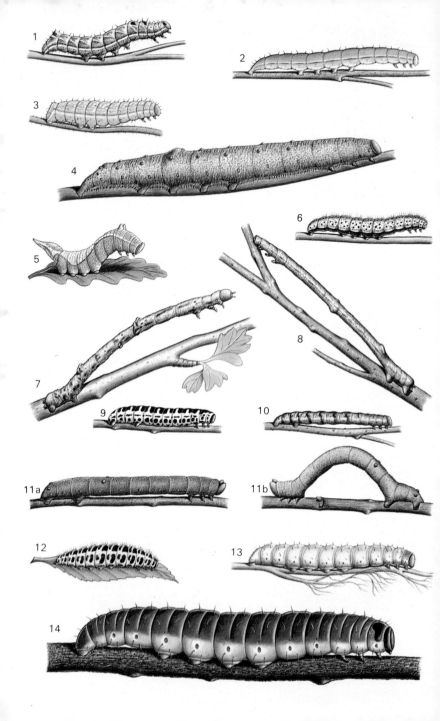

Family **Noctuidae** (Contd.)
1. Spectacle – *Unca triplasia*
2. Herald – *Scoliopteryx libatrix*
3. Burnished brass – *Plusia chrysitis*
4. Red underwing – *Catocala nupta*

Family **Drepanidae**
5. Oak hooktip – *Drepana binaria*

Family **Geometridae**
6. Treble bar – *Anaitis plagiata*
7. Large thorn – *Ennomos autumnaria*
8. Swallowtailed – *Ourapteryx sambucaria*
9. Magpie moth – *Abraxas grossulariata*
10. Mottled umber – *Erannis defoliaria*
11a. Peppered moth – *Biston betularia*
11b. Peppered moth in looping attitude

Family **Zygaenidae**
12. Six-spot burnet moth – *Zygaena filipendulae*

Family **Hepialidae**
13. Ghost swift – *Hepialus humuli*

Family **Cossidae**
14. Goat moth – *Cossus cossus*

various other insects with clear wings. Also called the stigma (Fig. p. 64)

Pterygote Any member of the sub-class Pterygota, meaning any insect apart from the primitive wingless bristletails, springtails, and proturans (see page 58)

Ptilinum A tiny balloon-like structure found in certain Diptera as they emerge from the puparia. The ptilinum emerges from the front of the head and, as it is inflated, it pushes off the lid of the puparium. Having done its job, it is deflated and withdrawn. Its position is marked by the ptilinal suture (Fig. p. 208)

Pubescent Covered with short soft hairs

Pulvillus The little pad which is found beneath each claw on the foot of a fly (Diptera) (Fig. p. 212)

Punctate Covered with tiny pits or depressions, as the elytra of many beetles and the thorax of many Hymenoptera

Pupa The third stage in the life history of Lepidoptera and other insects undergoing a complete metamorphosis. It is during the pupal stage, which does not feed and does not usually move about, that the larval body is rebuilt into that of the adult insect (Fig. p. 28)

Puparium The barrel-shaped case in which the pupa of many flies (Diptera) is concealed. It is formed from the last larval skin and, unlike the actual pupa, it carries no indication of the positions of the wings or other appendages

Pupate To pupate is to turn into a pupa

Pupiparous Insects which give birth to a fully grown larvae which pupate almost immediately are said to be pupiparous. The main examples are various parasitic flies (p. 242)

Quadrilateral A cell near the base of the damselfly wing, whose shape is important in separating the families (Fig. p. 64)

Radial Sector The posterior of the two main branches of the radius, usually abbreviated to Rs. It usually has several branches of its own.

Radius One of the longitudinal veins near the front of the wing, usually abbreviated to R. It gives off a posterior branch called the radial sector, and the smaller branches of these veins are numbered R_1, R_2, and so on (Fig. p. 22)

Raptorial Adapted for seizing and grasping prey, like the front legs of a mantis (Plate 7)

Reticulate Covered with a network pattern

Rostrum A beak or snout, applied especially to the piercing mouthparts of bugs (Hemiptera) and the elongated snouts of weevils (Fig. p. 318)

Rudimentary Poorly developed

Scape the first segment of the antenna, especially if it is longer than the other segments

Scarabaeiform Scarabaeiform larvae, typified by those of the lamellicorn beetles (p. 293), are those with thick soft bodies and well developed heads and thoracic legs, but without legs on the hind region. Often permanently curved into a C

Sclerite Any of the individual hardened plates which make up the body wall

Scopa Name given to the pollen-collecting apparatus of a bee, whether it be the pollen basket (corbicula) on the leg or a brush of hairs on the abdomen

Scopula A small tuft of hairs

Scutellum The third of the major divisions of the dorsal surface of a thoracic segment: usually obvious only in the mesothorax, and very large in some bugs (Hemiptera) (Fig. p. 111)

Scutum The middle of the three main divisions of the dorsal surface of a thoracic segment (Fig. p. 210)

Segment One of the rings or divisions of the body, or one of the sections of a jointed limb between two joints

Serrate Toothed like a saw

Sessile Attached to one place and unable to move, as many female scale insects (p. 138)

Seta A bristle

Setaceous Bristle-like, applied especially to antennae

Species The basic unit of living things, consisting of a group of individuals which all look more or less alike and which can all breed with each other to produce another generation of similar creatures. Many species are divided into sub-species. These normally inhabit different areas and they may differ in appearance, but they can still all interbreed

Spinose Spiny

Spiracle One of the breathing pores – openings of the tracheal system: occurring on most segments of the body but most clearly seen in certain caterpillars (Fig. p. 163)

Spur A large and usually moveable spine, normally occurring on the legs

Spurious Vein A false vein formed by a thickening of the wing membrane and usually unconnected with any of the true veins: well marked in hover-flies (Plate 32)

Squama Any of the membranous flaps that rise near the base of the wing in many Diptera (plural: squamae) (Fig. p. 211)

Stadium The time interval between successive moults in an insect's life

Sternite The plate or sclerite on the underside of a body segment

Stigma See Pterostigma

Striae Grooves running across or along the body: applied especially to the grooves on the elytra of beetles

Stridulation The production of sounds by rubbing two parts of the body together: best known in grasshoppers and other Orthoptera

Style A slender bristle arising at the apex of the antenna

Stylet A needle-like object: applied to various components of piercing mouthparts and also to a part of the sting of a bee or other Hymenoptera (Fig. p. 258)

Sub-Apical Situated just before the apex or tip

Subcosta Usually the first of the longitudinal veins behind the front margin of the wing, although it is often missing or very faint. Abbreviated to Sc

Sub-Imago Found only among the mayflies (p. 59), the sub-imago is the winged insect which emerges from the nymphal skin. It is rather dull in colour but it very soon moults again – the only example of a winged insect undergoing a moult – to reveal the imago. Also called a dun

Sub-Marginal Cells Cells in the front wing of certain Hymenoptera, lying just behind the stigma. Important in the classification of bees (Fig. p. 279)

Sub-species See Species

Suture A groove on the body surface which usually divides one plate or sclerite from the next. Also the junction between the elytra of a beetle

Synonym One of two or more names which have been given to a single species. The earliest name usually takes precedence

Tarsus The 'foot' of the insect: primitively a single segment but now usually divided up into several sub-segments

Tegmen Name given to the leathery front wing of a grasshopper or other similar insect, including cockroaches (plural: tegmina)

Tegula A small lobe or scale overlying the base of the front wing like a 'shoulder pad' (Fig. p. 249)

Tergite The primary plate or sclerite forming the dorsal surface of any segment of the body

Tergum The dorsal surface of any body segment

Thorax The middle of the three major divisions of the insect body. The wings and legs (if present) are always attached to the thorax

Tibia One of the segments of the leg, between the femur and the tarsus (Fig. p. 20)

Trachea One of the tiny tubes which permeate the insect body and carry air to all parts. The tracheae open to the air at the spiracles

Transverse Suture A suture running across the thorax of many flies (Diptera) and dividing the mesonotum into a scutum and a prescutum

Triangle A region near the base of the wing in dragonflies. It is triangular in shape and may or may not be divided into smaller cells (Fig. p. 64)

Triungulin Name given to the active first instar larva of the oil beetles and some of their relatives (p. 314), which appears to have three claws on each foot (Fig. p. 313)

Trochanter A segment of the insect leg between the coxa and the femur: often very small and easily overlooked (Fig. p. 20)

Truncate Abruptly ending: squared off

Tymbal The sound-producing 'drum skin' of a cicada (p. 133)

Tympanum The auditory membrane or ear drum of various insects (Fig. p. 85)

Type The type specimen of a species is the actual insect from which the original description of the species was produced.

If several specimens were used for this purpose, one of them should have been designated as the type. Because the type can be only of one sex, it is usual to designate a certain individual of the opposite sex as the allotype. The original type specimen is then called the holotype. These types are very important specimens in museum collections

Ventral Concerning the lower side of the body

Vertex The top of the head, between and behind the eyes (Fig. p. 16)

Vestigal Poorly developed

Vibrissae See Oral Vibrissae

Viviparous Bringing forth living or active young instead of laying eggs

Selected Bibliography

of works dealing with the Biology and Identification of Insects

The works listed here are mainly in English and they deal mainly with British insects. Many of them contain further references.

Insects occurring in France may be identified with the aid of the *Nouvel Atlas d'Entomologie* – a series of pocket books by various authors – and the various volumes in the Faune de France series.

General Entomology
Askew, R. R. 1971 *Parasitic Insects* Heinemann
Borror, D. J. and DeLong, D. M. 1954 *An Introduction to the Study of Insects* Holt, Rinehart & Winston
Ford, R. L. E. 1963 *Practical Entomology* Warne
Imms, A. D. 1957 *A General Textbook of Entomology* (9th edition, revised by O. W. Richards and R. G. Davies) Methuen
Imms, A. D. 1971 *Insect Natural History* (3rd edition) Collins
Kerrich, G. J., Meikle, R. D. and Tebble, N. 1967 *Bibliography of the Key Works for the Identification of the British Flora and Fauna*
Kloet, G. S. & Hincks, W. D. 1945 *Check List of British Insects*
Klots, A. B. & Klots, E. B. 1959 *Living Insects of the World* Hamish Hamilton
Oldroyd, H. 1958 *Collecting, Preserving and Studying Insects* Hutchinson
Oldroyd, H. 1968 *Elements of Entomology* Weidenfeld & Nicolson
Sanders, E. 1946 *An Insect Book for the Pocket* O.U.P.
Tweedie, M. W. F. 1968 *Pleasure from Insects* David & Charles

Apterygote Insects
Chopard, L. 1947 *Orthoptères et Aptérygotes de France* France
Delany, M. J. 1954 *Handbooks for the Identification of British Insects* Vol. 1, Part 2: *Thysanura and Diplura*
Womersley H. *Ent. mon. Mag.* 1927 **63**, 140-154

Mayflies
Goddard, J. 1966 *Trout Fly Recognition* Black
Goddard, J. 1970 *Trout Flies of Stillwater* Black
Harris, J. R. 1956 *An Angler's Entomology* (2nd edition) Collins
Kimmins, D. E. 1950 *Handbooks for the Identification of British Insects* Vol. 1, Part 9: *Ephemeroptera*
Kimmins, D. E. 1954 Freshwater Biological Assoc. Sci. Publ. No. 15
Mellanby, H. 1953, *Animal Life in Fresh Water* Methuen
Needham, J. G., Traver, J. R., and Hsu, Y. 1935 *The Biology of Mayflies* U.S.A.

Dragonflies
Corbet, P. S. 1962 *A Biology of Dragonflies* Witherby
Corbet, P.S., Longfield, C., and Moore, N.W. 1960 *Dragonflies* Collins
Fraser, F. C. 1956 *Handbooks for the Identification of British Insects* Vol. 1, Part 10: *Odonata*
Longfield, C. 1949 *The Dragonflies of the British Isles* Warne
Lucas, W. J. 1900 *British Dragonflies (Odonata)* London
Tillyard, R. J. 1917 *The Biology of Dragonflies* Cambridge

Stoneflies

Goddard, J. 1966 *Trout Fly Recognition* Black

Harris, J. R. 1956 *An Angler's Entomology* (2nd edition) Collins

Kimmins, D. E. 1950 *Handbooks for the Identification of British Insects* Vol. 1, Part 6:
  Plecoptera

Orthoptera (*Saltatoria*)

Chopard, L. 1947 *Orthoptères et Aptérygotes de France* France

Harz, K. 1969 *The Orthoptera of Europe* (Vol. 1) (Crickets, Bush Crickets, and Mole
  Crickets) The Hague

Hincks, W. D. 1956 *Handbooks for the Identification of British Insects* Vol. 1, Part 5:
  Dermaptera and Orthoptera

Ragge, D. R. 1965 *Grasshoppers, Crickets, and Cockroaches of the British Isles* Warne

Ragge, D. R. et al. 1965 *Songs of the British Grasshoppers and Crickets.* [A Companion
  Record to the above book]

Stick Insects

Chopard, L. 1947 *Orthoptères et Aptérygotes de France* France

Ragge, D. R. 1965 *Grasshoppers, Crickets and Cockroaches of the British Isles* Warne

Earwigs

Chopard L. 1947 *Orthoptères et Aptérygotes de France* France

Hincks, W. D. 1956 *Handbooks for the Identification of British Insects* Vol. 1, Part 5:
  Dermaptera and Orthoptera

Web-spinners

Davis, C. *Ann. ent. Soc. Amer.*, 1940, **33**, 677-682

Cockroaches and Mantises

Chopard, L. 1947 *Orthoptères et Aptérygotes de France* France

Hincks, W. D. 1956 *Handbooks for the Identification of British Insects* Vol. 1, Part 5:
  Dermaptera and Orthoptera

Ragge, D. R. 1965 *Grasshoppers, Crickets, and Cockroaches of the British Isles* Warne

Termites

Howse, P. E. 1970 *Termites* Hutchinson

Booklice (Psocids)

Badonnel, A. 1943 *Psocoptères* France

Lice

Clay, T. *Trans. R. ent. Soc. Lond.* 1951, **102**, 171-194

Clay, T. *Bull. Brit. Mus. Nat. Hist. (Ent.)*, 1969, **24**, 1-26

Craufurd-Benson, H. J. *Parasitology* 1941, **33**, 331-358

Hopkins, G. H. E. *Proc. zool. Soc. Lond.*, **119**, 387-604

Hopkins, G. H. E. and Clay, T. 1952 *A Check List of the Genera and Species of
  Mallophaga* Brit. Mus. (Nat. Hist.)

Bugs

Buckton, G. B. 1876-83 *Monograph of British Aphides* (4 vols.) Ray Society

Butler, E. A. 1923 *A Biology of British-Hemiptera-Heteroptera* London

Edwards, J. 1896 *The Hemiptera-Homoptera (Cicadina and Psyllina) of the British
  Islands* London

Le Quesne, W. J. 1965 *Handbooks for the Identification of British Insects* Vol. 2, Part 2:
  (a): *Hemiptera-Homoptera: Cicadomorpha* (part)
    1969 Vol. 2, Part 2 (b): *Hemiptera-Homoptera:Cicadomorpha* (cont.)

1960 Vol. 2, Part 3: *Hemiptera-Homoptera: Fulgoromorpha*

Newstead, R. 1901-3 *Monograph of British Coccidae* (2 vols.) Ray Society

Southwood, T. R. E. and Leston, D. 1959 *Land and Water Bugs of the British Isles* Warne

Theobald, F. V. 1926-29 *The Aphididae of Great Britain* (3 vols.) London

Thrips

Morison, G. D. 1949 *Thysanoptera of the London Area* – London Naturalist Reprint 59

Lacewings and other Neuroptera

Fraser, F. C. 1959 *Handbooks for the Identification of British Insects* Vol. 1, Parts 12-13: *Mecoptera, Megaloptera, Neuroptera*

Killington, F. J. *Trans. ent. Soc. Hants & S. England*, 1929, (5), 1-36

Killington, F. J. 1936-37 *Monograph of the British Neuroptera* (2 vols.) Ray Society

Scorpion Flies

Fraser, F. C. 1959 *Handbooks for the Identification of British Insects*, Vol. 1, Parts 12-13: *Mecoptera, Megaloptera, Neuroptera*

Hobby, B. M. and Killington, F. J. *Trans. Soc. Brit. Ent.*, 1934, **1**, 39-49

Withycombe, C. L. *Trans. ent. Soc. Lond.*, 1921, 312-318

Butterflies and Moths

Beirne, B. P. 1954 *British Pyralid and Plume Moths* Warne

Bradley, J. D. and Martin, E. L. *An Illustrated List of the British Tortricidae* (2 parts, reprinted from Entomologists' Gazette)

Ford, E. B. 1957 *Butterflies* (3rd edition) Collins

Ford, E. B. 1972 *Moths* (3rd edition) Collins

Higgins, L. G. and Riley, N. D. 1970 *A Field Guide to the Butterflies of Britain and Europe* Collins

Mansell, E. and Newman, L. Hugh 1968 *The Complete British Butterflies in Colour* Ebury Press

Meyrick, E. 1928 *Revised Handbook of British Lepidoptera* Classey (1968 reprint)

Sanders, E. 1939 *A Butterfly Book for the Pocket* O.U.P.

South, R. 1906 *The Butterflies of the British Isles* Warne

South, R. 1961 *The Moths of the British Isles* (2 vols. – 'Macros' only) Warne

Stokoe, W. J. 1944 *The Caterpillars of British Butterflies* Warne

Stokoe, W. J. 1948 *The Caterpillars of British Moths* (2 vols. – 'Macros' only) Warne

Warnecke, G. 1964 *Butterflies* (including some Continental species and some moths) Burke

Caddis Flies

Goddard, J. 1966 *Trout Fly Recognition* Black

Hickin, N. E. 1952 *Caddis* (mainly concerned with young stages) Methuen

Hickin, N. E. 1967 *Caddis Larvae* Hutchinson

Mellanby, H. 1963 *Animal Life in Fresh Water* (deals with larvae) Methuen

Mosely, M. E. 1939 *The British Caddis Flies (Trichoptera): A Collector's Handbook* Routledge

True Flies (Diptera)

Coe, R. L. 1953 *Handbooks for the Identification of British Insects* Vol. 10 Part 1: *Diptera: Syrphidae*

Coe, R. L. 1966 *Handbooks for the Identification of British Insects* Vol. 10 Part 2 (c): *Diptera: Pipunculidae*

Coe, R. L., Freeman, P. and Mattingly, P. F. 1950 *Handbooks for the Identification of British Insects* Vol. 9 Part 2: *Diptera: Nematocera* (part)

Colyer, C. N. and Hammond, C. O. 1968 *Flies of the British Isles* Warne

Edwards, F. W., Oldroyd, H. and Smart, J. 1939 *British Blood-Sucking Flies* Brit. Mus. (Nat. Hist.)

Emden, F. I. van 1954 *Handbooks for the Identification of British Insects* Vol. 10 Part 4 (a): *Diptera: Cyclorrhapha (Tachinidae, Calliphoridae)*

Fonseca, E. C. M. d'Assis 1968 *Handbooks for the Identification of British Insects* Vol. 10 Part 4 (b): *Diptera: Cyclorrhapha (Muscidae)*

Marshall, J. F. 1938 *The British Mosquitoes* Brit. Mus. (Nat. Hist.)

Oldroyd, H. 1964 *The Natural History of Flies* Weidenfeld & Nicolson

Oldroyd, H. 1970 *Handbooks for the Identification of British Insects* Vol. 9 Part 1: *Diptera: Introduction and Key to Families*

Oldroyd, H. 1969 *Handbooks for the Identification of British Insects* Vol. 9 Part 4: *Diptera: Tabanoidea and Asiloidea*

Smith, K. G. V. 1969 *Handbooks for the Identification of British Insects* Vol. 10 Part 2 (ai): *Diptera: Lonchopteridae*

Smith, K. G. V. 1969 *Handbooks for the Identification of British Insects* Vol. 10 Part 3 (a): *Diptera: Conopidae*

West, L. S. 1951 *The House-fly, its Natural History, Medical Importance and Control* Constable

Fleas

British Museum (Nat. Hist.) 1958 *Fleas: their Medical and Veterinary Importance*

Rothschild, M. and Clay, T. 1952 *Fleas, Flukes, and Cuckoos* Collins

Smit, F. G. A. M. 1957 *Handbooks for the Identification of British Insects* Vol. 1 Part 16: *Siphonaptera*

Bees, Wasps, Ants, and other Hymenoptera

Andrewes, Sir Christopher 1969 *The Lives of Wasps and Bees* Chatto & Windus

Askew, R. R. 1968 *Handbooks for the Identification of British Insects* Vol. 8 Part 2 (b): *Hymenoptera: Chalcidoidea* (cont.)

Benson, R. B. 1951-58 *Handbooks for the Identification of British Insects* Vol. 6 Parts 2 (a), 2 (b), 2 (c): *Hymenoptera: Symphyta*

Butler, C. G. 1954 *The World of the Honey-bee* Collins

Cameron, P. 1882-92 *Monograph of the British Phytophagous Hymenoptera* (4 vols.)

Darlington, A. 1968 *The Pocket Encyclopaedia of Plant Galls in Colour* Blandford

Donisthorpe, H. St J. K. 1927 *British Ants, their Life History and Classification* London

Donisthorpe, H. St J. K. 1927 *The Guests of British Ants, their Habits and Life Histories* London

Eady, R. D. and Quinlan, J. 1963 *Handbooks for the Identification of British Insects* Vol. 8 Part 1 (a): *Hymenoptera: Cynipoidea* (part)

Evans, H. E. 1964 *Wasp Farm* Harrap

Ferriere, Ch. and Kerrich, G. J. 1958 *Handbooks for the Identification of British Insects* Vol. 8 Part 2 (a): *Hymenoptera: Chalcidoidea* (part)

Free, J. B. and Butler, C. G. 1959 *Bumble-bees* Collins

Nixon, G. E. J. 1957 *Handbooks for the Identification of British Insects* Vol. 8 Part 3 (dii): *Hymenoptera: Proctotrupoidea* (part)

Perkins, J. F. 1959-60 *Handbooks for the Identification of British Insects* Vol. 7 Parts 2 (ai) and 2 (aii): *Hymenoptera: Ichneumonoidea*

Ribbands, C. R. 1953 *The Behaviour and Social Life of Honey-bees* London

Richards, O. W. 1953 *The Social Insects* MacDonald

Richards, O. W. 1956 *Handbooks for the Identification of British Insects* Vol. 6 Part 1: *Hymenoptera: Introduction and Key to Families*

Saunders, E. 1896 *The Hymenoptera Aculeata of the British Islands* London

Wheeler, W. M. 1928 *The Social Insects* London

Beetles

Balfour-Browne, F. 1940-50 *British Water Beetles* (2 vols.) Ray Society

Balfour-Browne, F. 1953 *Handbooks for the Identification of British Insects* Vol. 4 Part 3: *Coleoptera: Hydradephaga*

Britton, E. B. 1956 *Handbooks for the Identification of British Insects* Vol. 5 Part 11: *Coleoptera: Scarabaeoidea*

Buck, F. D. 1954 *Handbooks for the Identification of British Insects* Vol. 5 Part 9: *Coleoptera: Lagriidae to Meloidae*

Crowson, R. A. 1956 *Handbooks for the Identification of British Insects* Vol. 4 Part 1: *Coleoptera: Introduction and Key to Families*

Duffy, E. A. J. 1952 *Handbooks for the Identification of British Insects* Vol. 5 Part 12: *Coleoptera: Cerambycidae*

Duffy, E. A. J. 1953 *Handbooks for the Identification of British Insects* Vol. 5 Part 15: *Coleoptera: Scolytidae and Platypodidae*

Fowler, W. W. 1887-1913 *The Coleoptera of the British Islands* (6 vols.) London

Halstead, D. G. H. 1963 *Handbooks for the Identification of British Insects* Vol. 4 Part 10: *Coleoptera: Histeroidea*

Hinton, H. E. 1945 *A Monograph of the Beetles associated with Stored Products* British Museum (Nat. Hist.)

Johnson, C. 1966 *Handbooks for the Identification of British Insects* Vol. 4 Part 6 (a): *Coleoptera: Clambidae*

Joy, N. H. 1932 *A Practical Handbook of British Beetles* (2 vols.) Witherby

Linssen, E. F. 1959 *Beetles of the British Isles* (2 vols.) Warne

Pearce, E. J. 1957 *Handbooks for the Identification of British Insects* Vol. 4 Part 9: *Coleoptera: Pselaphidae*

Pope, R. D. 1953 *Handbooks for the identification of British Insects* Vol. 5 Part 7: *Coleoptera: Coccinellidae and Sphinididae*

Thompson, R. T. 1958 *Handbooks for the Identification of British Insects* Vol. 5 Part 5 (b): *Coleoptera: Phalacridae*

Tottenham, C. E. 1954 *Handbooks for the Identification of British Insects* Vol. 4 Part 8 (a): *Coleoptera: Staphylinidae* (part)

Walsh, G. B. and Dibb, J. R. (Eds.) *A Coleopterist's Handbook* Amateur Entomologist's Society

Stylopids

Hassan, A. I. *Trans. ent. Soc. Lond.*, 1939, **89**, 345-384

Perkins, R. C. L. *Ent. mon. Mag.*, 1918, **54**, 67-72 and 115-131

Linssen, E. F. 1959 *Beetles of the British Isles* (Vol. II) Warne

Entomological Suppliers

The Butterfly Farm*
Bilsington,
ASHFORD,
Kent

L. Christie
137 Gleneldon Road,
Streatham,
LONDON, S.W.18

Janson
44 Gt. Russell Street,
LONDON

Entech Services
46 Mersey View,
LIVERPOOL, 22
  (suppliers of portable light traps
  only)

GBI (Labs.) Ltd.
Heaton Mills,
Heaton Street,
Denton,
MANCHESTER, M34 3RG
  (sole suppliers of Euparal for wing
  mounts, etc.)

Watkins and Doncaster
Four Throws,
HAWKHURST,
Kent

World Wide Butterflies Ltd.*
Over Compton,
SHERBORNE
Dorset

Entomological books may be obtained from:
E. W. Classey Ltd.
353 Hanworth Road,
Hampton,
Middlesex

[Sole Agents for Handbooks for the Identification of British insects]

*Suppliers of living material as well as equipment

Index

Figures in *italics* refer to colour plates

348 INDEX

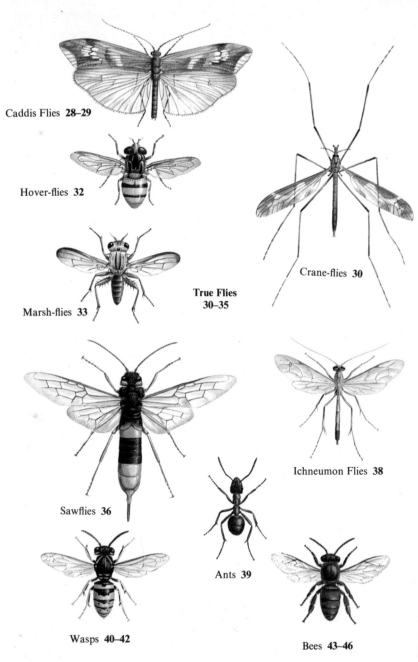

Caddis Flies **28–29**

Hover-flies **32**

Marsh-flies **33**

True Flies 30–35

Crane-flies **30**

Sawflies **36**

Ants **39**

Ichneumon Flies **38**

Wasps **40–42**

Bees **43–46**

Bees, Wasps, Ants, etc. 36–46